COMMERCIAL RADIO OPERATOR THEORY COURSE

by

MARTIN SCHWARTZ

Formerly Instructor at American Radio Institute

Published by
AMECO PUBLISHING CORP.
314 Hillside Avenue
Williston Park, New York 11596

COMMERCIAL
RADIO OPERATOR
THEORY COURSE

REVISED AND PRINTED 1974

Copyright 1972
by the
AMECO Publishing Corp.

Library of Congress Catalog No. 70-181771

Printed in the United States of America

EXPLANATION OF COURSE

The Commercial Radio Operator Theory Course has been written for the purpose of preparing the prospective radio operator for the Federal Communications Commission Radiotelephone First and Second Class Examinations. The subject matter covers the examination requirements for Elements 3 and 4.

The FCC issues study guides for the various examination elements. These study guides contain a series of questions that cover the scope of the material required for the FCC examinations. All of the information called for by these study guides is thoroughly discussed in this course. In addition, the course is complete in its coverage of radio theory. It starts at the very beginning of basic electricity and continues on through radio transmission and reception.

There are a number of practice questions at the end of each lesson. These practice questions will serve to test the student's knowledge of the material in the lesson. The questions are of the multiple-choice type because this type of question is used exclusively by the FCC on their examinations. At the end of the course, there are final examinations for Elements 3 and 4. These tests provide an added means of preparation for the actual FCC examinations, and also serve as an accurate gauge of preparedness. The answers to all the questions are given on Page 435.

This course covers the material for both the Element 3 and Element 4 examinations. Most of the information in the course is common to the requirements of both elements. Part of the balance of the material is specifically for Element 3 and the rest is specifically for Element 4. If one is studying for one of the examinations, it is not necessary to study the details that are required exclusively for the other examination. The information that is exclusively required for the Element 3 examination is indicated by a "3" in front of a bold-face subheading or paragraph and extends till the next bold-face subheading. The information that is exclusively required for the Element 4 examination is indicated by a "4" in front of a bold-face subheading or paragraph and extends till the next subheading. Therefore, when studying for the Element 3 examination, the Element 4 material can be ignored, and when studying for the Element 4 examination, the Element 3 material can be ignored.

The Ameco Publishing Corp. also publishes a series of license guides for these examinations. See back cover for detailed listing. These guides list the study questions that are issued by the FCC and give a detailed answer for each question. These detailed answers are taken from this course. It is the contention of the author that the student who thoroughly covers the material in this course will be prepared to pass the Commercial Radio Operator's examinations. However, if the prospective radio operator wishes to have a complete FCC listing of the study questions and answers, he may obtain one or more of these guides.

The following shows the examination elements that one must pass in order to obtain the indicated Radio Operator's license or permit issued by the FCC:

Radiotelephone 1st Class Operator's License - Elements 1, 2, 3, 4.

Radiotelephone 2nd Class Operator's License - Elements 1, 2, 3.

Radiotelephone 3rd Class Operator's Permit - Elements 1, 2.

Radiotelephone 3rd Class Operator's Permit Endorsed for Broadcast Operation - Elements 1, 2, and 9.

Radiotelegraph 1st Class Operator's License - Elements 1, 2, 5, 6.

Radiotelegraph 2nd Class Operator's License - Elements 1, 2, 5, 6.

Radiotelegraph 3rd Class Operator's Permit - Elements 1, 2, 5.

Aircraft Radiotelegraph Endorsement on 1st or 2nd Class License - Element 7.

Ship Radar Endorsement on Radiotelegraph or Radiotelephone 1st or 2nd Class License - Element 8.

This course does not contain information on Elements 1, 2 and 9. These are short, simple elements that pertain solely to International Laws and FCC Rules and Regulations. They are completely covered in Ameco publication #8-01 listed on the back cover. The tests for Elements 1 and 2 must be passed before the test for Element 3 can be taken.

The FCC examination for Element 3 consists of 100 multiple-choice questions, similar to the examination on Page 417. One percent (1%) credit is allowed for each question answered correctly and 75% is the passing mark. The Element 3 test must be passed before the Element 4 test can be taken.

The FCC examination for Element 4 consists of 50 multiple-choice questions, similar to the examination on Page 429. Two percent (2%) credit is allowed for each question answered correctly and 75% is the passing mark.

GOOD LUCK!

TABLE OF CONTENTS

LESSON 1
FUNDAMENTALS OF ELECTRICITY

MATTER. Matter is a general term that is used to describe all the material things about us. Matter includes all man-made structures, liquids, metals, gases, etc.; in other words, everything that has weight and occupies space.

All matter, regardless of size, quality or quantity, can be broken down into approximately one hundred and five different elements. Some of the more common elements are iron, copper, aluminum and oxygen. Elements may exist alone or they may exist in combination with other elements. For instance, copper wire consists only of the element copper. On the other hand, water is a combination of two elements: oxygen and hydrogen.

An element consists of many tiny particles, called ATOMS. An atom is the smallest unit into which an element can be broken down and still retain its original characteristics. An atom consists of electrons, protons and neutrons. Fig. 1-1 illustrates an atom of aluminum. Note that it contains 13 electrons, 13 protons and 14 neutrons. The protons and neutrons are present in the nucleus of the atom, while the electrons revolve about the nucleus in orbits.

The atom is too small to be seen by the most powerful microscope. However, we do have a considerable amount of knowledge about the atom and its parts. The proton differs physically and electrically from the electron. The proton is about 1850 times as heavy as the electron and, electrically, we say that the proton is POSITIVELY CHARGED. The tiny, revolving electron, on the other hand, is NEGATIVELY CHARGED. The neutron can be thought of as consisting of a proton and an electron. Thus, it has the same approximate weight as the proton. However, it is neutral in charge because the positive charge of the proton cancels out the negative charge of the electron.

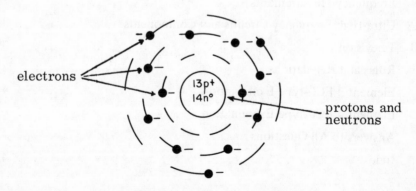

FIG. 1-1. AN ATOM OF ALUMINUM.

THE LAW OF ELECTRIC CHARGES. Most objects, such as a piece of wood, normally have a neutral or zero charge; that is, they contain as many electrons (negatively charged particles) as they do protons (positively charged particles). If this piece of wood can be made to have an excess of electrons, it would lose its neutral charge and become negatively charged. On the other hand, if the wood could be made to have a deficiency of electrons, the protons would predominate and it would become positively charged.

If we took a positively charged body and brought it near a negatively charged body, the two bodies would be drawn together. If, however, the two objects had the same charge (both positive or both negative), then they would repel each other. These two reactions form the basis of our first law of electricity, THE LAW OF ELECTRIC CHARGES. The law states: "LIKE CHARGES REPEL AND UNLIKE CHARGES ATTRACT." Fig. 1-2 illustrates this law.

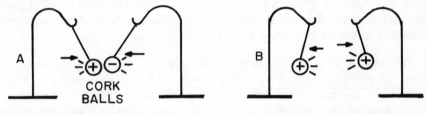

A. Unlike charges attract.   B. Like charges repel.

FIG. 1-2. LAW OF ELECTRIC CHARGES.

DIFFERENCES OF POTENTIAL. If we were to connect a copper wire between two equally and oppositely charged bodies, an electron flow would result. Electrons will flow from the negatively charged body to the positively charged body. This is because the positively charged body, which has a deficiency of electrons, will attract and take away the excess electrons from the negatively charged body. This action will continue until the deficiency and excess of electrons has disappeared and the two bodies become neutral or uncharged. See Fig. 1-3.

A difference in charge between two objects will always result in the development of an electrical pressure between them. This electrical pressure

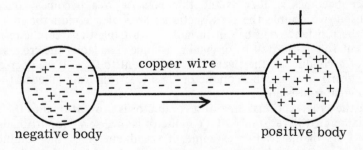

FIG. 1-3. FLOW OF ELECTRONS.

is defined as a DIFFERENCE OF POTENTIAL and will cause electrons to flow when a copper wire is connected between two oppositely charged bodies. The flow of electrons is referred to as a current flow or current.

CONDUCTORS AND INSULATORS. Materials through which current can easily flow are called CONDUCTORS. Conductors incorporate a large number of free electrons in their basic structure. These free electrons are not held tightly and will move freely through the conductor when stimulated by external electrical pressure. Examples of good conductors, in the order of their conductivity, are: silver, copper, aluminum and zinc.

Those materials through which electrons flow with great difficulty are called INSULATORS. The electrons are tightly held in the atomic structure of an insulator and therefore, cannot move about as freely as in conductors.

A distinction is made between insulators which are good enough at commercial power frequencies and those which are good at radio frequencies. Examples of good radio frequency insulators are: quartz, teflon, mica and polystyrene. Wood, silk, glass and phenolic can be used as insulators at power frequencies, but not at radio frequencies.

RESISTANCE AND RESISTORS. The ability of a material to oppose the flow of electrons is called RESISTANCE. All materials exhibit a certain amount of resistance to electron flow. In order to compare the resistances of various materials, we require some standard unit of resistance measurement. The unit of resistance that was adapted for this purpose is the OHM. The Greek letter Omega (Ω) is its symbol. One ohm may be defined as the amount of resistance inherent in 1,000 feet of #10 copper wire. For example, 5,000 feet of #10 copper wire would have a resistance of 5 ohms; 10,000 feet of #10 copper wire would have 10 ohms, etc. Although the ohm is the basic unit, the MEGOHM, meaning 1,000,000 ohms, is frequently used. The instrument used to measure resistance is the OHMMETER.

There are four factors which determine the resistance of a conductor. They are:

(1) LENGTH. The resistance of a conductor is directly proportional to its length. The longer the conductor, the greater is the resistance. The electrons have to flow through more material in a longer conductor, and therefore, meet more opposition.

(2) CROSS-SECTIONAL AREA. The resistance of a conductor is inversely proportional to the cross-sectional area. This means that the resistance becomes smaller as the thickness or area becomes larger. For example: if we double the cross-sectional area of a conductor of a given length, the resistance will be cut in half. If we triple the area, the resistance will be cut to one-third of its original resistance. The larger the cross-sectional area of a conductor, the easier it is for current to flow. If we decrease the cross-sectional area of the conductor, less electrons can squeeze through; hence, a greater resistance.

Since the cross-sectional area of a conductor is proportional to the square of its diameter, the resistance of a conductor is inversely proportional to the square of its diameter. For example, if the diameter of the conductor is doubled, its resistance becomes one-quarter of what it was; if the diameter is tripled, the resistance becomes one-ninth of what it was, etc.

8

(3) TEMPERATURE. In practically all conductors, with the exception of carbon, the resistance varies directly with the temperature. As the temperature of a conductor rises, its resistance increases; as the temperature drops, the resistance decreases.

(4) MATERIAL MAKE-UP. The resistance of a conductor depends upon the material of which it is made. Because of their material structure, some conductors have more resistance than others. For example, silver has a very low resistance, whereas nichrome has a high resistance.

RESISTORS. The resistor is a common radio part. Each resistor has a specific amount of resistance. Resistors which are made of mixtures of carbon and clay are called CARBON RESISTORS. Carbon resistors are used in low power circuits. WIRE WOUND RESISTORS, which contain special resistance wire, are used in high power circuits. Fig. 1-4 illustrates several types of fixed resistors which are used in radio circuits. The symbol which is used to represent them in circuit diagrams is also shown.

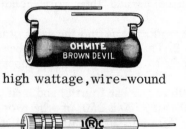

high wattage, wire-wound

fixed resistor symbol

carbon resistor

precision resistor

FIG. 1-4. FIXED RESISTORS.

When it becomes necessary to vary the amount of resistance in a circuit, we use adjustable or VARIABLE RESISTORS. The adjustable resistor has a sliding collar which may be moved along the resistance element to select any desired resistance value.

Variable resistors are used in circuits when a resistance value must be changed frequently. Variable resistors are commonly called potentiometers or rheostats, depending on their use. The volume control in a radio is a typical example of a variable resistor. Fig.1-5B shows a potentiometer that may be used as a volume control in a receiver. Fig. 1-5C is a potentiometer, wound of heavy wire, that can be used in a power supply circuit. Fig. 1-5A illustrates a variable resistor that can be used where frequent adjustment is not required.

3 RESISTOR COLOR CODE. Carbon resistors of two watts and under contain color bands to indicate their values and tolerances. The most popular standard method of marking resistors is shown in Fig. 1-6.

Band A represents the first figure of the value. Band B represents the second figure. Band C represents the number of zeros after the first two numbers. Band D indicates the tolerance (the guaranteed percentage of

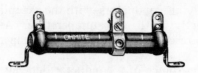

A. adjustable power resistor.

variable resistor symbol.

B. volume control potentiometer.

C. power supply rheostat.

FIG. 1-5. VARIABLE RESISTORS.

accuracy of the color coded value). The colors and their corresponding numbers are given in the table of Fig. 1-6C.

To illustrate how the resistor color code works, let us find the value of the resistor in Fig. 1-6B. Red corresponds to 2. Therefore, the first number of the resistor value is 2. Green corresponds to 5. The second number is therefore 5. The third band is red, indicating 2. This tells us that two zeros follow the 25. This resistor is therefore 2500 ohms. The fourth band is silver. Silver indicates a 10% tolerance factor. 10% of 2500 is 250. In other words, the resistor is guaranteed to be between 2250 ohms and 2750 ohms. If the fourth band is gold, the tolerance factor is 5%. If there is no fourth band, it is understood that the tolerance is 20%.

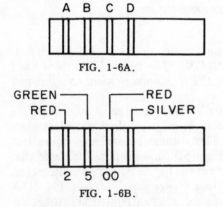

FIG. 1-6A.

FIG. 1-6B.

black 0	violet 7
brown 1	gray 8
red 2	white 9
orange 3	
yellow 4	Tolerance
green 5	silver 10%
blue 6	gold 5%

FIG. 1-6C.

CONDUCTANCE. Conductance is the ability of an electrical circuit to pass or conduct electricity. A circuit having a high conductance has a low resistance; a circuit having a low conductance has a high resistance.

Conductance is, therefore, the reciprocal of resistance.

$$(1-1) \quad \text{Conductance} = \frac{1}{\text{Resistance}}.$$

The symbol for conductance is G, and the unit of conductance is the MHO. A resistance of one ohm has a conductance of one MHO; a resistance of 10 ohms has a conductance of .1 MHO (1/10 = 0.1). In other words, to determine the conductance, we divide the number 1 by the amount of the resistance in ohms. We frequently use the term MICROMHO, meaning one millionth of a mho.

VOLTAGE AND CURRENT. Voltage is another term used to describe the difference of potential or electrical pressure which we spoke about earlier. It is the force which pushes or forces electrons through a wire, just as water pressure forces water through a pipe. Some other terms used to denote voltage are ELECTROMOTIVE FORCE (e.m.f.), IR DROP and FALL OF POTENTIAL. The unit of voltage is the VOLT, and the instrument used to measure voltage is the VOLTMETER. The KILOVOLT is equal to 1000 volts.

CURRENT is the term commonly used to describe the flow of electrons. It is the result of the application of a difference of potential to a circuit. If we increase the number of electrons flowing past a point in a given amount of time, we have more current. Conversely, if we decrease the number of electrons flowing past a point in a given amount of time, we decrease the current. The unit of current is the AMPERE, and it is equal to 6,300,000,000,000,000,000 electrons flowing past a point in one second. MILLIAMPERE and MICROAMPERE are terms used to denote one-thousandth and one-millionth of an ampere respectively. Current is measured by an AMMETER, MILLIAMMETER or MICROAMMETER.

Another term used in electrical work is the COULOMB. The coulomb is the unit of electrical QUANTITY. The coulomb is the number of electrons contained in one ampere. One coulomb flowing past a point in one second is equal to one ampere. Many people confuse the COULOMB with the ampere. The difference is this: the ampere represents the RATE OF FLOW of a number of electrons, whereas the coulomb represents only the quantity of electrons and has nothing to do with the RATE OF FLOW or movement of the electrons. The coulomb is a unit that is seldom used in radio and electronics.

METHODS OF PRODUCING ELECTRICITY. There are several methods that are used to produce electricity or an e.m.f. They are:

(1) Thermal action or the heating of connected dissimilar metals.

(2) Electromagnetic action or the movement of conductors in a magnetic field.

(3) Piezo-electric action or the application of physical pressure on a crystal such as quartz.

(4) Photo-electric action or the reaction of light on certain chemical substances.

(5) Electrostatic action which produces charges on objects by mechanical means.

(6) Chemical action, such as that produced by a dry cell or battery.

THE DRY CELL AND BATTERY. One of the most common methods of producing electricity by chemical means is the dry cell that is found in a

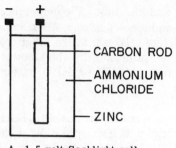

CARBON ROD

AMMONIUM
CHLORIDE

ZINC

A. 1.5 volt flashlight cell.   B. 45 volt "B" battery.

FIG. 1-7. THE DRY CELL.

flashlight. The dry cell contains a carbon rod, which acts as the positive terminal, surrounded by a core consisting of zinc chloride, manganese dioxide, carbon particles, glycerin and sawdust. Around this "core" is a moist chemical paste, called an electrolyte, made up of ammonium chloride solution in starch. A zinc can is used as the container of the cell and also acts as the negative terminal. See Fig. 1-7A.

The chemical reaction between the carbon, the zinc and the electrolyte causes the carbon rod to acquire a positive charge and the zinc container a negative charge. Therefore, a potential difference exists between the two electrodes.

The composition of the electrodes themselves, determines the difference of potential developed between them; not the type of electrolyte or the physical size of the cell. In the case of a cell consisting of a carbon rod and a zinc container as electrodes, the voltage produced is always 1.5 volts.

A battery is composed of a number of cells. Therefore, a battery may be 3 volts, 6 volts, 7.5 volts, etc., depending upon the number of cells it contains. The battery of Fig. 1-7B contains 30 dry cells. The fact that a cell is larger than another one indicates that the larger cell is capable of delivering a given amount of current for a longer period of time than the smaller one.

One of the results of the dry cell's chemical reaction is the production of positive hydrogen ions around the carbon rod. This is known as POLARIZA-TION. Polarization increases the internal resistance of the cell and decreases its ability to produce current. The manganese dioxide in the cell acts as a depolarizing agent which counteracts the polarization and therefore, increases the cell's life.

3 Dry cells are cheap and portable, but cannot be recharged. A cell that cannot be recharged after it has run down, is called a PRIMARY CELL. On the other hand, a SECONDARY CELL is one that can be restored to its original condition after it has run down. This is done by "charging" the cell with direct current. A secondary cell is also known as a STORAGE CELL.

3 THE LEAD-ACID STORAGE CELL. The most popular type of storage cell in use today is called the LEAD-ACID cell. A simplified diagram of it is shown in Fig. 1-8. The negative electrode is made up of pure sponge lead and the positive electrode is lead peroxide. The electrolyte consists of sulphuric acid and distilled water. The lead-acid cell generates 2.1 volts.

When current is drawn from the cell, we say it is discharging. Internally, the following chemical action takes place during discharge: the sulphate of

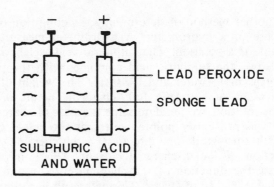

FIG. 1-8. THE LEAD-ACID STORAGE CELL.

the sulphuric acid combines with the lead of the negative and positive electrodes to form lead sulphate. The hydrogen of the sulphuric acid combines with the oxygen in the positive electrode to form water. This process continues until the electrodes both become lead sulphate, and the sulphuric acid disappears by combining with the electrodes. Under these conditions, we no longer have a cell. The two electrodes are the same and there is no electrolyte. The voltage drops from 2.1 volts down to 0 volts.

Long before the cell gets to 0 volts, the discharging process should be stopped, and the cell should be charged. A cell is charged by passing direct current through the cell in the direction opposite to its discharge direction. The internal chemical reaction is then reversed. The charging process is continued until all the sulphate is out of the electrodes and the electrolyte is restored to its original state.

3 SULPHATION. Sulphation is the formation of excess lead sulphate in the electrodes of the battery. The sulphate tends to cover the entire area of the plates and it increases the internal resistance of the cell. This, in turn, increases the heating inside the cell and causes the electrodes to buckle and deteriorate. If the sulphation process continues too long, it may be impossible to restore the cell to its original condition by charging it.

Sulphation is caused by using or discharging the cell for too long a time before charging.

3 DISCHARGING AND CHARGING THE LEAD-ACID CELL. If we discharge a cell at too high a current rate, the internal heating losses will be high and the plates may buckle. Also, the capacity of the cell will be reduced. It will not be able to deliver as much current for as many hours as it can when discharging at a lower rate. Since the current drawn from a battery depends upon the load, we can see that a battery must be chosen for a particular load where the battery has a much greater current capacity than will be used.

The condition of the lead-acid cell can be determined by two popular methods. One is to measure the voltage of the battery under load (while current is being drawn). It was previously stated that the approximately fully charged voltage of a lead acid cell is 2.1 volts. If the voltage falls below 1.8 volts, it should be charged.

Another method of determining the condition of a lead-acid cell involves the use of a hydrometer. A hydrometer measures the specific gravity or weight of a solution. The sulphuric acid weighs more than water. During discharge, the sulphuric acid combines with the plates and the electrolyte becomes more water and less acid. The weight of the solution will be less than when the battery is fully charged. Therefore, by measuring the weight of the solution, we can determine the state of charge of the cell.

It was previously pointed out that the cell is charged by passing direct current through it. The direction of the charging current is opposite to the direction of the discharging current. This is important. If we mistakenly reverse the direction of the charging current, the battery will continue to discharge instead of charge. This will result in sulphation and overheating.

Charging should be done at a slow rate. That is, one should use as long a time as possible to charge a battery. Charging at too high a rate will cause gassing, heating and a reduction in the battery life. The charging voltage should be slightly above the fully charged voltage of the battery. 2.5 volts per cell is generally used.

3 **CAPACITY OF BATTERIES.** Batteries are generally rated in ampere-hours. The rating tells us how many hours a battery can deliver a certain amount of current. For instance, if a certain battery can deliver 8 amperes for 12 hours, we say that the battery has a capacity or rating of 8 x 12 or 96 ampere-hours. This also tells us that we can draw 4 amperes for 24 hours (4 x 24 = 96). In actual practice, the number of ampere-hours which may be obtained from a battery varies with the rate of charge. If a battery is rated "80 ampere-hours for 8 hours," it means that 10 amperes can be drawn continuously for 8 hours. However, if we draw only 5 amperes from the battery, we can perhaps continue to draw the 5 amperes for 20 hours, for a capacity of 100 ampere-hours (5 x 20 = 100). If we draw the 5 amperes on an intermittent basis rather than a continuous basis, we can get still more life out of the battery. On the other hand, if we took the above 80 ampere-hour battery and drew 20 amperes from it instead of 10 amperes, we probably couldn't get more than 3 hours of useful life, or 60 ampere-hours of capacity.

Thus, we see that the capacity of a battery is increased if we draw less than its rate current, and is decreased if we draw more than the rated current.

CELLS IN SERIES AND PARALLEL. In order to get the highest voltage from a group of cells, we hook them up in series, as shown in Fig. 1-9A. The total voltage available is simply the sum of the individual cells. We are all familiar with the 12.6 volt storage battery that is used in autos. It consists of six lead-acid storage cells hooked up in series. (6 x 2.1 = 12.6).

If we want to draw more current than a single cell is capable of providing, or if we want cells to last longer for a given load, we hook them up in parallel. See Fig. 1-9B. The total voltage is the same as that of each cell. However, the amount of current available is the sum of the available currents of each cell.

3 **CARE OF STORAGE BATTERIES.** Storage batteries require a certain

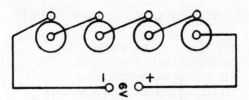

FIG. 1-9A. CELLS IN SERIES.

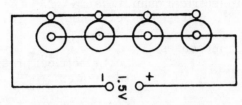

FIG. 1-9B. CELLS IN PARALLEL.

amount of care and attention. If proper care is provided, they will last longer and the chance of accidents will be diminished. The following rules should be observed in caring for batteries:

(1) Storage batteries should be inspected regularly, at least once a week. Take hydrometer and voltage readings.

(2) Batteries should be kept in a cool, but not cold, area. Extreme temperatures must be avoided because they shorten the life of the battery.

(3) The battery compartment should have adequate ventilation. Hydrogen and oxygen gases are given off during charging. These gases are highly combustible. Because of this, there should be no smoking or lighting of matches in the battery area.

(4) The batteries should be kept clean and dry at all times. The electrical connections should be clean, tight and free of corrosion. To help prevent corrosion, the cell terminals should be coated with a thin layer of pure vaseline.

(5) The level of the electrolyte should be approximately one-half inch above the plates. Distilled water or tap water, approved by the battery manufacturer, should be added to bring the electrolyte up to the proper level. If impure water is added, unwanted local action may occur. Acid should not be added to the electrolyte. The acid does not evaporate; the water does. Therefore, water should be added to make up for its evaporation. The only time that acid should be added is when the electrolyte has spilled out. This must be done carefully and in the manner prescribed by the battery manufacturer and acid maker.

(6) Batteries should not be charged at too high a rate. This will avoid "gassing" (giving off of oxygen and hydrogen), and "wearing" of the plate material.

(7) Batteries, not in use, should have a "trickle" charge at all times. This prevents the batteries from slowly discharging due to local action. It keeps the batteries fully charged and ready for operation at all times.

PRACTICE QUESTIONS - LESSON 1*

1. In a conductor, the free electrons: (3)*
   a. are tightly bound to their atoms
   b. are not tightly bound to their atoms
   c. must be neutralized before they can flow
   d. must have their electrostatic fields in one direction

2. The unit of electrical quantity is:
   a. ampere   b. volt   c. coulomb   d. watt

3. A voltmeter measures:
   a. current   c. electrical pressure
   b. amperes   d. power

4. A good high frequency insulator is: (3)
   a. rubber   b. bakelite   c. mica   d. glass

5. Which of the following factors does not influence the resistance of a conductor?
   a. length   b. diameter   c. temperature   d. color

6. Resistance is measured by a/an:
   a. ammeter   b. voltmeter   c. ohmmeter   d. wavemeter

7. The unit of electrical current is:
   a. ampere   b. volt   c. watt   d. farad

8. Sulphation does not cause: (3)
   a. high internal I^2R losses   c. excessive heating
   b. buckling of plates   d. increase in cell's capacity

9. What is the value of a resistor that is color-coded red, green and black?
   a. 35 ohms   b. 250 ohms   c. 240 ohms   d. 25 ohms

10. Electrical energy is measured by a/an: (3)
    a. watt-hour meter   c. ammeter
    b. wavemeter   d. voltmeter

11. Which of the following is not a good conductor?
    a. silver   b. copper   c. gold   d. none of the others

12. The electrolyte of a lead-acid cell contains: (3)
    a. hydrochloride acid   c. sulphuric acid
    b. lead dioxide   d. ammonium sulphate

---

* The "(3)" or "(4)" to the right of the practice questions indicates that the question is exclusive to element 3 or 4 respectively.

13. Which of the following is not correct? **(3)**
    a. batteries should be in a cool area
    b. batteries should have a "trickle" charge when not in use
    c. acid should be added to the electrolyte when it evaporates
    d. hydrometer readings should be taken once a week

14. A kilovolt is:
    a. 100 volts   c. 1000 volts
    b. one-thousandth of a volt   d. one-millionth of a volt

15. A battery is rated at 60 ampere-hours for 6 hours. Which of
    the following can be drawn and permit us to obtain more life
    out of the battery than the rated capacity indicates? **(3)**
    a. 10 amperes   c. 12 amperes
    b. 6 amperes   d. 15 amperes

16. The total voltage of four 1-1/2 volt dry cells, hooked in par-
    allel, is:
    a. 1-1/2 volts   c. 3 volts
    b. 6 volts   d. .375 volts

17

LESSON 2
DIRECT CURRENT THEORY

DIRECT CURRENT. If we take a flashlight bulb or lamp and connect it to a dry cell, as shown in Fig. 2-1, the bulb will light up. The lamp lights up because current flows through the filament of the bulb. The current leaves the cell at the negative terminal (−), flows through the bulb to the positive terminal (+), and then flows through the cell back to the negative terminal. This type of current flow is known as DIRECT CURRENT (DC). DIRECT CURRENT is current that flows only in ONE direction.

The heavy arrows in Fig. 2-1 indicate the direction of the current flow. As long as we can trace the current from the negative terminal of the cell, all around the circuit, and back to the positive terminal, we have a complete electrical path. It is important to remember that current will only flow through a complete circuit.

The necessary parts for a complete circuit are:
(1) A source of voltage - the dry cell of Fig. 2-1.
(2) Connecting leads - the copper wire conductors.
(3) A load - the flashlight bulb.

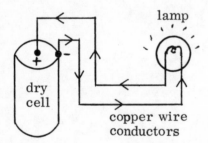

FIG. 2-1. A COMPLETE ELECTRICAL CIRCUIT.

SCHEMATICS. In drawing an electrical circuit on paper, it is impractical to draw the actual battery or lamp as was done in Fig. 2-1. Instead, we use simple symbols to represent the various electrical parts. For example:

A cell is shown as

A battery is shown as

A resistor is shown as

Note that we indicate the negative (−) battery terminal by a short line and the positive (+) terminal by a long line.

Fig. 2-1 can now be redrawn as follows:

18

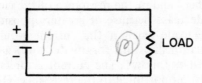

FIG. 2-2. COMPLETE CIRCUIT.

When talking about the electrical properties of Fig. 2-1, we can consider the bulb, or load, as a resistor or resistance, as shown in Fig. 2-2.

OPEN AND SHORT CIRCUITS. If we were to break one of the conducting leads, or remove the load in Fig. 2-2, no current would flow. We would then have an OPEN CIRCUIT. Fig. 2-3 illustrates the open circuit condition.

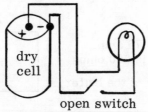

open switch

FIG. 2-3. OPEN CIRCUIT.

If we place a piece of wire directly across the two terminals of the cell, no current will flow through the load. The current by-passes the load and flows through the path of least resistance, which is the piece of wire. This condition is illustrated in Fig. 2-4 and is known as a SHORT CIRCUIT. It is important to avoid a short circuit condition because it causes a severe current drain which rapidly wears down the battery.

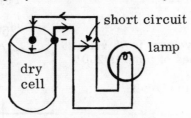

FIG. 2-4. SHORT CIRCUIT.

OHM'S LAW. So far we have discussed voltage, current and resistance. Now we shall study the important relationships that exist between these three factors.

If we were to increase the source of voltage of Fig. 2-2, more current would flow through the circuit because of the greater electrical pressure exerted. If we were to decrease the voltage, the flow of current would decrease. On the other hand, if the resistance of the circuit were made larger, the current would decrease because of greater opposition to current flow. If the resistance were made smaller, the current would increase by similar reasoning. These relationships are formulated into a law known as OHM'S LAW, which is stated as follows: The current is directly proportional to the voltage and inversely proportional to the resistance. Ohm's law, mathematically stated, says that the current, in amperes, is equal to the voltage, in volts, divided by the resistance, in ohms. The three formulas of Ohm's law are:

$$(2\text{-}1) \quad I = \frac{E}{R} \qquad (2\text{-}2) \quad E = IR \qquad (2\text{-}3) \quad R = \frac{E}{I}$$

"I" stands for the current in amperes, "E" is the voltage in volts, and "R" is the resistance in ohms. If two out of the three factors of Ohm's law are known (either E, I or R), the unknown third factor can be found by using one of the three above equations. Several examples will clarify the use of Ohm's law:

PROBLEM:
Given: Current is .75 amp.
Resistance is 200 ohms.

Find: The voltage of the battery.

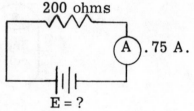

200 ohms

(A) .75 A.

E = ?

SOLUTION: Since we are interested in finding the voltage, we use formula (2-2) because it tells us what the voltage is equal to. We then substitute the known values and solve the problem as follows:

E = IR

E = .75 x 200

E = 150 V.

```
   200
 x .75
  1000
 1400
150.00
```

PROBLEM:
Given: Battery voltage is 75 volts.
Resistance of lamp is 250 ohms.

Find: Current in circuit.

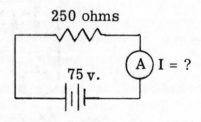

250 ohms

(A) I = ?

75 v.

SOLUTION: Use formula (2-1) to find the current.

$$I = \frac{E}{R} \qquad I = \frac{75}{250} \qquad I = .3 \text{ amp.}$$

```
        .3
250 ) 75.0
      75 0
      00 0
```

20

PROBLEM:

Given: Current in circuit is 2 amp.
Battery is 45 volts.

Find: Resistance of circuit.

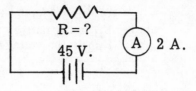

SOLUTION: Use formula (2-3) and substitute for E and I to find R.

$$R = \frac{E}{I} \qquad R = \frac{45}{2} \qquad R = 22.5 \text{ ohms.}$$

RESISTORS IN SERIES. If two or more resistors are connected end to end, as shown in Fig. 2-5A, we say that the resistors are connected in a SERIES CIRCUIT. Any current flowing through one of the resistors will also flow through the others. The arrows indicate the direction of current flow.

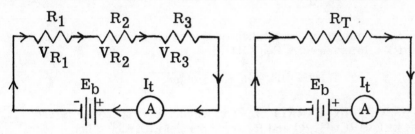

FIG. 2-5A. SERIES CIRCUIT.   FIG. 2-5B. EQUIVALENT CIRCUIT.

Since the same current flows through each resistor, the CURRENT IS THE SAME AT EVERY POINT IN A SERIES CIRCUIT. Similarly, the total current is the same as the current in any part of the series circuit. To put it mathematically:

$$(2-4) \quad I_{(total)} = I_{R1} = I_{R2} = I_{R3}.$$

It is important to note that the current in Fig. 2-5A will remain unchanged if the three resistors are replaced by a single resistor whose resistance value is equal to the sum of the three resistors. Fig. 2-5B illustrates the equivalent circuit of Fig. 2-5A. We can, therefore, say that THE TOTAL RESISTANCE IN A SERIES CIRCUIT IS EQUAL TO THE SUM OF THE INDIVIDUAL RESISTANCES.

$$(2-5) \quad R_T = R1 + R2 + R3, \text{ etc.} \quad \text{where } R_T \text{ is total resistance.}$$

Whenever current flows through a resistance in a circuit, a part of the source voltage is used up in forcing the current to flow through the particular resistance. The voltage that is used up in this manner is known as the VOLTAGE DROP, or fall of potential across that particular resistor. The voltage drop is equal to the current through the resistor, multiplied by the resistance of the resistor.

If we add up the voltage drops across all the parts of a series circuit, the sum would be equal to the source or battery voltage.

21

$$(2-6) \quad E_B = E_{R1} + E_{R2} + E_{R3}, \text{ etc.}$$

where: E_B is the battery voltage, E_{R1} is the voltage across R1
E_{R2} is the voltage across R2, etc.

PROBLEM

Find the resistance of R_2

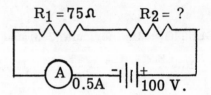

SOLUTION: Since we know the total current and the battery voltage, we can use Ohm's law to find the total resistance.

$$R_T = \frac{E}{I} = \frac{100}{.5} = 200.$$

Since the total resistance in this series circuit is 200 ohms and R1 = 75; then $R2 = R_T - R1$.

$$R2 = 200 - 75 = 125 \text{ ohms.}$$

RESISTORS IN PARALLEL. The circuit in Fig. 2-7A is called a PARALLEL CIRCUIT. R1 and R2 are in parallel with each other.

The current in the circuit now has two paths to flow through. If we remove resistor R1 or R2 from the circuit, the current has only one path to flow through from the negative to the positive end of the battery. Since it is easier for the current to flow through two paths instead of one, THE TOTAL RESISTANCE OF A PARALLEL COMBINATION IS LESS THAN THE RESISTANCE OF EITHER RESISTOR IN THE CIRCUIT. The more resistors we add in parallel, the less becomes the total resistance. This is because we increase the number of paths through which the current can flow.

If each resistor in Fig. 2-7A has a value of one ohm, it would be twice as easy for the current to pass through the parallel combination than it would be for it to pass through either one of the resistors alone. The total parallel resistance would, therefore, be one-half of either one of the resistors, or

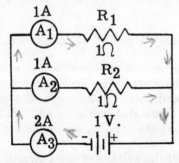

FIG. 2-7A. PARALLEL CIRCUIT.

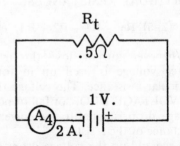

FIG. 2-7B. EQUIVALENT CIRCUIT.

22

one-half ohm. THUS, WE CAN SAY THAT THE TOTAL RESISTANCE OF TWO EQUAL RESISTORS IN PARALLEL IS EQUAL TO HALF OF ONE OF THEM. The schematic diagram in Fig. 2-7B shows the equivalent circuit of Fig. 2-7A.

The total resistance of ANY TWO resistors in parallel may be found by using the following formula:

$$(2-7) \quad R_T = \frac{R1 \times R2}{R1 + R2}$$

For example, if R1 and R2 of Fig. 2-7A are 3 and 6 ohms respectively, the total resistance would be:

$$R_T = \frac{R1 \times R2}{R1 + R2} \qquad R_T = \frac{3 \times 6}{3 + 6} = \frac{18}{9} = 2 \text{ ohms}.$$

The total resistance of ANY NUMBER of resistors in parallel may be found by applying the following formula:

$$(2-8) \quad R_T = \frac{1}{\dfrac{1}{R1} + \dfrac{1}{R2} + \dfrac{1}{R3} + \text{etc.}}$$

For example, if three resistors of 5, 10, and 20 ohms are connected in parallel, the total resistance would be:

$$R_T = \frac{1}{\dfrac{1}{R1} + \dfrac{1}{R2} + \dfrac{1}{R3}} \qquad R_T = \frac{1}{\dfrac{1}{5} + \dfrac{1}{10} + \dfrac{1}{20}} \qquad \text{(least common denominator is 20)}$$

$$\frac{1}{\dfrac{4 + 2 + 1}{20}} = \frac{1}{\dfrac{7}{20}} \qquad 1 \times \frac{20}{7} = 2\frac{6}{7} \text{ ohms}.$$

SUMMARY OF PARALLEL CIRCUIT CHARACTERISTICS

(1) The total resistance of several resistors hooked in parallel is less than that of the smallest resistor.

(2) Different amounts of current flow through the different branches of a parallel circuit. The amount of current flowing through each branch depends upon the resistance of the individual branch. The total current drawn from the battery is equal to the sum of the individual branch currents.

(3) The voltage across all the branches of a parallel circuit is the same; in Fig. 2-7A, the voltage across R1 is the same as the voltage across R2.

An example will illustrate the above principles.

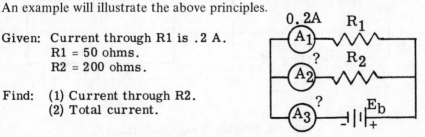

Given: Current through R1 is .2 A.
       R1 = 50 ohms.
       R2 = 200 ohms.

Find: (1) Current through R2.
     (2) Total current.

SOLUTION: Since we know the resistance of R1 and the current through R1, we can find the voltage across R1 by using Ohm's law.

$$E_{R1} = I_{R1} \times R1 \qquad E_{R1} = .2 \times 50 \qquad E_{R1} = 10 \text{ V}.$$

Since R1 is in parallel with R2, the voltage across R2 is the same as that across R1. Therefore, $E_{R2} = 10$ V.

Knowing the resistance of R2 (given) and the voltage across it, we can find the current through R2:

$$I_{R2} = \frac{E_{R2}}{R2} = \frac{10}{200} = .05 \text{ Amp}.$$

In a parallel circuit, the total current is equal to the sum of the individual branch currents; therefore:

$$I_T = I_{R1} + I_{R2}$$
$$I_T = .2 \text{ A. } + .05 \text{ A. } = .25 \text{ Amp}.$$

SERIES-PARALLEL CIRCUITS. Circuits A and B of Fig 2-8 are called SERIES-PARALLEL circuits. In circuit A, the 10-ohm resistors are in parallel with each other. But, this parallel combination is in series with the 20 ohm resistor. The total resistance of circuit A is computed as follows:

First find the resistance of the two 10-ohm parallel resistors, using formula (2-7).

$$R_T = \frac{R1 \times R2}{R1 + R2} = \frac{10 \times 10}{10 + 10} = \frac{100}{20} = 5 \text{ ohms}.$$

Since the parallel resistors are in series with the 20 ohm resistor, the total resistance of the combination is: 5 + 20 or 25 ohms.

In diagram B, the two 15-ohm resistors are in series with each other. This series combination is in parallel with the 30 ohm resistor. The total resistance of series-parallel circuit B is computed as follows:

The resistance of the two 15-ohm resistors in series is 15 + 15 or 30 ohms.

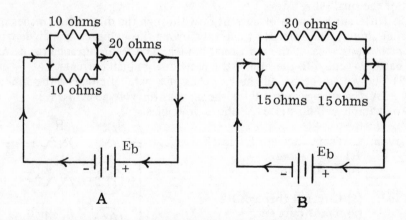

FIG. 2-8. SERIES-PARALLEL CIRCUITS.

24

Since this 30 ohms is in parallel with the 30-ohm resistor, the total resistance of the combination is:

$$R_T = \frac{30 \times 30}{30 + 30} = \frac{900}{60} = 15 \text{ ohms.}$$

POWER. Whenever current flows through a resistance, there is friction between the moving electrons and the molecules of the resistor. This friction causes heat to be generated, as does all friction. We could also say that electrical energy is changed to heat energy whenever current flows through a resistor. The rate at which the heat energy is generated is the power that the resistor consumes. This power consumption in the form of heat represents a loss because we do not make use of the heat generated in radio circuits.

It is important to know how much power a resistor is consuming or dissipating because it will burn up if it cannot stand the heat. Resistors are therefore rated, not only in ohms, but in the amount of power that they can dissipate without overheating. The unit of electrical power is the WATT or KILOWATT. One kilowatt is equal to 1,000 watts. A resistor rated at 5 watts is one which can safely dissipate up to 5 watts of power. If this resistor is forced to dissipate 10 watts, by increased current flow, it may become damaged.

Let us see how much power is dissipated in a particular circuit, and upon what factors the power dissipation depends. Since the power is the result of friction between the flowing electrons and the resistance in the circuit, the actual power dissipated depends upon the current and the resistance. The more current that flows, the more electrons there are to collide with the particles of the resistance material. Also, the greater the resistance, the greater is the resulting friction. The actual power dissipated in a resistor can be found by the following formula:

(2-9) $P = I^2 \times R$ where: **P is the power in watts**
(I^2 means I x I)   **I is the current in amperes**
                                     R is the resistance in ohms

A problem will illustrate the use of this formula:

PROBLEM: Find the power dissipated in a 2,000 ohm resistor with 50 milliamperes flowing through it.

SOLUTION: First change milliamperes to amperes. This is done by moving the decimal three places to the left. Thus, 50 milliamperes is equal to .05 ampere. Then, substitute the values given in formula (2-9):

$P = I^2 \times R$	.05	.0025
$P = .05 \times .05 \times 2000$	x .05	x 2000
$P = 5$ watts	.0025	5.0000

By using Ohm's law and algebraically substituting in formula 2-9, we arrive at two more formulas for obtaining power dissipation. Formula 2-10

(2-10) $P = E \times I$ where: **P is the power in watts,**
                                   E is the voltage in volts,
(2-11) $P = \dfrac{E^2}{R}$ **I is the current in amperes,**
                                 R is the resistance in ohms.

states that the power is equal to the product of the voltage across a resistor and the current through it.

Formula 2-11 states that the power is also equal to the square of the voltage across a resistor, divided by the resistance of the resistor.

A few problems will illustrate the use of these formulas.

PROBLEM: Find the power dissipated in a 110 volt lamp if 2.4 amperes is flowing through it.

SOLUTION: Use formula (2-10).

$$P = E \times I$$

$$P = 110 \text{ V.} \times 2.4 \text{ A.}$$

$$P = 264 \text{ watts}$$

$$\begin{array}{r} 110 \\ \times\, 2.4 \\ \hline 440 \\ 220 \\ \hline 264.0 \end{array}$$

PROBLEM: Find the current that will flow through a 2 watt lamp connected to a 12 volt source.

SOLUTION: Formula 2-10 involves power, voltage and current. However, it states what the power will be if we know the voltage and current. It does not tell us what the current is if we know the power and voltage. We must change formula 2-10 around so as to tell us what the current is equal to. We do this by dividing both sides by E as follows:

$$P = E \times I, \qquad \frac{P}{E} = \frac{E \times I}{E}, \qquad \frac{P}{E} = I \text{ or } I = \frac{P}{E}$$

We then substitute the values given in the problem and solve.

$$I = \frac{P}{E} = \frac{2}{12} = \frac{1}{6} \text{ Amp. or } .166 \text{ Amp. or } 166 \text{ ma.}$$

Note that we have changed .166 Amp. into 166 milliamperes by moving the decimal point three places to the RIGHT.

PROBLEM: If a 5 kilohm resistor is connected across 300 volts, what is the power dissipated in the resistor.

SOLUTION: Use formula 2-11 to solve the problem.

$$P = \frac{E^2}{R} = \frac{300 \times 300}{5,000} = \frac{90,000}{5,000} = 18 \text{ watts}$$

If we require a resistor where 18 watts is to be dissipated, we order one with a rating of at least 30 watts. It is always good design practice to use a resistor that is capable of handling about twice the power actually dissipated.

The instrument that is used to measure power is called a WATTMETER.

ENERGY. Power has been defined as the RATE of doing work. The actual work or capacity to do the work is called ENERGY. The energy represents the amount of power used in a specific amount of time. Energy is therefore equal to the power multiplied by the time. If a 100 watt lamp burned for two hours, the power would be 100 watts, but the energy consumed would be: 100 watts x 2 hours or 200 watt-hours. The unit of energy is the WATT-HOUR. The kilowatt- hour and the watt-second are also used as units of energy. Another term for the watt-second is the JOULE.

In purchasing electricity, we pay for the total energy consumed and not simply for the power. In other words, we are not billed for the rate at which electrical work is being performed; we pay for the total electrical work or energy that has been consumed. An example will make this clear.

PROBLEM: An electric company charges 6¢ per kilowatt-hour. How much does it cost to use two 120-volt, 75 watt lamps, for a period of 24 hours?

SOLUTION: The two lamps use 150 watts. The total energy consumed is the product of the power and the time: 150 x 24 = 3600 watt-hours. We divide by 1000 to get kilowatt hours.

$$\frac{3600}{1000} = 3.6 \text{ kilowatt-hours.}$$

Since the charge is 6¢ per kilowatt-hour, it would cost 6¢ x 3.6 or 21.6¢ to use the two bulbs for 24 hours.

REVIEW PROBLEM: The problem presented below is an excellent review of the principles of direct current theory learned to this point.

PROBLEM: Find:
(a) the total resistance
(b) the total current.
(c) the current in each resistor
(d) the voltage across each resistor
(e) the power dissipated by each resistor
(f) the total power dissipated in the circuit.

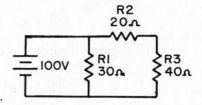

ANSWER: The resistors are arranged in a "pi" network. We use the term "pi" because the resistor arrangement resembles the Greek letter Π. Actually, the "pi" network is nothing more than the series-parallel circuit of Fig. 2-8B.

(a) R2 and R3 are in series. Their total resistance is equal to the sum of the two resistors or 20 + 40 = 60 ohms. The 60 ohms is in parallel with the 30 ohms. The resistance of this combination is found by using formula 2-7.

$$R_T = \frac{R1 \times R2}{R1 + R2} = \frac{30 \times 60}{30 + 60} = \frac{1800}{90} = 20 \text{ ohms}$$

The total resistance of the circuit is, therefore, 20 ohms.

(b) The total current is found by using Ohm's law:

$$I_T = \frac{E_T}{R_T} \qquad \frac{100 \text{ volts}}{20 \text{ ohms}} = 5 \text{ Amperes}$$

(c) The current in each resistor is also found by using Ohm's law.

$$\text{The current in R1} = \frac{100}{30} = 3.33 \text{ Amp.}$$

The current in R2 is the same as the current in R3 because they are in series with each other. The current through the two resistors is equal to:

$$I = \frac{E}{R} = \frac{100 \text{ V.}}{60 \text{ ohms}} = 1.66 \text{ Amp.}$$

(d) The voltage across R1 is obviously 100 volts. The 100 volt source is directly across R1. The voltage across R2 is found by Ohm's law.

$$E = I_2 \times R2 = 1.66 \times 20 = 33.2 \text{ volts.}$$

The voltage across R3 is found in a similar manner:

$$E = I_3 \times R3 = 1.66 \times 40 = 66.4 \text{ volts.}$$

(e) The power dissipated in each resistor is found by using the power formula, $P = I^2 R$.

$$P_{R1} = 3.33^2 \times 30 = 11.09 \times 30 = 332.7 \text{ watts.}$$

$$P_{R2} = 1.66^2 \times 20 = 2.76 \times 20 = 55.2 \text{ watts.}$$

$$P_{R3} = 1.66^2 \times 40 = 2.76 \times 40 = 110.4 \text{ watts.}$$

(f) The total power dissipated is equal to the sum of the individual powers dissipated.

$$P_T = P_{R1} + P_{R2} + P_{R3}$$

$$P_T = 332.7 + 55.2 + 110.4$$

$$P_T = 498.3 \text{ watts.}$$

The total power can also be found by using the total current and the total resistance in the power formula,

$$P_T = I_T^2 \times R_T = 5^2 \times 20 = 25 \times 20 = 500 \text{ watts.}$$

This checks with the above. The slight difference is due to rounding out numbers after the decimal point.

3
SOLDERING AND PRINTED CIRCUIT WIRING. This book will not deal with mechanical and electrical shop techniques. However, the FCC Study Guides do contain a few questions on soldering and printed circuits.

The following information should give the prospective operator sufficient knowledge to be able to answer any questions that may be asked on this subject.

QUESTION: List several precautions which should be taken in soldering electrical connections to assure a permanent junction.

ANSWER: The following precautions must be taken in order to make a good electrical connection:

(1) The parts to be soldered must be thoroughly cleaned. It would help if the parts to be soldered were tinned - that is, a thin coat of solder is applied to the parts prior to joining them together.

(2) A good mechanical connection should be made between the parts to be soldered prior to actual soldering.

(3) The tip of the soldering iron should be clean, smooth and tinned.

(4) A good grade of solder with a rosin core flux should be used. Acid flux should never be used.

(5) The soldering iron to be used should have a large enough tip and a high enough wattage to provide sufficient heat to the joint to be soldered.

(6) Heat the work to be soldered and apply the solder to the work. Do not heat the solder and simply allow it to drip on to the work.

(7) Do not move the parts while the solder is cooling. Apply only enough solder to cover the joint.

QUESTION: Discuss etched wiring printed circuits with respect to the following:

  (a) Determination of wiring breaks.
  (b) Excessive heating
  (c) Removal and installation of components.

ANSWER: A printed circuit board is made up of an insulating material such as mylar or epoxy. Thin copper strips or "leads" are etched or printed on one side of the board. The copper "leads" represent the actual wiring that connects various points together throughout the board. The component parts are inserted on the other side of the board and their leads or "pigtails" are brought through holes in the board to the copper side. Here, they are soldered to the copper strips.

Breaks in the copper etching can be physically observed by the naked eye or by a magnifying lens. Anyone working with printed circuit boards should own a magnifying lens because miniaturization makes it necessary. Breaks can also be determined with the aid of an ohmmeter, or, if the power is on, by tracing with a voltmeter.

A low wattage iron with a small, fine, properly tinned tip, should be used when working on a printed circuit board. A large iron is too clumsy to use on a printed circuit board. A large iron may cause adjacent copper strips to be accidently bridged with solder.

A minimum amount of heat should be used on a printed circuit board. Too much heat may cause the board to buckle, or it may cause the copper to break away from the board. This, in turn, may result in open circuits. Soldering on printed circuit boards should be quick and accurate.

When soldering a component to a printed circuit board, the pigtails of the component should be inserted into clean holes. In order to prevent a component from being exposed to too much heat, it can be mounted a slight distance above the board and the pigtails can be crimped to hold it there while soldering. When soldering transistors or diodes to a printed circuit board or for that matter, to any type of circuit, the part should be placed some distance from the board. This gives the heat of the iron a chance to dissipate itself before getting to the actual part itself. A heat sink, or other means of conducting heat, can be clipped to the lead between the part and the heating point to conduct and absorb the heat before it gets to the part.

In order to remove a part from a printed circuit board, we can carefully cut the part away and neatly solder another part in its place without necessarily putting the pigtails of the new part through the original holes. If there are not too many other parts going through the same hole, and the area of the part to be removed is not too crowded, the pigtails of the original defective component being removed, can be taken out by applying heat to the connection after the component has been clipped out, and quickly removing the pigtails. We then make sure that the holes are clean and clear for the pigtails of the replacement component to be inserted. We then apply a minimum of solder and a minimum of heat to the connection. After we are finished, the area should be inspected with a magnifying glass to make sure that the soldering joint is not "cold" and also that there are no soldering "bridges" across insulated copper strips.

PRACTICE QUESTIONS - LESSON 2

1. The instrument used to measure power is the:
a. ohmmeter   c. wattmeter
b. power meter   d. wavemeter

2. Ohm's law states that the:
a. current is equal to the voltage times the resistance
b. resistance is equal to the voltage divided by the current
c. voltage is equal to the current divided by the resistance
d. current is equal to the resistance divided by the voltage

3. Assume a DC circuit consisting of a 100 V source, a 250 ohm resistor across the source, and a 50 ohm resistor and 350 ohm resistor in series across the 250 ohm resistor. Find the voltage across the 50 ohm resistor.
a. 100 V.   b. 7.5 V.   c. 12.5 V.   d. 20 V.

4. The ratio of current to voltage in a circuit is known as:
a. inductance   b. capacitance   c. conductance   d. impedance

5. The resistance of two equal resistors connected in parallel is:
a. the sum of the two resistors
b. one-half of one of the resistors
c. one-quarter of one of the resistors
d. the average value of the resistors

6. The total current in a parallel circuit is:
a. the same in each branch
b. equal to the sum of the individual branch currents
c. equal to the current in each branch, multiplied by two
d. none of the above

30

7. In a series circuit, the source voltage is equal to:
a. the sum of the individual voltage drops
b. the average of the individual voltage drops
c. the total resistance multiplied by the total current
d. a and c are correct

8. The total current in a series circuit is equal to:
a. the current in any part of the circuit
b. the sum of the currents in each part
c. the total resistance divided by the voltage
d. the sum of the IR drops

9. A short circuit:
a. is found in every good electrical circuit
b. causes a heavy current to be drained from the electrical source
c. prevents current from flowing
d. decreases the conductance of the circuit

10. Find the source voltage
of the circuit shown:
a. 24 V.
b. 100 V.
c. 60 V.
d. 50 V.

30Ω   20Ω

$E = I \times R$

2A

11. The unit of energy is:
a. watt   b. joule   c. coulomb   d. electron

12. A 20 ohm resistor, a 15 ohm resistor and a 30 ohm resistor
are all hooked in parallel. What is their total resistance?
a. 6.7 ohms   b. 65 ohms   c. 15 ohms   d. 30 ohms

13. The total resistance of Fig. 13 is:
a. 150 ohms
b. 100 ohms
c. 66 ohms
d. 33 ohms   Fig. 13

50Ω

20Ω   80Ω

66V

14. The current through the 80 ohm resistor is:
a. .66 A.   b. .33 A.   c. 1.32 A.   d. .825 A.

15. The power dissipated by the 20 ohm resistor is:
a. 9 W.   b. 4-1/2 W.   c. 6.6 W.   d. 40 W.

16. Which of the following is correct?   (3)
a. the soldering tip must be square
b. a 40-60 rosin core flux should be used
c. the work should be heated, rather than the solder
d. the solder should drip on to the junction of the two parts

LESSON 3
MAGNETISM AND METERS

THE MAGNET. We are all familiar with the effects of magnetism. A horseshoe magnet will attract iron filings. A powerful crane electromagnet will pick up heavy pieces of iron. A compass needle will point to the North pole. A magnet, therefore, is any object which has the ability of attracting to itself magnetic materials such as iron or steel. Fig. 3-1 shows a horseshoe magnet attracting particles of iron filings.

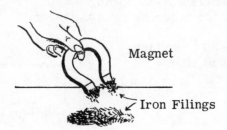

FIG. 3-1. MAGNET'S ATTRACTIVE POWER.

When a magnetized bar of iron is suspended from a string tied around its center so that it it free to rotate, it will come to rest with one end pointing almost directly North. The end that points North is called the North-seeking pole or the NORTH POLE and is marked N. The South-seeking pole of the magnet is called the SOUTH POLE and is marked S.

LAW OF MAGNETIC POLES. If the North pole end of one magnet is brought near the North pole end of another magnet, the magnets will repel each other. The same reaction of REPULSION will occur if two South pole ends are brought close to each other. If, however, a North pole and South pole are brought close to each other, the magnets will attract each other. The reason that the North pole of a suspended magnet points to the earth's North geographical pole is that the earth itself is a magnet. The earth's South magnetic pole is located near the North geographical pole.

The results of experiments in magnetic attraction and repulsion were formulated into the LAW OF POLES which states that OPPOSITE POLES ATTRACT EACH OTHER, WHEREAS LIKE POLES REPEL EACH OTHER. Fig. 3-2 illustrates this principle.

We cannot see the forces of repulsion or attraction that exist between the pole pieces of two magnets. However, we can assume that the North pole of one magnet sends out some kind of invisible force which has the ability to act through air and pull the South pole of the other magnet to it. This force which exists between two like poles is one of mutual repulsion and the force

32

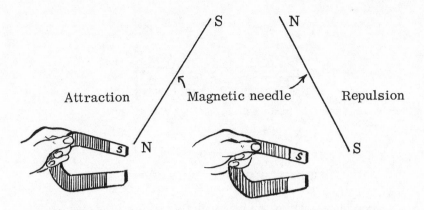

Attraction   Magnetic needle   Repulsion

FIG. 3-2. ATTRACTION AND REPULSION.

between two unlike poles is one of mutual attraction.

It is important to note that the strength of the force between the two poles varies inversely with the square of the distance between them. This means that the further apart the poles are placed from each other, the weaker the force between them will be. If we double the distance, the strength is one-quarter as great and if we triple the distance, the strength becomes one-ninth as great.

THE MAGNETIC FIELD AND MAGNETIC STRENGTH The invisible magnetic force which exists in the air or space surrounding a magnet is called the MAGNETIC FIELD. One way of showing what the magnetic field around a bar magnet is like, is to sprinkle iron filings on a piece of paper under which we place a bar magnet. The result is shown in Fig. 3-3. The iron filings arrange themselves so as to LOOK like the field that surrounds the magnet.

FIG. 3-3. PICTURE
OF IRON FILINGS.

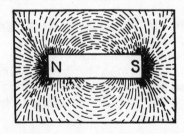

Another way of showing the magnetic field is to draw a picture which represents the intensity and the direction of the magnetic field around and through the magnet. The lines that are drawn are CALLED magnetic lines of force and the arrows indicate the direction of magnetic flow. See Fig. 3-4. Notice that the lines of force leave the magnet at the North pole and return to the magnet at the South pole. Note also that the magnetic field continues flowing inside the magnet from the South to the North pole. These magnetic lines, when taken as a homogeneous group, are called a Magnetic Field or

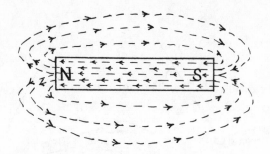

FIG. 3-4. MAGNETIC LINES OF FORCE.

Flux. The complete path of the magnetic flux is called the magnetic circuit. A magnetic flux can exist only if there exists a complete magnetic path.

Fig. 3-5 illustrates the magnetic field of attraction as it exists between the North and South poles of two magnets. Notice that the magnetic field appears to be "pulling" the two pole ends together.

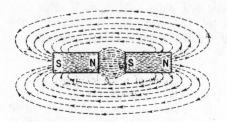

FIG. 3-5. UNLIKE MAGNETIC
POLES ATTRACT.

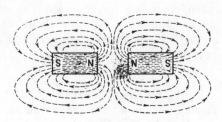

FIG. 3-6. LIKE MAGNETIC
POLES REPEL.

Fig. 3-6 illustrates the magnetic field of repulsion between two like poles. Notice that the magnetic fields appear to be "pushing" each other away.

3 THE NATURE OF MAGNETISM. The molecular theory of magnetism holds that each of the tiny molecules of a magnet is itself a tiny magnet. These tiny magnets are present in unmagnetized steel or iron. However, they are arranged in a haphazard form, as shown in Fig. 3-7A. With this arrangement, the magnetism of each of the molecules is neutralized by that of adjacent molecules, and no external magnetic effort is produced.

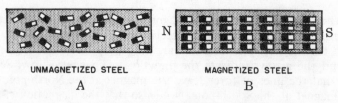

UNMAGNETIZED STEEL   MAGNETIZED STEEL
A   B

FIG. 3-7. MOLECULAR THEORY OF MAGNETISM.

When a magnetizing force is applied to an unmagnetized iron or steel bar, the tiny magnetic molecules become aligned so that the North poles point one way and the South poles point the other way. When this happens, the magnetic fields of all the tiny magnets add up and there is an external magnetic effect. The North poles of the molecular magnets all point to the North pole of the magnet, and the South poles of the molecular magnets point to the South pole of the magnet. See Fig. 3-7B.

The fact that tapping a steel bar in a magnetic field helps it become a stronger magnet is considered support for this theory. When we tap the bar, we are "helping the tiny magnets to move into their proper alignment".

SHIELDING. If a non-magnetic object, such as a tennis ball, is placed in the path of a magnetic field, as shown in Fig. 3-8, the lines of force would pass right through the ball, just as light shines through a piece of glass. However, if the tennis ball were covered up with a thick layer of soft iron, the lines of force would flow through the soft iron and not through the center of the ball. The reason for this is that the soft iron offers much less resistance to the magnetic flux than the air does. This is illustrated in Fig. 3-9. Notice that the area in the center of the ball is now free of magnetic flux. The above example illustrates the principle of magnetic shielding which is so extensively used in electronic circuits.

FIG. 3-8. NO SHIELDING.   FIG. 3-9. SHIELDING.

People who work near strong magnetic fields usually encase their watches in soft iron through which the magnetic field will not penetrate. The delicate watch movement is therefore protected and will not be adversely affected by the magnetic field.

TEMPORARY AND PERMANENT MAGNETS. Soft iron can be magnetized easily by placing it in a magnetic field. However, as soon as the iron is removed from the magnetic field, it loses most of its magnetism. Such a magnet is called a TEMPORARY MAGNET. The small amount of magnetism that does remain is called RESIDUAL MAGNETISM.

Steel or hard iron, which is difficult to magnetize, retains most of its magnetism after it has been removed from the magnetic field. A magnet of this type is called a PERMANENT MAGNET. Permanent magnets are usually made in the shape of a bar or a horseshoe. The horseshoe type has the stronger magnetic field because the magnetic poles are closer to each other. Horseshoe magnets are used in the construction of headphones. Loudspeakers use a form of bar magnet.

ELECTROMAGNETISM. The same type of magnetic field that exists around a magnet, also exists around wires that carry current. This can be proven by placing a compass next to a current-carrying conductor. It will be found that the compass needle will turn until it is at right angles to the conductor. Since a compass needle lines up in the direction of the magnetic field, the field must exist in a plane at right angles to the conductor. Fig. 3-10 illustrates a current-carrying conductor with its associated magnetic field. The current flows from left to right and the magnetic field is in the direction shown by the arrows. In Fig. 3-11, the current flows from right to left and the magnetic field is in the opposite direction. This magnetic field encircles the wire all along its length like a cylinder.

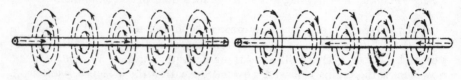

FIG. 3-10. CURRENT LEFT TO RIGHT.   FIG. 3-11. CURRENT RIGHT TO LEFT.

THE COIL. If the same conductor is wound in the form of a coil, the total magnetic field about the coil will be greatly increased because the magnetic fields of each turn add up to make one large resultant magnetic field. See Fig. 3-12. The coil is called a SOLENOID or ELECTROMAGNET. The electromagnet has a North and South pole, just like a permanent magnet. The rule for determining which end is the North pole and which end is the South pole is as follows: If we grasp the coil with the left hand so that the finger tips point in the direction of the current flow, the thumb will automatically point to the North pole of the electromagnet. Thus, we see that the polarity of an electromagnet depends upon both the way in which the turns are wound and the direction of the current flow. If we reverse either the direction of the current flow or the direction of the windings, the North pole will become the South pole, and the South pole will become the North pole.

A compass placed within a coil carrying an electric current, will point to the North pole of the coil. The reason for this is that the compass needle lines itself up in the direction of the magnetic lines of force. You will recall that inside a magnet, the direction of the field is from the South pole to the North pole. This is also true in the electromagnet illustrated in Fig. 3-12.

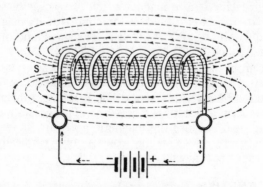

FIG. 3-12. MAGNETIC FIELD AROUND A COIL OF WIRE.

There are various factors which influence the strength of an electromagnet. They are:

(1) The number of turns. An increase in the number of turns in a coil increases the magnetic strength of the coil.

(2) The amount of current. If we increase the amount of current in a coil, the magnetic strength increases.

(3) Permeability of the core. The core of the coil is the material within the coil. It may be air, glass, wood or metal. If we wind the coil on an iron core, we find that the strength of the electromagnet is increased by several hundred times over what it is with an air core. The iron is said to have more permeability than air; permeability is the ability of a substance to conduct magnetic lines of force easily. Permeability is to a magnetic circuit as conductance is to an electrical circuit. If we have a core with a high permeability, we will have a large number of magnetic lines of force. This will result in a stronger magnetic field. Iron and permalloy are examples of materials having high permeability. Air is arbitrarily given a permeability of "one". The permeability of air is the basis for comparing the permeability of other materials. Iron and steel, for example, have a permeability of several hundred.

RELUCTANCE. Magnetic reluctance is similar to electrical resistance. Magnetic reluctance is the opposition that a substance offers to magnetic lines of force. It is the propery of a material that opposes the creation of a magnetic flux within itself. The unit of reluctance is the REL or the OERSTED.

MAGNETOMOTIVE FORCE. The magnetomotive force of a magnetic circuit is similar to the electromotive force of an electrical circuit. The magnetomotive force is the force which produces the magnetic lines of force or flux. The unit of magnetomotive force is the GILBERT. The number of gilberts in a circuit is equal to:

$$(3-1) \quad G = 1.26 \times N \times I$$

where: N is the number of turns in the coil and
I is the number of amperes.

N x I, alone, is also known by the term AMPERE-TURNS. It is the number of turns multiplied by the number of amperes flowing in the circuit.

3 RELAYS. The relay is a popular device that makes use of the principles of electromagnetism. The basic function of a relay is to control a switch or circuit from a remote point. The circuit to be switched may be some distance from the operator or, heavy currents may be involved and it may be impractical to bring these heavy currents to a small panel switch.

Fig. 3-13 illustrates two common types of relays. The relay in Fig. 3-13A is called a "make-contact" relay. Contacts A and B are normally open (as shown). When switch S is closed, current flows through the electromagnet and pulls the arm holding contact B. Contact B then touches contact A and the circuit that is connected to these two contacts remains closed as long as current flows through the magnet. As soon as switch S is open, the electromagnet loses its magnetism and the arm with contact B is pulled back to its normal position. The circuit that is connected to contacts A and B is now open. We refer to this relay as a "Make-Contact" relay because it makes contact when the magnet is energized.

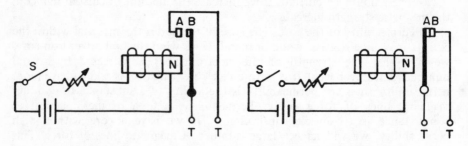

FIG. 3-13A. A MAKE-CONTACT RELAY   FIG. 3-13B. A BREAK-CONTACT RELAY.

Fig. 3-13B is a "Break-Contact" relay. It operates in a manner similar to that of Fig. 3-13A. We call it a break-contact relay because it is normally closed. When the relay coil is energized, the arm with contact A swings away from contact B and the circuit is "broken" or open.

Combination relays are in use that can close circuits and open others at the same time.

INDUCED VOLTAGE. If a coil of wire is made to cut a magnetic field, a voltage is induced in the coil of wire. The same reaction will occur if the magnetic field cuts the coil of wire. In other words, as long as there is relative motion between a conductor and a magnetic field, a voltage will be generated in the conductor. An induced voltage is sometimes called an induced e.m.f. (electromotive force).

Fig. 3-14A shows a bar magnet being thrust into a coil of wire. The dotted lines about the magnet represent magnetic lines of force. The relative movement between the coil and magnet will result in the turns of wire of the

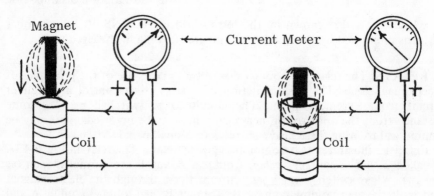

A. Magnet moving into coil.   B. Magnet moving out of coil.

FIG. 3-14. INDUCING A VOLTAGE IN A COIL OF WIRE.

38

coil being cut by the magnetic lines of force. The net result of this action will be an induced voltage generated in the turns of the coil. This induced voltage will, in turn, cause a current to flow in the coil. A galvanometer (an instrument used to detect the presence of small currents) will deflect to the right, indicating a current flow as a result of the induced e.m.f. Fig. 3-14B shows the magnet being pulled out of the coil. The galvanometer needle will now deflect to the left, indicating that the current is now in the opposite direction. Reversing the direction of the motion of the magnet in relation to the coil, reverses the direction of the induced e.m.f. This method of electromagnetic induction is used in the generators which supply us with our electricity.

If we wish to increase the strength of the induced e.m.f., we can do the following:

(1) Use a stronger magnet.

(2) Use more turns on the coil.

(3) Move the magnet or the coil back and forth at a faster rate.

(4) Have the coil cut the lines of force at right angles, if it is not already doing so. In other words, the more lines of force cut per second, the stronger is the induced e.m.f.

In order to determine the direction of the induced current, we use LENZ'S LAW. Lenz's law states: When a moving magnetic field induces an e.m.f. in a coil, a current will flow in such a direction as to form a magnetic field within the coil, which will oppose the motion of the original magnetic field.

METERS. There are many different types of meters and instruments used in the electronics field. However, the most common meters, such as the voltmeter, the ammeter and the ohmmeter, all make use of a basic meter movement known as the D'Arsonval type of meter movement.

3 D'ARSONVAL MOVEMENT. The D'Arsonval type of meter movement uses the principle of magnetic attraction and repulsion that has been described earlier in this chapter. A simplified illustration of the D'Arsonval movement is shown in Fig. 3-15. A coil of fine wire is suspended by two spiral springs in a magnetic field created by a permanent horse-shoe magnet.

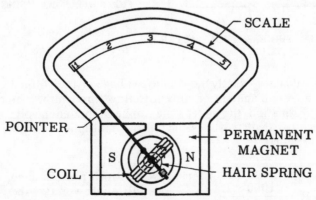

FIG. 3-15. THE D'ARSONVAL METER MOVEMENT.

A pointer is attached to the coil. If current flows through the coil, a magnetic field will be set up around the coil that will react with the field of the permanent magnet. If the current flows through the coil in the direction of the arrows, the left hand side of the coil will become a South magnetic pole and the right hand side will become a North magnetic pole. This will cause the coil to rotate in a clockwise direction (the South pole of the coil moves toward the North pole of the permanent magnet).

The spiral springs at the end of the coil (in Fig. 3-15 only one spring is shown; the other is hidden by the coil), tend to keep the coil from rotating. The magnetic reaction between the coil and the permanent magnet overcomes this resistance of the springs. If we increase the current through the coil, the coil will rotate more. This is due to the increased magnetic reaction between the permanent magnet and the stronger field of the coil. When the current through the coil is removed, the two springs force the coil to return to its original position.

The pointer that is attached to the coil deflects across a scale, thereby indicating relative amounts of current that flow through the movement.

If the D'Arsonval meter movement is used alone as an instrument, it is called a GALVANOMETER. The galvanometer merely indicates the presence of current; its scale is not calibrated to read amperes, volts or ohms.

THE VOLTMETER. By adding a high resistance in series with the basic D'Arsonval movement, we convert it to a VOLTMETER. This is shown in Fig. 3-16A. The series resistor is called a multiplier and it limits the flow of current through the delicate meter movement.

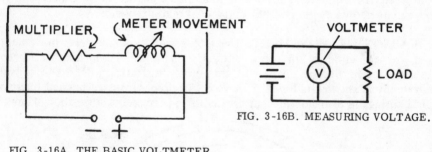

FIG. 3-16B. MEASURING VOLTAGE.

FIG. 3-16A. THE BASIC VOLTMETER
CIRCUIT.

We can calculate exactly how much voltage at the voltmeter's terminals will cause a certain amount of current to flow through the meter movement. With this information, the meter scale can be calibrated in volts.

In order to calculate the value of the multiplier resistor, we use the following formula:

$$(3\text{-}2) \quad R = \frac{1000 \times E}{I}$$

where: R = multiplier resistance,
E = full scale voltage and
I = full scale reading of the basic meter in milliamperes

40

PROBLEM: We have a basic meter movement that deflects full scale when 1 milliampere flows through it. (This meter is referred to as a 0-1 milliammeter). Find the value of the multiplier resistor required to convert the meter movement to a voltmeter that reads full scale when 400 volts is across it.

SOLUTION: The multiplier needed is found by using formula (3-2):

$$R = \frac{1000 \times E}{I}, \quad R = \frac{1000 \times 400}{1.0}, \quad R = 400,000 \text{ ohms.}$$

Thus, a 400,000 ohm multiplier is required.

A voltmeter's sensitivity depends on the current that is required to deflect it full scale. The less current that is required, the more sensitive is the meter. The sensitivity of the voltmeter is expressed in "ohms per volt" and is found by dividing the total resistance of the voltmeter by its full scale voltage. In the above example, the sensitivity would be:

$$\frac{400,000 \text{ ohms}}{400 \text{ volts}} = 1000 \text{ ohms per volt.}$$

Another way of finding the sensitivity of a voltmeter is to divide the full scale meter current into 1. In the above example, it would be:

$$\frac{1}{.001 \text{ amp.}} = 1000 \text{ ohms per volt.}$$

A voltmeter is always connected in parallel to, or across, the circuit that is being measured. See Fig. 3-16B.

THE AMMETER. To convert the D'Arsonval meter movement to an ammeter, we must add a SHUNT to it. A shunt is a very low value resistance that is connected in parallel to the meter movement. See Fig. 3-17A.

Because the shunt has a much lower resistance than the meter movement, most of the current flows through the shunt. Only a small amount of current flows through the meter movement itself. Since the coil in the meter movement is made of very thin wire, it would burn up if too much current flowed through it.

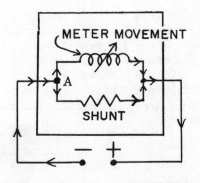

FIG. 3-17A. THE BASIC AMMETER
CIRCUIT.

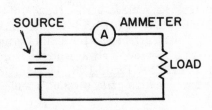

FIG. 3-17B. MEASURING CURRENT.

The scale is calibrated so that it reads the total current flowing through both the meter movement and the shunt. The value of the shunt resistance that is required to make the meter read a given full scale current range is found by using the following formula:

$$(3\text{-}3) \quad R_s = \frac{R_m \times I_m}{I_s}$$

where: R_s = shunt resistance
R_m = meter movement resistance
I_m = full scale meter movement current
I_s = shunt current

EXAMPLE: A 0-1 milliammeter, having a resistance of 15 ohms, is to be used to make a milliammeter whose full scale reading is to be 50 milliamperes. Find the value of the shunt resistor.

SOLUTION: Use formula (3-3). I_s is 49 ma. because the 50 ma. will divide so that 1 ma. will go through the meter and the balance (49 ma.) will go through the shunt.

$$R_s = \frac{15 \times .001}{.049} = \frac{.015}{.049} = .306 \text{ ohms.}$$

3 There are times when one must figure out an unknown current value using a milliammeter with a known shunt. The following problem illustrates this.
EXAMPLE: A one-milliampere meter having a resistance of 20 ohms was used to measure an unknown current by shunting the meter with a 5 ohm resistor. It then reads .7 milliampere. What was the unknown current value?

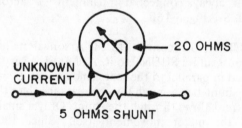

UNKNOWN CURRENT

20 OHMS

5 OHMS SHUNT

FIG. 3-18. CALCULATING
AN UNKNOWN CURRENT.

SOLUTION: If 0.7 ma. goes through the 20 ohm meter, the voltage across the meter is .0007 x 20 or .014 v. Since the shunt resistor is across the meter, the voltage across the shunt is also .014 v. The current through the shunt is E/R or .014/5 = 2.8 ma. The total unknown current is the sum of the meter current and the shunt current – 0.7 + 2.8 = 3.5 ma.

An ammeter is always hooked up in series with the circuit that is being measured. See Fig. 3-17B. An ammeter that is used to measure current in the order of milliamperes is called a milliammeter.

THE OHMMETER. The ohmmeter is a basic instrument that measures the resistance value of a resistor or circuit element. It is also used to test for shorted or open circuits, as well as circuit continuity.

The basic ohmmeter consists of a current meter movement, a source of low voltage DC and a current limiting resistor. This is shown in Fig. 3-19.

The battery causes a current to flow through the meter. Since different amounts of resistance at the ohmmeter terminals A and B will cause different amounts of meter deflection, we can calibrate the meter scale in ohms. Thus, we can place an unknown resistor at terminals A and B and read its resistance on the meter scale.

R1 is a limiting resistor. It limits the flow of current through the meter when terminals A and B are shorted. R2 is a zero adjust rheostat. It is used to set the meter to zero ohms when terminals A and B are shorted.

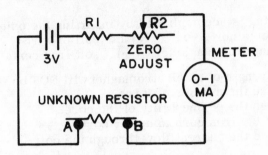

FIG. 3-19. THE BASIC OHMMETER CIRCUIT.

PRACTICE QUESTIONS - LESSON 3

1. The unit of magnetomotive force is:
a. henry   b. coulomb   c. farad   d. gilbert

2. If we placed a compass inside a coil carrying direct current, the North pole of the compass would:
a. point to the South pole of the coil
b. point to the North pole of the coil
c. point to the center of the coil
d. shift back and forth until the current was shut off

3. The opposition to the magnetic lines of force in a magnetic circuit is known as:
a. ampere-turns   c. resistance
b. reluctance   d. reactance

4. The magnetism remaining in a material after the magnetizing force has been removed, is known as:
a. residual magnetism   c. conductance
b. permeability   d. residual permeability

5. Ampere-turns may be defined as:
a. the square root of the number of turns, multiplied by current
b. the number of turns, multiplied by the square root of the current
c. the number of turns, multiplied by the current
d. one-half the number of turns, multiplied by the current

6. A relay does not use: (3)
a. an electromagnet   c. a source of current
b. contacts   d. a permanent magnet

7. The unit of reluctance is the:
   a. mho   b. gilbert   c. ampere-turns   d. oersted

8. Inside of a bar magnet, the path of the lines of force is:
   a. from the North pole to the South pole
   b. from the South pole to the North pole
   c. either way, depending on the type of magnet
   d. there are no lines of force inside a magnet

9. Shielding is accomplished by inserting the object in a:
   a. lead container   c. coil of wire
   b. non-magnetic container   d. soft iron container

10. The strength of an electromagnet will NOT be increased if we:
    a. increase the number of turns
    b. increase the permeability of the core
    c. change the iron core to an air core
    d. increase the current flow through the coil

11. What is the magnetomotive force, in gilberts, of a coil containing 50 turns with 200 ma flowing through it?
    a. 12,600   b. 10   c. 12.6   d. 25.2

12. Find the value of the multiplier resistor required to convert a 0-50 microampere meter movement to a voltmeter that reads full scale when 100 volts is across it.
    a. 20,000 ohms   c. 2,000 ohms
    b. 2,000 megohms   d. 2 megohms $R = \frac{E}{I} \quad \frac{100}{5 \times 10^{-5}}$

13. What is the sensitivity, in ohms per volt, of a 0-50 microampere meter?
    a. 20   b. 20,000   c. 50   d. 5,000 $\frac{E}{I}$

14. Find the value of the shunt that will convert a 20 ohm, 1 ma meter movement into a 1.0 ampere meter. $Rm \times Im$
    a. .002 ohms b. .02 ohms c. 20 ohms d. .18 ohms

15. A 200 microampere meter, having a resistance of 15 ohms, is used to measure an unknown current by shunting the meter with a 3 ohm resistor. The meter reads 120 microamperes. What is the value of the unknown current? (3)
    a. .48 ma b. 1.8 ma c. .6 ma d. .72 ma

16. What, in a D'Arsonval meter movement, opposes the meter action? (3)
    a. the springs   c. the electromagnet
    b. the permanent magnet d. none of the above

17. a relay whose contacts are normally closed, is known as a/an: (3)
    a. break-contact relay   c. open-contact relay
    b. closed-circuit relay   d. make-contact relay

44

LESSON 4
ALTERNATING CURRENT

ALTERNATING CURRENT. The three previous lessons dealt with direct current, a form of current that flows in one direction only. In this lesson, we will study alternating current (AC), a type of current that periodically reverses its direction of flow. Alternating current is produced by an AC generator or alternator.

DEVELOPMENT OF THE AC WAVE. Let us see how we can develop or generate AC. Fig. 4-1 shows a loop of wire which can be rotated between the poles of a magnet. (The magnetic field that exists between the North and South Poles is not shown in the diagram). If the loop of wire is rotated through the magnetic field, an electromotive force or voltage will be induced in the wire of the loop. This is because a conductor is cutting a magnetic field, and whenever this happens, a voltage is induced in the conductor. The voltage developed in the loop of wire will cause a flow of current. The milliammeter, in series with the loop, will indicate this current flow.

One of the factors influencing the strength of the induced e.m.f. is the relative cutting position of the loop, as compared to the direction of the magnetic field. When the conductors of the loop cut perpendicular to the

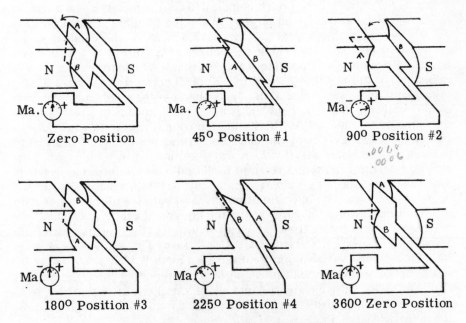

Zero Position   45° Position #1   90° Position #2

180° Position #3   225° Position #4   360° Zero Position

FIG. 4-1. GENERATING THE ALTERNATING CURRENT SINE WAVE.

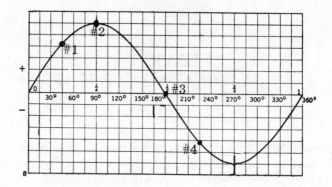

FIG. 4-2. THE SINE WAVE.

magnetic field, a maximum induced voltage will be generated. When the conductors of the loop are moving parallel to the magnetic field, no flux will be cut and therefore, no voltage will be generated. If the loop is rotated at a constant speed in a counterclockwise direction, a current will flow and its strength and direction will vary with different positions of the loop. The strength and direction of the current for different loop positions are indicated in Fig. 4-1. Fig. 4-2 is a graph showing the relationship between the amount of current and the different positions of the loop. Let us see exactly what happens at the various loop positions. At zero position, the loop begins its rotation with the ammeter indicating zero current. (The conductors of the loop are moving parallel to the magnetic flux; therefore, no induced e.m.f. will be generated.) When the loop has reached position #1 (45 degrees), the current flow, which is indicated on the meter, is in a direction which we shall arbitrarily call positive. When the loop has reached position #2 (90 degrees), the current is at a maximum, since the conductors are cutting into the magnetic field at right angles. The current flow is still in a positive direction. From position #2 to position #3, the current decreases in value, but is still positive. At position #3 (180 degrees) the current is zero once again, as it was at the start. This is because the conductor is moving parallel with the magnetic field and is not actually cutting it. From position #3, through #4 and back to the starting position, the current goes through the same changes as it went through from starting position (zero degrees) to position #3 (180 degrees). However, from position #3 to position zero, the direction of the current has reversed itself and is now considered negative. This is because the loop of wire is now cutting the magnetic field in the opposite direction. The opposite of positive is negative, and this is shown on the graph by drawing the curve below the horizontal center line. The curve of Fig. 4-2, representing the varying current through the loop, is a waveform known as the ALTERNATING CURRENT wave. The mathematical name for a fundamental alternating current wave is a SINE WAVE.

The action just described is the basis for the alternating current generators that supply us with electricity. Instead of one loop of wire, there is an armature that has many turns of wire and it is rotated through a strong magnetic field.

TO SUMMARIZE: ALTERNATING CURRENT, AS OPPOSED TO

DIRECT CURRENT, CONTINUOUSLY VARIES IN STRENGTH (OR AMPLITUDE) AND PERIODICALLY REVERSES ITS DIRECTION OF FLOW.

CHARACTERISTICS OF THE SINE WAVE. A sine wave has the following important characteristics:

(1) The complete wave, as shown in Fig. 4-3, is known as a CYCLE. The wave is generated in one complete revolution of the loop, from 0 to 360 degrees.

(2) An alternation is one-half cycle, from 0° to 180°, or from 180° to 360°.

(3) The frequency of a sine wave is the number of complete cycles in one second. If the sine wave of Fig. 4-3 takes one second to get from 0° to 360°, its frequency is one cycle per second. If 60 such cycles are completed in one second, the frequency would be 60 cycles per second. The time taken for one such cycle would be 1/60th of a second.

(4) The height of the wave at any point is known as its AMPLITUDE. The highest point of the wave is called the maximum or PEAK AMPLITUDE, which in Fig. 4-3, is one volt. In a sine wave, the peaks always occur at 90 degrees and 270 degrees; the zero points always occur at 0, 180 and 360 degrees.

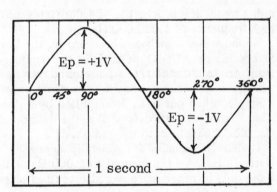

FIG. 4-3. THE SINE WAVE.

The peak voltage, E_p, is the voltage from the 0 line to the maximum point on either side of the 0 line. The Peak-to-Peak voltage is from the maximum point on the positive side of the 0 line to the maximum point on the other side of the 0 line. It is 2V. in Fig. 4-3. The sine wave of Fig. 4-3 represents AC current as well as AC voltage. Peak current or peak-to-peak current has similar meanings to their voltage counterparts.

FREQUENCY. The unit of frequency is CYCLES PER SECOND or simply, CYCLES. The abbreviation for cycles per second is CPS. In recent years, the electronics industry has adopted the term "HERTZ" instead of cycles per second. The abbreviation for Hertz is Hz. In keeping with this industry-wide change, we shall use the term Hertz to mean cycles per second. The frequency of the AC power that is supplied to most homes in the United States is 60 Hz. This is known as the POWER FREQUENCY. Radio waves transmitted by radio stations have a much higher frequency than the 60 Hz. power frequency; they are usually above 400,000 Hz. The abbreviation for

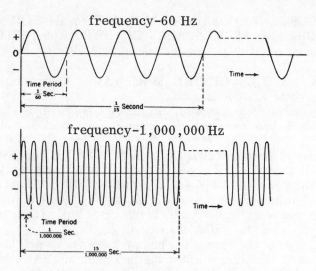

FIG. 4-4. LOW AND HIGH FREQUENCY WAVES.

radio frequency is RF. Fig. 4-4 illustrates a low frequency of 60 Hz and a high frequency of 1,000,000 Hz.

Sound waves which can be heard by the human ear are called AUDIBLE SOUNDS, or AUDIO SOUNDS. The frequency range of audio sounds is from 16 to 20,000 Hz. When sound waves are converted into electrical waves, they become known as audio frequencies (abbreviated AF). For example, when our voice is amplified by a public address system, the sound waves from our throats strike the microphone and are converted into electrical frequencies in the audio range.

Higher frequencies are generally expressed in kiloHertz (kHz) or mega-Hertz (MHz). A kHz is equal to 1,000 Hz. The prefix "kilo" stands for one thousand. In order to convert Hertz to kiloHertz, we divide the number of cycles by 1,000.

$$\text{For example: } 25,000 \text{ Hz} = \frac{25,000}{1,000} = 25 \text{ kHz}$$

A megaHertz (MHz) is equal to 1,000,000 Hertz. The prefix "meg" stands for one million. In order to convert Hertz into megaHertz we divide the number of Hertz by a million.

$$\text{For example: } 4,000,000 \text{ Hz} = \frac{4,000,000}{1,000,000} = 4 \text{ MHz}$$

FREQUENCY VERSUS TIME. It has been previously stated that it takes 1/60th of a second to complete one cycle of a 60 Hertz AC wave. A simple formula that gives the relationship between the time it takes to complete a cycle and the frequency, is:

$$(4\text{-}1) \quad \text{Time} = \frac{1}{\text{frequency}}$$

48

If we are interested in finding out how long it takes to complete a part of a cycle of a particular frequency, then we must multiply the answer from the above formula by a fraction representing that part of the cycle that we are interested in. An example will make this clear.

PROBLEM: How long does it take for a 2 megacycle wave to complete 45° of a cycle.

ANSWER: Using the formula (4-1), we find out low long it takes for one complete cycle:

$$\text{Time} = \frac{1}{2,000,000} = .0000005 \text{ sec.}$$

We can change the answer to microseconds (millionths of a second) by moving the decimal 6 places to the right.

.0000005 seconds = .5 microsecond (ms)

The fraction of a cycle for 45° is $\frac{45°}{360°}$ or $\frac{1}{8}$. In other words, 45° is completed in $\frac{1}{8}$ of the time of a full cycle.

$$.5 \text{ ms} \times \frac{1}{8} = .0625 \text{ ms}$$

Thus, it takes .0625 ms. to complete 45° of a cycle of a 2 megacycle wave.

THE MEANING OF PHASE RELATIONSHIP. If two alternating current generators are connected in series across a load, and if their armatures are started rotating together from exactly the same point, two voltages will be produced. Let us assume that the peak output of generator #1 is 4 volts and the peak output of generator #2 is 3 volts. Since both generators start from the same position, at the same time and at the same speed, they will both produce their maximum and minimum voltages at the same instant. This is illustrated in Fig. 4-5. Because the maximums and minimums of the two waves occur at the same time, we say that the two waves are IN PHASE with each other. Being in phase, the voltages become additive. Therefore, the resultant peak will be neither 4 volts nor 3 volts, but 7 volts, the combination of the two.

Now, let us assume that generator #2 is started an eighth of a revolution (45°) after generator #1 has started. The output of the two generators will reach maximum and minimum points at different times. They will now be

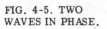
FIG. 4-5. TWO
WAVES IN PHASE.

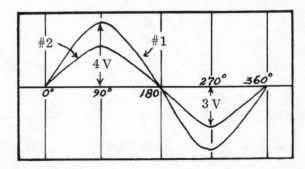

49

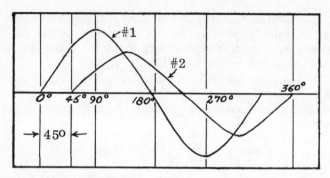

FIG. 4-6. TWO WAVES OUT-OF-PHASE.

OUT OF PHASE with each other, as shown in Fig. 4-6. It should be observed that the same voltages are being considered here as in Fig. 4-5, except that the 3 volt wave LAGS 45° behind the 4 volt wave. These waves are said to be out of phase by 45°. If the 3 volt wave had started 90° later, the 3 volt wave would lag the 4 volt wave by 90°. The angle by which one wave leads or lags another wave is known as the PHASE ANGLE.

COMBINING OUT-OF-PHASE VOLTAGES. Voltages that are out of phase cannot be added by simple addition, as we do with "in phase" voltages. In order to combine voltages or currents that are out of phase, we must use vector addition. Vectors are straight lines that are used to represent the magnitude and direction of a given quantity. The quantity can be a voltage, a current, a resistance, etc. The magnitude of the quantity is denoted by the length of the line. The direction is indicated by an arrow at one end of the line together with the angle that the vector makes with a horizontal reference vector.

The voltages of Fig. 4-6 are represented in vector form in Fig. 4-7. Note that the angle between the two vectors is 45°, the difference in phase between the two voltages. Also, note that the lengths of the lines corresponds to the voltages of the two waves. In order to add the two waves together, we use the "PARALLELOGRAM LAW". At the end of the 3 V. vector we draw a line parallel to the 4 V. vector. At the end of the 4 V. vector we draw a line parallel to the 3 V. vector. A parallelogram is formed. See Fig. 4-7B. The diagonal drawn from the junction of the two original vectors is called the resultant and it represents the sum of the two voltages.

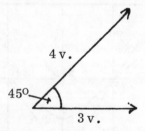

FIG. 4-7A. VECTORS REPRESENTING
VOLTAGES.

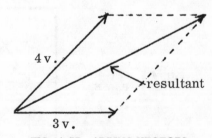

FIG. 4-7B. ADDING VECTORS.

50

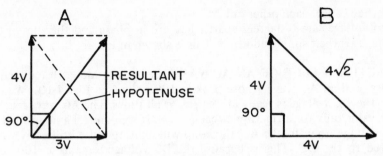

FIG. 4-8. VECTOR ADDITION IN A RIGHT TRIANGLE.

The length of the line represents the voltage of the sum and the angle that the resultant makes with the two original voltages represents its relative phase angle with respect to the other voltages.

If the phase angle between the two voltages is 90°, the parallelogram that is formed becomes a rectangle. See Fig. 4-8. Since the two diagonals of a rectangle are equal, the length of the hypotenuse (the side opposite the 90° angle) also gives us the magnitude of the vectorial sum of the two vectors. This can be found by measurement or by the formula for the hypotenuse of a right triangle.

$$(4\text{-}2) \quad X = \sqrt{a^2 + b^2}$$

where: X is the hypotenuse
a is one side
b is the other side

In fig. 4-8A, the vectorial sum of the two voltages is therefore:

$$X = \sqrt{a^2 + b^2} = \sqrt{3^2 + 4^2} = \sqrt{9 + 16} = \sqrt{25} = 5$$

Thus, the sum of a 4 volt sine wave and a 3 volt sine wave, 90° out of phase, is 5 volts.

If the two sides of the right triangle are equal, formula (4-2) becomes:

$$X = \sqrt{a^2 + a^2} = \sqrt{2a^2} = a\sqrt{2} = a \times 1.414 \text{ or } 1.414 \times a$$

Thus, the sum of two equal vectors, 90° apart; is equal to 1.414 times one of the vectors. This is shown in Fig. 4-8B.

If two vectors or voltages are 180° apart, as shown in Fig. 4-9A, they are opposite one another and tend to cancel each other. Their sum is their simple difference. If they are equal and 180° out of phase, their sum is zero

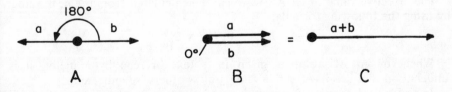

FIG. 4-9. ADDING VECTORS 180° OUT OF PHASE.

51

because they cancel each other out.

If two voltages are 0 degrees apart, they are in phase and the sum of the two voltages is their simple addition. This is shown in Fig. 4-9B.

EFFECTIVE VALUE OF AN AC WAVE. Let us consider a DC voltage of 100 volts, and an AC wave whose peak is 100 volts (see Fig. 4-10). We can see that the DC voltage is really at its peak at all times. The AC wave reaches its peak value only for a fraction of each cycle. If we connect a lamp, first to the DC voltage, then to the AC, the lamp will light up more brilliantly when connected to the DC. This is because the DC voltage remains at 100 volts continuously, whereas the AC voltage reaches 100 volts only at two points during each cycle. In order for the lamp to light with equal brilliance on AC as well as on DC, we find that we must raise the AC voltage to 141 peak volts. Effectively then, 141 peak volts of AC will light up a lamp as brilliantly as does 100 volts of DC. The EFFECTIVE value of the 141 volt peak AC wave is therefore 100 volts. This is illustrated in Fig. 4-11. Another term for effective value is RMS value. RMS stands for ROOT MEAN SQUARE.

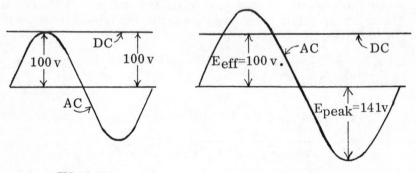

FIG. 4-10.

DC LEVEL EQUALS PEAK OF AC WAVE.

FIG. 4-11.

EFFECTIVE VALUE OF A SINE WAVE.

The effective value of an AC wave (either voltage or current), is 0.707 times its peak value. For example, the effective value of the above AC wave is 0.707 x 141 volts or 100 volts.

CALCULATION OF PEAK AND EFFECTIVE VALUE. The peak value of AC wave can be calculated from its effective value by using the following formula:

$$(4-3) \quad E_{peak} = 1.41 \text{ x } E_{eff}$$

The effective value of an AC wave can be calculated from the peak value by using the following formula:

$$(4-4) \quad E_{eff} = 0.707 \text{ x } E_{peak}$$

Whenever an AC value is given in a text or read by a meter, it is understood that it is its effective value, unless otherwise indicated.

In order to determine the peak value of an AC wave, the reading of an AC meter is multiplied by 1.414. In addition to this method, there are other ways of determining peak AC voltages. There are special peak reading vacuum tube voltmeters that measure the peak voltage or current directly. (The vacuum tube voltmeter is discussed in lesson 8). Another way of determining the peak voltage of an AC wave is to use the device that actually exhibits the wave signal on the face of a large tube. Such a tube is called a CATHODE RAY TUBE, and is fully discussed in lesson 8. The face of the cathode ray tube can be calibrated with known voltages, and by comparing these to the unknown voltage, we can determine the value of the unknown voltage.

AVERAGE VALUE The average value of an AC sine wave is the mathematical average of the instantaneous values of the sine wave. Since half of the sine wave is negative and half is positive, the average value of a sine wave is zero. However, when we use the term "average value" electrically, we mean the average of an alternation or half cycle. The average value of an AC wave is found to be 0.637 of the peak value. The following formulas state this relationship:

(4-5) $E_{av} = 0.637 \times E_{peak}$ and (4-6) $I_{av} = 0.637 \times I_{peak}$

The average value is used in rectifier systems, which will be discussed in a later lesson.

INDUCTANCE. In a previous paragraph we learned that a current-carrying coil of many turns behaves just like a magnet. The current causes a magnetic field to surround the coil. If the current flowing through the coil is alternating, the magnetic field will also be alternating. Fig. 4-12 shows a coil with alternating current flowing through it. This alternating current produces an alternating magnetic field around the coil which expands and collapses in step (or in phase) with the alternating current. When the current is zero, the magnetic field is zero; when the current reaches its peak at 90°, the magnetic field reaches its maximum value. This is shown in Fig. 4-13. Since the field starts from zero and builds up to a maximum, it is an expanding field. This expanding field must cut through the conductors of the coil itself. According to Lenz's law, the cutting action induces an e.m.f. in the coil which opposes the original current. In other words, alternating current flowing through a

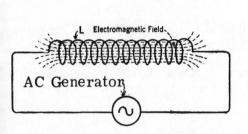

FIG. 4-12.
AC FLOWING THROUGH COIL.

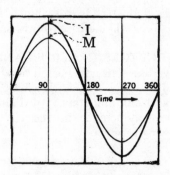

FIG. 4-13. MAGNETIC FIELD
AND CURRENT IN PHASE.

53

coil induces a voltage into the coil that is in opposition to the original voltage. The process wherein an induced e.m.f. is generated in a coil is called SELF-INDUCTION. The coil of wire is called an INDUCTANCE. The unit of inductance is the HENRY, and the abbreviation of henry is h. The symbol for inductance is L. Smaller and more practical units of inductance are the millihenry (mh) and the microhenry (μh).

$$1 \text{ millihenry} = \frac{1}{1000} \text{ of a henry}$$

$$1 \text{ microhenry} = \frac{1}{1,000,000} \text{ of a henry}$$

The energy stored in the magnetic field surrounding an inductance carrying an electric current is found by using the following formula:

(4-7) $W = \dfrac{LI^2}{2}$ where W (watt-second) is in joules, L is in henries and I is in amperes

The schematic symbol for inductance is —⁀⁀⁀⁀⁀— or ⌒⌒⌒

FACTORS AFFECTING THE INDUCTANCE OF A COIL.

(1) Number of turns. The inductance of a coil varies as the square of the number of turns.

$$(4-8) \quad \frac{L1}{L2} = \frac{T1^2}{T2^2}$$

For example, if we have two coils of the same length and diameter and coil #1 has four turns while coil #2 has eight turns, the inductance of coil #2 will be four times the inductance of coil #1.

(2) Core material. The inductance of a coil varies with the core material. An iron-core coil will have a higher inductance than an air-core coil. Since iron has a higher permeability than air, there will be a stronger magnetic field around the iron- core coil which results in a higher inductance.

(3) Length of coil. As the length of a coil increases, the number of turns remaining. constant, the inductance of the coil decreases. This is because the reluctance of the magnetic circuit increases due to the increased coil length. This results in a weakening of the magnetic field.

(4) Diameter of coil. The inductance of a coil varies directly as the square of the diameter. For example, if we double the diameter of a coil, the inductance will increase four times.

INDUCTORS IN SERIES AND PARALLEL.
Series-connected inductors behave like series-connected resistors. The total value of inductors in series is the sum of their individual values.

The total inductance of inductors in parallel is always less than the smallest inductance in the circuit, and can be computed by using the following formula:

$$(4-9) \quad L_T = \frac{1}{\dfrac{1}{L1} + \dfrac{1}{L2} + \dfrac{1}{L3}}$$

54

The above rules for inductances in series or parallel are true only if the inductances are far enough apart so that the magnetic fields around the individual inductors do not affect any of the other inductors in the circuit. If this is not the case, formulas (4-11) or (4-13) must be used.

MUTUAL INDUCTANCE AND COEFFICIENT OF COUPLING. When AC is applied to coil A of Fig. 4-14, a varying magnetic field will develop around it. This field will induce a voltage into coil B. Since this induced

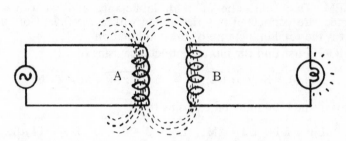

FIG. 4-14. MUTUAL INDUCTANCE.

voltage is the result of current flowing in coil A, we speak of the mutual inductance between the two coils. It is the effect of one coil upon the other, and vice versa. The mutual inductance of two coils depends upon the distance between the two coils and the angle between the two coils. The smallest amount of coupling occurs when the coils are at right angles to each other and/or when they are far apart from each other. The greatest amount of coupling occurs when the coils are wound in phase, one over the other, and on a closed iron core. When all of the magnetic flux of one coil passes through all of the turns of the second coil, we have the maximum coupling. This is sometimes referred to as UNITY COEFFICIENT OF COUPLING and is given the numerical value of one. The coefficient of coupling is a measure of the amount of coupling between two coils, and it varies from zero to one. The formula for the coefficient of coupling is:

$$(4\text{-}10) \quad K = \frac{M}{\sqrt{L1 \times L2}}$$

where: K is the coefficient of coupling. It is a number from 0 to 1. M is the mutual inductance between the two coils. L1 is coil 1; L2 is coil 2.

PROBLEM: What is the coefficient of coupling between two coils having inductances of .4 and .9 henry, respectively, if the mutual inductance between the two coils is .4 henry?
SOLUTION:

$$K = \frac{.4}{\sqrt{.4 \times .9}}, \quad K = \frac{.4}{\sqrt{.36}}, \quad K = \frac{.4}{.6}, \quad K = .667$$

Where mutual inductance is present, and their fields are in phase (series aiding), the total inductance of two coils in series is found by using the following formula:

55

(4-11) $L_T = L1 + L2 + 2M$ where: L_T = total inductance.
L1 = inductance of coil 1.
L2 = inductance of coil 2.
M = mutual inductance.

M is either given or can be derived from formula (4-10). It is equal to:

(4-12) $M = K \times \sqrt{L1 \times L2}$ where K is the coefficient of coupling.

PROBLEM: Two coils, one of 2 μh inductance and the other of 8 μh inductance, are connected in series aiding with a coefficient of coupling of .5. What is the total inductance of the combination?
SOLUTION: First find the mutual inductance using (4-12).

$$M = K \sqrt{L1\,L2}; \quad M = .5 \sqrt{2 \times 8}; \quad M = 2 \,\mu h$$

Next find the total inductance, using (4-11).

$$L_T = L1 + L2 + 2M; \quad L_T = 2 + 8 + 4; \quad L_T = 14 \,\mu h.$$

If the fields of the two coils in series are out of phase (series opposing), the formula for the total inductance is:

(4-13) $L_T = L1 + L2 - 2M.$

INDUCTIVE REACTANCE. Due to the counter electromotive force of self-induction, an inductance resists a change of current flow. This resistance or holding-back effect is measured in ohms. Instead of being called a resistance, however, it is called a reactance, an INDUCTIVE REACTANCE. The symbol for inductive reactance is X_L.
The formula for computing inductive reactance is:

(4-14) $X_L = 2\pi f L$ where $\pi = 3.14$
f = frequency of applied voltage in Hz
L = inductance of the coil in henries

PROBLEM: Find the inductive reactance of a 10 millihenry coil at a frequency of 60 Hz.
SOLUTION: First convert 10 mh to h; then use formula (4-14).

(1) $10 \text{ mh} = \dfrac{10}{1000} h = \dfrac{1}{100} h$ (2) $X_L = 2\pi f L$

(3) $2 \times 3.14 \times 60 \times \dfrac{1}{100} = 3.768 \text{ ohms.}$

An inductance is sometimes called a "choke" because it opposes or "chokes" an alternating current flow. A filter choke is an inductance that is found in power supplies. Its purpose is to oppose the flow of AC power frequencies while allowing DC to pass through unopposed. An audio choke is an inductance that is found in audio circuits. Its purpose is to oppose the flow of audio frequencies while allowing DC to flow. A radio frequency choke (RFC) is an inductance that is found in radio frequency (high

56

frequency AC) circuits. Its purpose is to oppose the flow of radio frequency currents while allowing the lower frequencies and direct current to flow.

IMPEDANCE OF AN INDUCTIVE CIRCUIT. In Fig. 4-15A, the total resistance which opposes the flow of current is R1 + R2. The total resistance to current flow in a series circuit is the sum total of the individual resistances. If the circuit consists of resistance and inductive reactance, as shown in Fig. 4-15B, the total resistance to the flow of current is called the IMPEDANCE. The symbol for impedance is Z. The unit of impedance is the ohm. Unlike the resistive circuit, the impedance of an inductive circuit is NOT equal to the simple sum of the resistance and the inductive reactance.

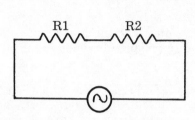

FIG. 4-15A.
RESISTIVE CIRCUIT.

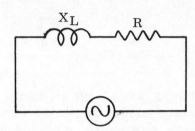

FIG. 4-15B.
INDUCTIVE-RESISTIVE CIRCUIT.

The impedance of an inductive circuit can be calculated by using the following formula:

where:

(4-15) $Z = \sqrt{R^2 + X_L^2}$

Z is the total impedance in ohms,
X_L is the inductive reactance in ohms,
R is the series resistance in ohms.

Problem: If a circuit contains a coil and resistor in series, and if the coil has an inductive reactance of 12 ohms and the resistor is 5 ohms, what is (1) the total impedance and (2) the current? The source voltage is 130 volts.
Solution: Note that the impedance IS NOT simply the sum of R and X_L, or 17 ohms. The impedance in an INDUCTIVE CIRCUIT must be calculated by using formula (4-15).

$$Z = \sqrt{R^2 + X_L^2} = \sqrt{5^2 + 12^2} = \sqrt{25 + 144} = \sqrt{169} = 13 \text{ ohms}$$

The current in the circuit is simply the total voltage divided by the impedance. This is in accordance with Ohm's Law.

$$I = \frac{E}{Z} = \frac{130}{13} = 10 \text{ amperes}$$

3 SKIN EFFECT. When direct current flows through a wire, it flows through the entire cross-sectional area of the wire. This is also true of low-frequency alternating current. However, as the frequency of the alternating current increases, we find that an inductive reactance or opposition to the current flow develops in the center of the wire. We can see from the formula for inductive reactance that it increases with increasing frequency. The opposition at the center of the wire causes the high frequencies to flow at or near its surface. This phenomenon is known as SKIN EFFECT.

The effects of skin effect can be reduced by using large diameter wires and by coating the surface with a low resistivity metal such as silver. Hollow copper tubing can be used for high frequency circuits since very little current would normally flow through the conductor's center.

3 **ADMITTANCE.** Just as the conductance is the reciprocal or opposite of resistance, admittance is the reciprocal or opposite of impedance. While impedance is the total opposition to AC, the admittance of a circuit represents the ability of a circuit to conduct AC. The unit of admittance is the mho. The formula for admittance is:

$$(4\text{-}16) \quad Y = \frac{1}{Z}$$

where Y is the admittance in mhos and Z is the impedance in ohms

PHASE ANGLE OF AN INDUCTIVE CIRCUIT. If AC is applied to an ordinary resistive circuit, the voltage and current are in phase with one another. However, this is not true if AC is applied to an inductive circuit. If we apply AC to a "pure" inductive circuit (one that contains only inductance and no resistance), the current will lag the impressed voltage by 90°. This is illustrated in Fig. 4-16. The waveform E starts 90° ahead of the

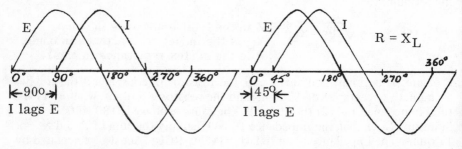

FIG. 4-16.
PURE INDUCTIVE CIRCUIT.

FIG. 4-17.
INDUCTIVE-RESISTIVE CIRCUIT.

waveform I. We say that the phase angle between the voltage and current is 90°. Since, in actual practice, a coil or inductance will always have some resistance (the resistance of the wire), the phase angle between the applied voltage and the current becomes less than 90°. The greater the proportion of resistance, the smaller will be the phase angle. Fig. 4-17 illustrates the current lagging the voltage by 45° in a circuit containing equal amounts of resistance and inductive reactance. When there is all resistance and no inductance, the phase angle becomes 0 degrees. The current and voltage are then in phase. This is to be expected since it is the counter-e.m.f. of the inductance which causes the current to lag.

To find the phase angle of the current with reference to the voltage in an inductive-resistance circuit, we use the following formula:

$$(4\text{-}17) \quad \mathrm{Tan}\,\theta = \frac{X_L}{R}$$

where: Tan θ is the tangent of the
phase angle.
X_L is the inductive reactance.
R is the resistance.

The answer gives us the tangent of the phase angle. By referring to the trigonometry table, we can find the actual phase angle.

CAPACITANCE. We have thus far studied two radio parts that exert a limiting effect upon current flow: (1) resistors, and (2) inductors. A third limiting device which has a tremendous application in radio is the CAPACITOR. A capacitor is a device having, in its simplest form, two conducting plates separated by an insulator.

The symbol for capacitance is C. The unit of capacitance is the FARAD; the symbol for farad is f. Since the farad is an extremely large unit of capacitiance, it is very rarely used. The more common, smaller units of capacitance are the microfarad (mf) which is equal to one millionth of a farad and the micromicrofarad (mmf) which is equal to one millionth of a millionth of a farad. The term, micromicrofarad, is no longer used. It has been replaced by the term picofarad (pf).

The range of capacitors used in radio work may vary all the way from 1 pf up to 1000 mf.

The dielectric is nothing more than the name for the insulating material between the plates of a capacitor. Examples of dielectrics used in capacitors are mica, ceramic, glass, oil and waxpaper. Capacitors with different dielectric materials will have different capacitances. For example, a capacitor with a mica dielectric will have a larger capacitance than an air dielectric capacitor of similar dimensions. The dielectric determines the ability of a capacitor to hold more or less charge.

Fig. 4-18 illustrates a two-plate capacitor connected across a battery. When the switch is closed, a certain number of free electrons on plate A will be attracted to the positive side of the battery. Plate A will therefore be left with a positive charge. At the same time, plate B will have the same number of electrons pushed onto it by the negative side of the battery. This electron flow continues until a charge or voltage is built up on the capacitor plates.

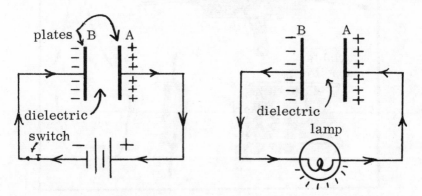

FIG. 4-18. CHARGING A CAPACITOR.   FIG. 4-19. CAPACITOR DISCHARGING.

This voltage is equal to the battery voltage. The plates of the capacitor are now said to be electrically charged. Notice that the accumulated electrons on plate B cannot cross to the other plate because of the insulator or dielectric between them. The arrows indicate electron flow.

The electrons on the negative plate are actually held there by the mutual attraction of the corresponding positive charges on the positive plate. This mutual attraction creates an electrostatic or electric field through the dielectric. This electric field is, in many respects, similar to a magnetic field. It has electric lines of force or flux. These lines of force originate on the negatively charged plate and terminate on the positively charged plate.

The charge on the capacitor plates depends on the size of the plates (the capacitance) and the voltage of the battery. The symbol for charge is Q (quantity of charge) and the unit of charge is the coulomb. The formula for the charge on a capacitor is:

$$(4\text{-}18) \quad Q = CE$$
where: Q is the charge in coulombs.
C is the capacitance in farads.
E is the applied voltage in volts.

The energy stored in a capacitor which has a charge is found by using one of the following formulas:

$$(4\text{-}19) \quad W = \frac{QE}{2} \qquad (4\text{-}20) \quad W = \frac{CE^2}{2} \qquad (4\text{-}21) \quad W = \frac{Q^2}{2C}$$

where: W is the energy in joules

If we disconnect the battery from the capacitor, the capacitor will continue to hold its charge. If a lamp is now connected across the charged capacitor (Fig. 4-19), the excess electrons on plate B will flow through the lamp and onto positive plate A. This is because electrons are attracted to a positively charged body. During the brief time of the electron flow, the lamp

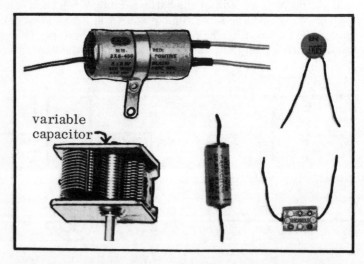

variable capacitor

FIG. 4-20. VARIOUS TYPES OF CAPACITORS USED IN RADIO.

will light for an instant, indicating that a current is passing through it. The electrons will continue to flow until plate B no longer has a surplus of electrons. Plate B is then said to have a zero charge. Plate B is now neutral and of course, plate A will have regained its electrons so that it also is neutral. The capacitor is now said to be DISCHARGED. A capacitor, then, is a device in which electricity may be stored for a period of time. Fig. 4-20 illustrates several different types of capacitors used in radio work.

3 **FACTORS AFFECTING THE VALUE OF CAPACITANCE.** The capacitance of a capacitor depends upon the following factors:

(1)THE AREA OF THE PLATES. The capacitance of a capacitor is directly proportional to the area of the plates. More electrons or charge can be stored if the plate area is larger. By the same token, if the plate area is smaller, the capacitance is smaller.

(2) THE DISTANCE BETWEEN PLATES. The capacitance is inversely proportional to the distance between plates. The greater the distance, the less is the capacity; the less the distance, the greater is the capacity.

(3) THE TYPE OF DIELECTRIC USED. The use of different dielectric materials changes the capacity of a capacitor. For instance, if we substitute mica for air as the dielectric, the capacitance increases by a factor of six. We say that mica has a DIELECTRIC CONSTANT six times as great as air. The various dielectric materials used in capacitors are assigned dielectric constants. As the dielectric constant goes up, the capacitance goes up and vice versa.

The capacitance formula (for a simple two plate capacitor) that ties these factors together, is:

(4-22) $C = 0.2249 \left(\dfrac{KA}{D} \right)$

where:
C is the capacitance in picofarads. A is the area of one of the plates in square inches. D is the distance between plates in inches. K is the dielectric constant of the material separating the plates.

3 **CAPACITOR COLOR CODE.** In most cases, the value of a capacitor is marked on its body. This is true for tubular types and ceramic capacitors. However, most mica ("postage-stamp" type) capacitors use color codes to indicate their values. There are several color codes in existence. The most popular one is the one adopted by the Electronic Industries Association (EIA). See Fig. 4-21. The colors are read clockwise, starting at the upper left hand corner. The first color indicates the code being used. White would indicate the EIA code. Black would indicate the JAN (Joint Army-Navy) code and silver indicates the AWS (American War Standards) code. In the EIA system, the second color is the first significant figure of the capacitance value in picofarads. The third color gives the second significant figure. The fourth color (lower right hand corner) tells us how many zeros must be added. The fifth color gives the tolerance and the sixth color indicates the temperature coefficient. Fig. 4-21B illustrates a typical mica capacitor. Its value is 220 pf, with a 5% tolerance. It uses the EIA code and has a temperature coefficient of 0-70 ppm per degree C. The color-number table

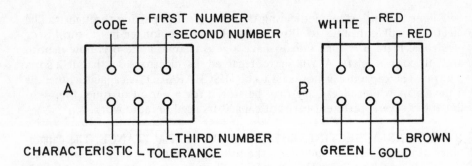

FIG. 4-21. CAPACITOR COLOR CODE. **C**

0 black	7 violet
1 brown	8 gray
2 red	9 white
3 orange	Tolerance
4 yellow	5% gold
5 green	10% silver
6 blue	20% no color

for capacitors is given in Fig. 4-21C.

THE VARIABLE CAPACITOR. Fig. 4-22 shows the schematic symbol of a capacitor whose capacitance can be varied. This capacitor is known as a **VARIABLE CAPACITOR**, and is used whenever the capacitance in a circuit

FIG. 4-22. VARIABLE CAPACITOR SYMBOLS.

OR

indicates rotor

must be changed frequently. The station selector in a radio receiver is a typical example of a variable capacitor. A variable capacitor is shown in Fig. 4-23.

A typical operating range for a variable capacitor is from 25 pf to 40 pf. Most variable capacitors are of the air dielectric type. A simple variable

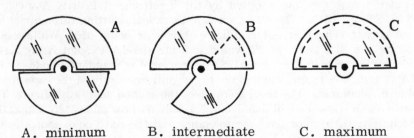

A. minimum   B. intermediate   C. maximum

FIG. 4-23. VARIABLE CAPACITOR SETTINGS.

capacitor consists of two sets of metal plates insulated from each other and so arranged that one set of plates can be moved in relation to the other set. The stationary plates are the stator; the moveable plates, the rotor. As the rotor is turned so that its plates mesh with the stator plates, the capacitance increases. Fig. 4-23 illustrates the rotor position of a variable capacitor for minimum, intermediate and maximum capacitances. If several variable capacitors are connected on a common shaft so that all may be controlled at the same time, the result is known as a "ganged" capacitor.

THE FIXED CAPACITOR. Fixed capacitors are capacitors that have a non-adjustable value of capacitance. (See Fig. 4-20). They are usually made of thin pieces of metal foil acting as the plates and a thin, solid dielectric which is sandwiched between the plates. The most common solid dielectrics used are paper, mica and ceramic. Typical values of fixed capacitors range from 1 pf to 1 mf.

3 **THE ELECTROLYTIC CAPACITOR.** The electrolytic capacitor is most commonly used where a large value of capacitance is needed. (See Fig. 4-20). Values of electrolytic capacitors are from 1 mf up to 1 f. The plates are usually made of aluminum foil with a liquid or paste chemical compound between them. When a voltage is applied across the plates of an electrolytic capacitor, a thin electro-chemical film is formed on the plates which acts as the dielectric. This type of capacitor has polarity and its terminals or leads are marked positive (+) and negative (−). The polarity must be observed when using an electrolytic capacitor in a circuit.

VOLTAGE RATING OF A CAPACITOR. Capacitors are rated not only in capacitance, but also by the maximum voltage they can handle before breaking down. If the voltage across a capacitor is too high, the electrical pressure will force the electrons to jump from the negative plate to the positive plate. This will puncture the dielectric and, in most cases, will ruin the capacitor. A typical capacitor would be rated as follows:

Capacitor - 8 mf
DC working voltage - 450 V.

DC WORKING VOLTAGE indicates that the capacitor may be used in any circuit as long as the DC voltage or the AC peak voltage across it does not exceed 450 volts.

CAPACITORS CONNECTED IN SERIES COMBINATION. When two or more capacitors are connected end to end, as shown in Figs. 4-24 and 4-25, the capacitors are said to be connected in series.

THE EFFECT OF CONNECTING CAPACITORS IN SERIES IS TO DECREASE THE TOTAL CAPACITANCE OF THE CIRCUIT, just as the total resistance of circuit is decreased when resistors are connected in parallel.

The total capacitance of capacitors connected in series can be computed by using the following formula:

63

$$(4\text{-}23) \quad C_T = \cfrac{1}{\dfrac{1}{C1} + \dfrac{1}{C2} + \dfrac{1}{C3} + \text{etc.}}$$

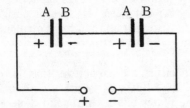

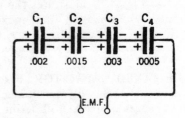

FIG. 4-24. CAPACITORS IN SERIES.   FIG. 4-25. PROBLEM.

PROBLEM: If four capacitors with capacitances as shown in Fig. 4-25 are connected in series, what is the total capacitance?

SOLUTION: Substitute in formula 4-23 and solve.

$$C_T = \cfrac{1}{\dfrac{1}{.002} + \dfrac{1}{.0015} + \dfrac{1}{.003} + \dfrac{1}{.0005}}$$

Dividing .002 into 1, we get,500, etc.

$$C_T = \cfrac{1}{500 + 667 + 333 + 2000} = \cfrac{1}{3500} = .00029 \text{ mf or } 290 \text{ pf.}$$

From the above example, it should be clear that in a series arrangement of capacitors, the total capacity of the series combination is always less than the capacitance of any individual capacitor.

In a series AC circuit, the voltage across each capacitor is directly proportional to the voltage of the source and inversely proportional to the capacitance of the capacitor.

PROBLEM: Four capacitors having capacitances of 5, 10, 20, and 25 mf respectively, are connected in series across a 110 volt source, as shown in Fig. 4-26. What voltage will appear across each capacitor?

SOLUTION: The total capacitance in the circuit is found from formula (4-23).

FIG. 4-26.
PROBLEM.

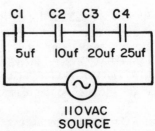

64

$$C_T = \cfrac{1}{\cfrac{1}{C1} + \cfrac{1}{C2} + \cfrac{1}{C3} + \cfrac{1}{C4}} \, , \quad C_T = \cfrac{1}{\cfrac{1}{5} + \cfrac{1}{10} + \cfrac{1}{20} + \cfrac{1}{25}}$$

$$C_T = \cfrac{1}{.2 + .1 + .05 + .04} \, , \quad C_T = \cfrac{1}{.39} \, , \quad C_T = 2.564 \text{ mf.}$$

The voltage across each capacitance is found by taking the product of the total capacitance, C_T, and the source voltage, Es, and dividing by the capacitance of the capacitor in question, Cx.

$$(4\text{-}24) \quad E_x = \frac{C_T \times E_s}{C_x}$$

$$E1 = \frac{C_T \times E_s}{C1} \, , \quad E1 = \frac{2.564 \times 110}{5} \, , \quad E1 = 56.41 \text{ volts}$$

$$E2 = \frac{C_T \times E_s}{C2} \, , \quad E2 = \frac{2.564 \times 110}{10} \, , \quad E2 = 28.2 \text{ volts}$$

$$E3 = \frac{C_T \times E_s}{C3} \, , \quad E3 = \frac{2.564 \times 110}{20} \, , \quad E3 = 14.1 \text{ volts}$$

$$E4 = \frac{C_T \times E_s}{C4} \, , \quad E4 = \frac{2.564 \times 110}{25} \, , \quad E4 = 11.29 \text{ volts}$$

CAPACITORS CONNECTED IN PARALLEL COMBINATION. Fig. 4-27 illustrates three capacitors hooked together in parallel. Connecting capacitors in parallel results in greatly increasing the effective plate area. Since the

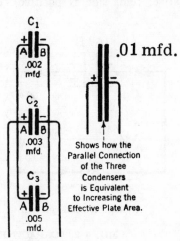

FIG. 4-27. CAPACITORS IN PARALLEL.

65

effective plate area is increased, the effective capacitance is also increased, as shown in Fig. 4-27.

When capacitors are connected in parallel, the resulting capacitance is equal to the sum of the individual capacitances.

PROBLEM: If three capacitors of .002, .003 and .005 mf are connected in parallel, what is the total capacitance?

SOLUTION:

(1) $C_T = C1 + C2 + C3$

(2) $C_T = .002 + .003 + .005 = .01$ mf.

THE CAPACITOR IN AN ALTERNATING CURRENT CIRCUIT. If a capacitor is placed across an AC generator in series with an AC ammeter (Fig. 4-28A) the following action occurs: When the left side of the generator is negative, electrons flow from the negative terminal of the generator to the capacitor plate A. At the same time, electrons flow off plate B, through the ammeter, to the right side of the generator. When the polarity of the AC generator reverses, as in Fig. 4-28B, the electrons reverse in direction and flow from the left plate, through the generator and ammeter, onto the right plate. This reversal of current flow occurs many times in one second, depending upon the frequency of the generator. The ammeter registers a reversal of current flow since electrons flow through it, first in one direction and then in the other. In other words, although an electric current does not flow through the capacitor itself, it does flow in and out of the plates of the capacitor and therefore, flows back and forth through all the components connected in series with the capacitor. When it is said that AC flows through a capacitor, what is actually meant is that the current is flowing in and out of the plates of the capacitor. As far as the other components in the circuit are concerned, the AC might just as well be flowing through the capacitor itself.

CAPACITIVE REACTANCE. Fig. 4-28A shows a capacitor connected across an AC generator. At the instant shown (left side of generator is negative, right side is positive), electrons rush from the left side of the

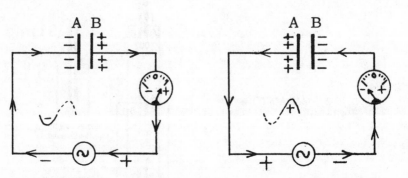

A. Negative alternation.　　　　B. Positive alternation.

FIG. 4-28. CAPACITOR ACROSS AN AC GENERATOR.

66

generator to the left plate of the capacitor. At first only a few electrons will reach the capacitor plate, A. However, these few electrons will attempt to repel the electrons that are approaching this capacitor plate. This same action occurs on the plate B when the polarity of the generator reverses itself. (See Fig. 4-28B). Every time the polarity of the generator reverses, the first few electrons that pile up on the capacitor will repel the remaining electrons. Thus we see that a capacitor offers a certain amount of opposition to alternating current. This opposition is actually a COUNTER-E.M.F., since the original charge on the capacitor plates represents an opposition voltage to the generator voltage. This counter-e.m.f. will vary inversely with the capacitance of the capacitor and the frequency of the AC generator.

The opposition or resistance that the capacitor offers to AC is called CAPACITIVE REACTANCE. The symbol for capacitive reactance is Xc, and its unit is the OHM.

In order to compute the capacitive reactance of a capacitor in an AC circuit, the following formulas are used:

(1) When the capacitance is given in farads:

$$(4\text{-}25) \quad X_c = \frac{1}{2\pi fc}$$

where X_c = capacitive reactance in ohms,
π = 3.14,
f = frequency of AC in Hertz,
c = capacitance in farads

(2) When the capacitance is given in microfarads:

$$(4\text{-}26) \quad X_c = \frac{1,000,000}{2\pi fc} = \frac{10^6}{2\pi fc}$$

where X_c = capacitive reactance in ohms, 2π = 6.28,
f = frequency of AC in Hertz,
c = capacitance in microfarads

PROBLEM: Find the capacitive reactance of a 15 mf capacitor in an AC circuit where the frequency of the generator is 1 kHz.
SOLUTION: Use formula (4-26)

$$X_c = \frac{10^6}{2\pi fc} \qquad X_c = \frac{10^6}{6.28 \times 1000 \times 15}$$

$$X_c = \frac{10^6}{94.2 \times 10^3} = 10.6 \text{ ohms}$$

There are times when we wish to find the value of a capacitor that will give us a certain amount of capacitive reactance. In order to do this, we simply take the above formula and transpose the Xc and the C. Mathematically, we have a right to do this. In effect, we are multiplying both sides by C, then we divide both sides by Xc. The result is formula (4-27).

$$(4\text{-}26) \quad X_c = \frac{1,000,000}{2\pi fc} \quad , \quad (4\text{-}27) \quad C = \frac{1,000,000}{2\pi fX_c}$$

A problem will illustrate the use of this formula:
PROBLEM: Find the value of capacitance that will yield 3000 ohms of capacitive reactance in a circuit where the frequency is 10 kHz.

$$C = \frac{1,000,000}{2\pi f X_c} = \frac{1,000,000}{6.28 \times 10,000 \times 3000} = \frac{1,000,000}{188,400,000} = .0053 \text{ mf}$$

A capacitor acts somewhat differently than a coil. The inductance of the coil OPPOSES CURRENT CHANGES by means of a self-induced e.m.f.; a capacitor OPPOSES VOLTAGE CHANGES by means of the counter-e.m.f. developed on its plates.

4 CAPACITIVE REACTANCE VERSUS FREQUENCY. An examination of the formula for capacitive reactance indicates that the reactance of a capacitor is inversely proportional to the frequency. In other words, as the frequency goes up, the reactance goes down, and vice versa.

The proportional equation that shows this is:

$$\frac{X_{c1}}{X_{c2}} = \frac{f2}{f1}$$

where f1 is the frequency that gives us X_{c1} and f2 is the frequency that gives us X_{c2}

If we know three of the four items in the formula, we can find the fourth by algebraically solving for it. Assume that we know Xc2, f2 and f1. We want to find Xc1. We simply multiply both sides of the equation by Xc2 and arrive at the following equation:

$$X_{c1} = \frac{f2 \, X_{c2}}{f1}$$

PROBLEM: What is the reactance of a capacitor at 1500 Hz if its reactance is 500 ohms at 900 Hz?
SOLUTION: Use the formula developed in the above paragraph:

$$X_{c1} = \frac{f2 \, Xc2}{f1} = \frac{500 \times 900}{1500} = \frac{450,000}{1500} = 300 \text{ ohms}$$

THE PHASE ANGLE. In an inductive circuit, we found that the current lags the impressed voltage. In a capacitive circuit, the opposite is true; THE CURRENT LEADS THE IMPRESSED VOLTAGE. The current leads the source voltage by 90 degrees in a pure capacitive circuit (see Fig. 4-29). If we introduce some resistance into the circuit, the current will lead the voltage

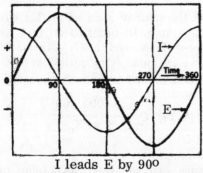

I leads E by 90°

FIG. 4-29. PURE CAPACITIVE CIRCUIT.   FIG. 4-30. R-C SERIES CIRCUIT.

68

by less than 90 degrees. When the resistance and capacitive reactance are equal, the current will lead the voltage by 45 degrees. The greater the resistance in the circuit, the smaller is the phase angle.

To find the phase angle of current with reference to the voltage in a capacitive-resistive circuit, we use the following formula:

$$(4\text{-}27) \quad \mathrm{Tan}\,\theta = \frac{X_c}{R}$$

where: $\mathrm{Tan}\,\theta$ is the tangent of the phase angle.

The answer gives us the tangent of the phase angle. By referring to the trigonometry table, we can find the actual phase angle.

IMPEDANCE OF A RESISTANCE-CAPACITANCE SERIES CIRCUIT. In a previous paragraph, we discussed the impedance of a series circuit containing resistance and inductive reactance. We learned that the total impedance of the circuit was not the simple sum of the resistance and the inductive reactance. The same is true for the impedance of a circuit containing resistance and capacitive reactance. (Fig. 4-30). The formula used to determine the impedance of a capacitive circuit is:

$$(4\text{-}28) \quad Z = \sqrt{R^2 + X_c^2}$$

where:
R = series resistance in ohms.
X_c = capacitive reactance in ohms.

PROBLEM: If, in a series resistive-capacitive circuit, Xc = 4 ohms and R = 3 ohms, what is the total impedance?
SOLUTION: Use formula (4-28).

$$Z = \sqrt{R^2 + X_c^2} \quad Z = \sqrt{3^2 + 4^2} \quad Z = \sqrt{9 + 16} \quad Z = \sqrt{25} = 5 \text{ ohms}$$

TIME CONSTANT OF AN R-C CIRCUIT. Figure 4-31 shows a capacitor in series with a resistor. At the instant that the switch is closed, current starts to flow and the voltage across the capacitor begins to build up. After a while, the voltage across the capacitor will be the same as the battery voltage. The time that it takes for the voltage on the capacitor to reach the battery voltage depends upon the values of the capacitor and the resistor. The larger these two values are, the longer it will take for the full voltage to appear across the capacitor. This relationship is expressed by a factor called the "time constant." The time constant is equal to the time it takes for a capacitor to charge up to 63% of its final value. Its formula is:

$$(4\text{-}29) \quad T = RC$$

Where: T is the Time constant in seconds,
R is the resistance in ohms and
C is the capacitance in farads.

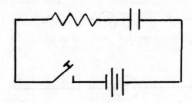

FIG. 4-31. AN R-C CIRCUIT.

The time constant is also equal to the time it takes for the voltage to drop, or discharge to 37% of its initial value.

PROBLEM: What is the time constant of an R-C circuit composed of a 500 ohm resistor and a 10 mf capacitor?

SOLUTION: Use formula (4-29)

$$T = RC = 500 \times 10 \times 10^{-6} = 5 \times 10^{-3} = .005 \text{ sec.}$$

3 TIME CONSTANT OF AN R-L CIRCUIT. The time constant of an R-L circuit is the time it takes for the current in the inductor to build up to 63.2% of its maximum value. The formula for the time constant of an R-L circuit is:

(4-30) $\quad T = \dfrac{L}{R} \qquad$ where T is time constant in seconds,
$\qquad\qquad\qquad\qquad$ L is inductance in henries,
$\qquad\qquad\qquad\qquad$ R is resistance in ohms

The curve for the current build-up is exactly the same as the voltage build-up curve across the capacitors in an R-C circuit.

A SERIES R-L-C CIRCUIT. The series circuit of Fig. 4-32 contains resistance, inductance and capacitance. Since the inductive reactance and the capacitive reactance act in an opposite manner to the current flow, they tend to cancel one another. If the inductive reactance is equal to the capacitive reactance, the resultant reactance will be zero. If the inductive reactance is larger than the capacitive reactance, the resultant reactance will be the difference between the two and it will be inductive. Conversely, if the capacitive reactance is larger than the inductive reactance, the resultant reactance remaining will be the difference between the two and it will be capacitive. In other words, if a circuit contains 20 ohms of capacitive reactance and 15 ohms of inductive reactance, the total reactance in the circuit is equal to 5 ohms of capacitive reactance.

The following formula is used to find the impedance of a series circuit containing resistance, inductance and capacitance:

(4-31) $\ Z = \sqrt{R^2 + (X_L - X_c)^2}$

where:
Z is the total impedance in ohms.
R is the resistance in ohms.
X_L is the inductive reactance in ohms.
X_c is the capacitive reactance in ohms.

PROBLEM: Find the impedance of a series circuit which contains a resistance of 5 ohms, an inductive reactance of 22 ohms and a capacitive reactance of 10 ohms (Fig. 4-32).

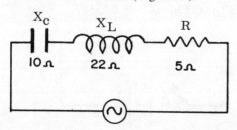

FIG. 4-32. R-L-C
SERIES CIRCUIT.

70

SOLUTION: Use formula (4-31).

$$Z = \sqrt{R^2 + (X_L - X_c)^2} \qquad Z = \sqrt{R^2 + (22 - 10)^2}$$

$$Z = \sqrt{25 + (12)^2} = \sqrt{25 + 144} = \sqrt{169} = 13 \text{ ohms}$$

There are times when we may want to know the value of the reactances when the impedance and the other reactances are known. Let us assume that we wish to find the capacitive reactance if we know the impedance, resistance and inductive reactance. We take the formula given above for impedance and algebraically solve for Xc.

$$Z = \sqrt{R^2 + (X_L - X_c)^2}, \quad Z^2 = R^2 + (X_L - X_c)^2,$$

$$Z^2 - R^2 = (X_L - X_c)^2 \qquad \sqrt{Z^2 - R^2} = X_L - X_c$$

$$\sqrt{Z^2 - R^2} - X_L = -X_c , \quad \text{or transposing, } X_c = X_L - \sqrt{Z^2 - R^2}$$

PROBLEM: Find the capacitive reactance of a series circuit if the impedance is 13 ohms, the inductive reactance is 6 ohms and the resistance is 5 ohms.

$$X_c = X_L - \sqrt{Z^2 - R^2} = 6 - \sqrt{13^2 - 5^2} = 6 - \sqrt{144} = 6 - \pm 12$$

The square root of 144 is plus or minus 12. This gives us two solutions: $6 - 12 = -6$ and $6 + 12 = 18$. The negative value is obviously wrong. The answer is therefore 18 ohms.

Since current flows through the various components of the series circuit of Fig. 4-33, there will be voltage drops across each component. However, these voltage drops do not add up to the source voltage as they do when all the components are resistors. Let us see how this comes about. Assume that the current is 2 amperes. The voltage drops can be calculated with Ohm's law:

$$E_c = I_c \times X_c = 2 \times 10 = 20 \text{ V.}$$

$$E_L = I_L \times X_L = 2 \times 22 = 44 \text{ V.}$$

$$E_R = I_R \times R = 2 \times 5 = 10 \text{ V.}$$

In order to calculate the source voltage, we use Ohm's Law. In the problem of Fig. 4-32, we found the impedance to be 13 ohms. Therefore:

$$E = IZ = 2 \times 13 = 26 \text{ V.}$$

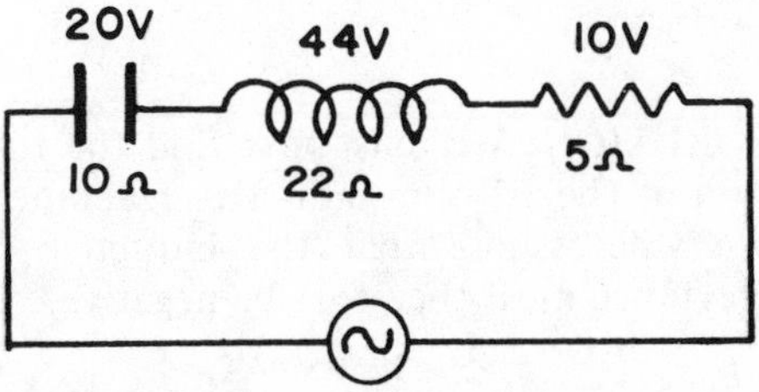

FIG. 4-33. R-C-L SERIES CIRCUIT.

71

The sum of the individual voltage drops is 74 volts whereas the source voltage is 26 volts. Why is there such a large discrepancy? The answer lies in the fact that the various voltage drops are out of phase with each other. They are not acting at the same time. Also, the voltages across the capacitor and inductor are opposite to one another and tend to cancel each other out. Therefore, we cannot add these voltages up by ordinary addition. We must add them vectorially. Vectorial addition takes into account the phases of the voltages in addition to their magnitudes.

PARALLEL R-C-L CIRCUITS. If similar reactances are in parallel, as in Fig. 4-34, the total reactance is found by using the formula for parallel resistors.

$$(4\text{-}32) \quad X_T = \cfrac{1}{\cfrac{1}{X_{C1}} + \cfrac{1}{X_{C2}} + \cfrac{1}{X_{C3}}}$$

On the other hand, if different reactances are in parallel, as in Fig. 4-35, we must take into account the fact that the reactances are acting OPPOSITE to one another.

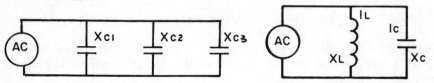

Fig. 4-34. CAPACITIVE REACTANCES IN PARALLEL. FIG. 4-35. DIFFERENT REACTANCES IN PARALLEL.

If one of the reactances is considered positive, we must consider the other one as negative. Thus, the total reactance of Fig. 4-35 is:

$$(4\text{-}33) \quad X_T = \cfrac{1}{\cfrac{1}{X_L} - \cfrac{1}{X_C}}$$

or, since we are dealing with only 2 reactances in parallel, we can have

$$X_T = \frac{X_L \text{ x } -X_C}{X_L - X_C}$$

An example will make this rule clear.
PROBLEM: Find the total impedance of the circuit of Fig. 4-36.

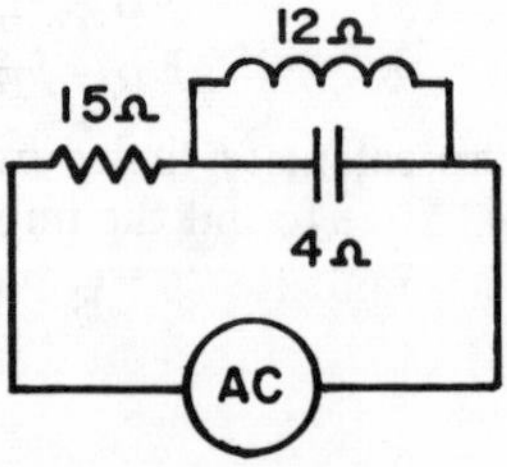

FIG. 4-36.

SOLUTION: We must first find the total reactance of the parallel combination of the 12 ohm inductive reactance and the 4 ohm capacitive reactance. We will assume that the inductive reactance is positive. The capacitive reactance must therefore be negative.

$$X_T = \frac{X_L \text{ x } -X_C}{X_L - X_C} = \frac{12 \text{ x } -4}{12 - 4} = \frac{-48}{8} = -6 \text{ ohms}$$

The negative answer indicates that the resultant reactance of the combination is capacitive. This is to be expected because the capacitive reactance is smaller than the inductive reactance and more capacitive current will flow than inductive current. If the inductive reactance were smaller, we would have a larger inductive current and the resultant reactance would be inductive. In series circuits, the resultant reactance is inductive if the inductive reactance is larger and capacitive if the capacitive reactance is larger. This is because there is a larger reactive voltage across the larger reactance.

The total impedance of the series circuit is found by using a simplified version of the impedance formula.

$$Z = \sqrt{X^2 + R^2} = \sqrt{(-6)^2 + 15^2} = \sqrt{36 + 225} = \sqrt{261} = 16.15 \text{ ohms}$$

4 Another way of calculating the impedance of a parallel circuit containing inductive and capacitive reactance is to assume a voltage across the parallel circuit. Then, using Ohm's law, we can calculate the currents through each reactance. The total current of the parallel circuit is then calculated by simple subtraction because the two reactances are 180 degrees opposed to one another. The total reactance of the parallel circuit is then found by using Ohm's law.

We can use this method in the problem of Fig. 4-36 and see if it checks with the other method. Assume a voltage of 24 volts across the parallel branch. The currents would then be:

$$I_L = \frac{E_L}{X_L} = \frac{24}{12} = 2 \text{ A.} \qquad I_c = \frac{E_c}{X_c} = \frac{24}{4} = 6 \text{ A.}$$

$$\text{Current, } I = I_c - I_L = 6 - 2 = 4 \text{ A.}$$

$$Z_{LC} = \frac{E}{I} = \frac{24}{4} = 6 \text{ ohms.}$$

This checks with the impedance found in the previous method.

PROBLEM: Given the values of Fig. 4-37, Find the total current.

SOLUTION: We first find the current in each branch.

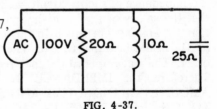

FIG. 4-37.

$$I_R = \frac{E}{R} = \frac{100}{20} = 5 \text{ A.} \qquad I_{X_L} = \frac{E}{X_L} = \frac{100}{10} = 10 \text{ A.}$$

$$I_{X_C} = \frac{E}{X_C} = \frac{100}{25} = 4 \text{ A.}$$

The total current in a parallel circuit consisting of X_L, X_C and R cannot be found by adding up the individual branch currents. They are not in phase. They must be added vectorially and to do this, we use the following

73

formula:

$$(4\text{-}34) \quad I_T = \sqrt{I_R^2 + (I_{X_L} - I_{X_C})^2}$$

$$I_T = \sqrt{5^2 + (10 - 4)^2} = \sqrt{25 + 36} = \sqrt{61} = 7.8A.$$

4 THE PHASE ANGLE OF A SERIES R-L-C CIRCUIT. To find the phase angle of current with reference to voltage in a series R-L-C circuit, we use the following formula:

$$(4\text{-}35) \quad Tan\,\theta = \frac{X}{R} \qquad \text{where: X is the reactance in the circuit.}$$

Since X_L and X_C oppose each other, we subtract one from the other to find the resultant reactance. If X_L is greater than X_C, the reactance is inductive and the current lags the voltage. If X_C is greater than X_L, the reactance is capacitive and the current leads the voltage.

PROBLEM: A potential of 100 volts is applied to a series R-L-C circuit containing an inductive reactance of 50 ohms, a capacitive reactance of 25 ohms and a resistance of 25 ohms. What is the phase relationship between the applied voltage and the current in the circuit?

SOLUTION: Use formula (4-35).

$$Tan\,\theta = \frac{X}{R}, \quad X = X_L - X_C \text{ (because } X_L \text{ is larger),}$$

$$X = 50 - 25, \quad X = 25 \text{ ohms.} \quad Tan\,\theta = \frac{25}{25}, \quad Tan\,\theta = 1.0$$

From a trigonometry table, we find that the tangent of 45° equals 1.0. The phase angle is, therefore, 45°. Since X_L predominates over X_C, the reactance is inductive and, therefore, the current lags the voltage by 45°.

SERIES RESONANCE. In a previous section, we studied a series AC circuit containing resistance, inductance and capacitance. In order to find the impedance of such a circuit, we had to use formula (4-31). Let us assume that the values of L, C and the frequency of the AC generator are so chosen that X_L and X_C are equal. In this case, the quantity $(X_L - X_C)$ in formula (4-31) would be equal to zero. The two reactances are equal and cancel each other. The only opposition that remains in the circuit is the resistance, R. Therefore, the IMPEDANCE IN A CIRCUIT, CONTAINING EQUAL AMOUNTS OF INDUCTIVE AND CAPACITIVE REACTANCE, IS EQUAL TO THE RESISTANCE IN THE CIRCUIT. The current flowing in the circuit is at its maximum value; and the IMPEDANCE OF THE CIRCUIT IS AT ITS MINIMUM VALUE. The condition where the inductive reactance is equal to the capacitive reactance in a circuit is known as RESONANCE. Since the components of this circuit are in series, the circuit is known as a SERIES RESONANT CIRCUIT. The frequency of the generator at resonance is called the RESONANT FREQUENCY.

If the frequency of the AC generator is increased, the inductive reactance will go up and the capacitive reactance will go down. The difference between the two reactances is a number larger than zero. Our circuit is, therefore, no longer resonant. The impedance of the circuit has increased since the resistance is no longer the sole opposition to current flow. The impedance of the circuit is now determined by formula (4-31). Since the circuit impedance has increased, the current will now decrease below its resonance value.

If the generator frequency is decreased, the inductive reactance goes down and the capacitive reactance goes up. The reasoning in the preceding paragraph applies here as well. In this case, the current also decreases below its resonance value. We can therefore conclude that the current is a maximum at resonance, and decreases on either side of the resonant frequency.

THE SERIES RESONANCE CURVE. If we were to draw a curve of the variations of current with changes in generator frequency, we would obtain a curve known as a RESONANCE CURVE. This is illustrated in Fig. 4-38 for a series resonant circuit. The vertical direction represents the amount of current flowing in the current for different frequencies. The horizontal direction represents the different generator frequencies. As the frequency of the generator is varied above and below the resonant frequency, the current will vary in the manner indicated. Notice that the current reaches a peak only at resonance, and decreases in value at either side of resonance.

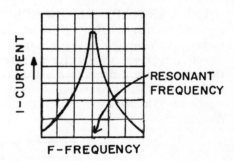

FIG. 4-38. THE SERIES
RESONANCE CURVE.

PARALLEL RESONANCE. Fig. 4-39 shows a coil and capacitor connected in parallel across an AC generator. Note that R_L represents the DC resistance of the coil. If the frequency of the generator is adjusted so that X_L is equal to X_C, we would have a condition of resonance known as PARALLEL RESONANCE. In a parallel resonant circuit, there are two different currents flowing. First, there is the line current (I_{line}) which flows from the generator, through the resonant circuit, and back to the generator. At resonance, the line current is very low in value. The line current increases

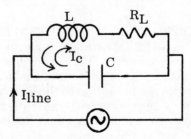

FIG. 4-39.
PARALLEL RESONANCE.

75

in value above and below resonance. At resonance, the line current supplies just enough energy to the parallel circuit to overcome the losses in the resistance of the coil. Secondly, there is the current which flows back and forth between the coil and capacitor. This current, Ic, is called the INTERNAL CIRCULATING CURRENT. At resonance, the internal circulating current is very high compared to the line current. Since the reactance of the coil and capacitor are equal and cancel each other, the only opposition to the internal circulating current at resonance is the resistance of the coil, R_L.

If the parallel resonant circuit has no resistance, no energy is dissipated as the internal circulating current flows back and forth between the coil and the capacitor. (Energy can only be dissipated in a resistance). Therefore, the generator would not have to supply any energy, since none would be lost in the circuit. Consequently, the line current would be zero. Practically speaking, there will always be some resistance present in the circuit. Energy will necessarily be dissipated in the circuit, since the internal circulating current must flow through the resistance of the coil. In order to replenish this lost energy, the generator will have to supply energy by way of the line current flowing into the circuit.

THE PARALLEL RESONANCE CURVE. The resonance curve of a parallel resonant circuit is illustrated in Fig. 4-40. The vertical scale represents the amount of line current flowing in the circuit. The horizontal direction represents the different generator frequencies. As the frequency of the generator is varied above and below the resonant frequency, the current will vary in the manner indicated. Notice that the current reaches a minimum value only at resonance, and increases in value at either side of resonance.

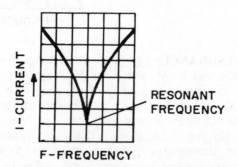

FIG. 4-40. THE PARALLEL-RESONANCE CURVE.

IMPEDANCE OF THE PARALLEL RESONANT CIRCUIT. The average TANK CIRCUIT (parallel resonant circuit) encountered in radio has a very low coil resistance. The energy dissipated will therefore be very low, and the line current will also be very low. Since the line current is small, the impedance (opposition to the line current) of a parallel resonant circuit must be very high. Compare this with the low impedance of a series resonant circuit. We will also find that the impedance of the parallel resonant circuit decreases as the frequency of the energy that is injected into the tank circuit varies above and below the resonant frequency.

The characteristics of series and parallel resonant circuits are summarized in the following table:

SUMMARY OF CHARACTERISTICS OF SERIES AND PARALLEL RESONANT CIRCUITS

	Series Resonant Circuit	Parallel Resonant Circuit
Impedance	low	high
Current	high	line current - low. Internal circulating current - high.
E across circuit	low	high

Fig. 4-41 shows a circuit that is commonly encountered in radio equipment. C1 and L1 form a parallel resonant circuit. Coil L1 is magnetically coupled to L2. Radio frequency AC is fed into the circuit at terminals A and B. As C1 is varied, a point is reached where the C1, L1 tank circuit is resonant to the incoming frequency. At this resonant point, the internal circulating current of the tank circuit is maximum and it induces a maximum e.m.f. into L2. The meter across L2 reads this maximum value that occurs at resonance. As we vary C1 on both sides of resonance, the meter reading drops. Thus, we can tell by a maximum meter reading when the tank circuit is at resonance.

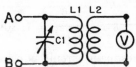

FIG. 4-41. MAGNETIC COUPLING.

RESONANT FREQUENCY. For every value of inductance and capacitance in a resonant circuit, there is ONE frequency at which the inductive reactance equals the capacitive reactance. This frequency is referred to as the RESONANT FREQUENCY. The resonant frequency can be calculated by using the following formula:

(4-36) $\quad f_R = \dfrac{1}{2\pi\sqrt{LC}}$

where:
f_R is the resonant frequency in Hertz
2π is 6.28
L is the inductance in henries
C is the capacitance in farads.

In order to find the resonant frequency when L and C are given in more common units such as microhenries and microfarads, the above formula is modified as follows:

(4-37) $\quad f_R = \dfrac{10^6}{2\pi\sqrt{LC}}$

where:
f_R is the resonant frequency in Hertz
2π is 6.28
L is the inductance in microhenries
C is the capacitance in microfarads

77

It is important to remember that the resonant frequency of a circuit goes up when either the inductance or capacitance goes down. This becomes apparent if we inspect either formula (4-36) or (4-37).

There are two important variations of the formula (4-36). They are formula (4-38) which is used for finding the inductance of a resonant circuit, and formula (4-39) which is used for finding the capacitance of a resonant circuit.

$$(4\text{-}38) \quad L = \frac{10^{12}}{4\pi^2 f_R^2 C}$$

where:

f_R is the resonant frequency

π is 3.14

L is the inductance in microhenries

$$(4\text{-}39) \quad C = \frac{10^{12}}{4\pi^2 f_R^2 L}$$

C is the capacitance in microfarads

PROBLEM: In a series resonant circuit composed of an inductance of 100 μh and a capacitance of 150 pf, what is the resonant frequency?

SOLUTION: Use (4-37).

$$f_R = \frac{10^6}{2\pi\sqrt{LC}}, \quad 150 \text{ pf} = 150 \times 10^{-6} \text{ mf}$$

$$f_R = \frac{10^6}{6.28 \times \sqrt{100 \times 150 \times 10^{-6}}} = \frac{10^6}{6.28 \times \sqrt{150 \times 10^{-4}}}$$

$$f_R = \frac{10^6}{6.28 \times 12.25 \times 10^{-2}} = \frac{10^6}{.7693} = 1,300,000 \text{ Hz or } 1.3 \text{ MHz}$$

PROBLEM: In a parallel resonant circuit consisting of a coil having an inductance of 50 μh, what is the value of the shunt capacitor in order that the circuit resonate at 2.0 MHz?

SOLUTION: Use (4-39).

$$C = \frac{10^{12}}{4\pi^2 f_R^2 L}, \quad 2 \text{ MHz} = 2.0 \times 10^6 \text{ Hz}$$

$$C = \frac{10^{12}}{4 \times 9.86 \times 4 \times 10^{12} \times 50}, \quad C = \frac{1}{9.86 \times 800},$$

$$C = \frac{1}{7.888 \times 10^3}, \quad C = .127 \times 10^{-3},$$

$$C = 127 \times 10^{-6} \text{ mf}, \quad \text{or } C = 127 \text{ pf}$$

THE Q OF A RESONANT CIRCUIT. The Q of a resonant circuit is the gain or figure of merit of the circuit at the resonant frequency. The formula for Q is:

$$(4\text{-}40) \quad Q = \frac{X}{R}$$

where:

X is equal to the reactance (inductive or capacitive since both are equal in a resonant circuit).

R is the AC resistance.

From the formula it can be seen that the Q falls as the resistance increases. Thus it is important to keep the resistance as low as possible.

For frequencies below 30 MHz, the resistance in the circuit is due mainly to the resistance in the wire used in winding the inductor. At frequencies above 30 MHz, the capacitor becomes inefficient due to the dielectric becoming a poor insulator and causing energy loss. This energy loss is the same as if series resistance were added to the circuit.

The Q of a tuned circuit determines its sharpness or selectivity. The higher the Q, the sharper the response curve or selectivity. The lower the Q, the broader is the response curve and the selectivity is poorer. We can deliberately broaden the response curve of a resonant circuit by loading the tuned circuit down with resistance.

The Q of a resonant circuit is also the voltage gain of the resonant circuit. A voltage introduced into a resonant circuit gets multiplied Q times to give us a higher output voltage.

Just as we speak of the Q of a tuned circuit, we can speak of the Q of a coil or the Q of a capacitor. The Q of a coil is its figure of merit. It is equal to its ability to store energy divided by the energy lost in the coil. The ability to store energy is really its inductive reactance and the energy lost in the coil is determined by the effective resistance of the coil. Hence the Q of a coil is equal to:

$$(4\text{-}41) \quad Q = \frac{X_L}{R} \qquad \text{where: } X_L \text{ is the reactance of the coil and } R \text{ is the total effective resistance.}$$

In most circuits, the Q of the coil is very close in value to the Q of the tuned circuit. This is because the capacitor has very little resistance.

A-C POWER. In Lesson 2, we learned that the power consumed in a DC circuit is determined by using the following formulas:

$$P = EI \qquad P = I^2 R \qquad P = \frac{E^2}{R}$$

The power consumed in a pure resistive AC circuit is similarly determined, using the same formulas where E and I are ineffective values.

In an AC circuit containing either inductance or capacitance, the voltage and current are out of phase. (They are not acting together at the same instant.) Therefore, the above formulas cannot be used to determine the TRUE POWER in a reactive circuit. The product of $E_{eff.}$ and $I_{eff.}$ is called the APPARENT POWER. This power is actually larger than the true power consumed in the circuit. The true power is the heat dissipated in the circuit. The electric company charges you for the true power consumed over a period of time. Power can only be dissipated or used up in a resistive element. Power cannot be dissipated in a pure capacitive or pure inductive circuit.

The apparent power can be determined from the readings of voltmeter and ammeter placed in the circuit, as illustrated in Fig. 4-42. The product of these readings, volts times amperes or VOLT-AMPERES, is the apparent power. The true power dissipated will always be indicated by a WATT-METER.

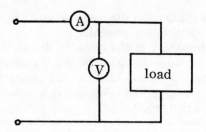

FIG. 4-42. DETERMINING
APPARENT POWER.

The one formula that can be used to determine the true power consumed in both DC and AC circuits is:

(4-42) $P = I^2 R$

where: I is either the direct current or the effective alternating current.
R is the resistance of the load.

POWER FACTOR. The power factor (PF) is the ratio of the true power to the apparent power. The formula is:

$$(4\text{-}43) \quad PF = \frac{\text{True power}}{\text{Apparent power}}$$

It is also equal to the cosine of the phase angle between the voltage and current. The power factor is an indication of whether or not the circuit is reactive and to what extent. The greater the reactance, the smaller is the power factor. Another formula for power factor is:

$$(4\text{-}44) \quad PF = \frac{R}{Z}$$

where: R is resistance in ohms and
Z is impedance in ohms.

3 **THE WATTMETER.** It has previously been stated that the true power can always be determined by the use of a WATTMETER. Fig. 4-43 shows an elementary type of wattmeter. It contains two coils; a movable coil and a stationary coil. The movable coil with a series resistance forms the voltage element and the stationary coils constitute the current element. Note that

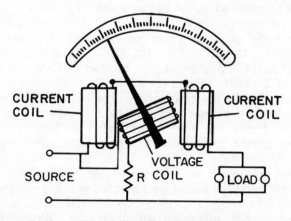

FIG. 4-43. A WATTMETER.

the stationary coils are in series with the load and source, whereas the movable coil is across the load and source. The magnetic strength of the field around the movable coil depends upon the voltage. The magnetic field around the stationary coils depends upon the current. The two fields react with one another and cause the movable coil to rotate. The meter deflection is proportional to the product of the voltage across the movable coil and the current through the current coils. Since the product of the voltage and the current is equal to the wattage, it is obvious that the wattmeter is reading the actual power that is consumed.

If the current in a line is reversed, the direction of current in both coils is reversed and the pointer continues to read up-scale. Therefore, this type of wattmeter can be used to measure either AC or DC.

THE TRANSFORMER. You will recall from our earlier discussion of AC voltage, that an e.m.f. will be induced in a loop of wire which cuts a magnetic field. As long as there is relative motion between the loop and the magnetic field, a voltage will be generated. If the loop is kept stationary and the magnetic field cuts across the loop of wire, the result obtained will be the same as if the loop were in motion instead of the magnetic field. In either case, a voltage will be induced in the conductors of the loop. Transformer operation is based upon a varying magnetic field inducing a voltage in a stationary coil of wire.

OPERATION OF THE TRANSFORMER. Every time current flows through a conductor, a magnetic field builds up around the conductor. The magnetic field is in phase with the current at all times. Therefore, if an alternating current flows through a coil of wire, an alternating magnetic field will exist around this coil. This alternating magnetic field expands outwardly, away from the coil, and collapses back into the coil periodically. If a second coil with a lamp across it, is placed in the vicinity of coil #1, as illustrated in Fig. 4-44, the alternating magnetic field will cut across coil #2 and induce an AC voltage in it. This voltage will cause the lamp to light. Notice that no electrical connection exists between the coils. Energy is transferred from coil #1 to coil #2 by the varying magnetic field. We say that the coils are MAGNETICALLY COUPLED. This method of transferring energy from one coil to another is known as TRANSFORMER ACTION. The entire device, consisting of two coils magnetically coupled, is called a TRANSFORMER. Coil #1, which is connected to the voltage source, is called the PRIMARY. Coil #2 is called the SECONDARY.

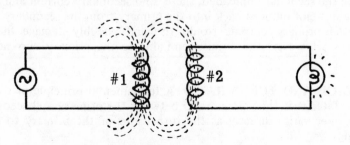

FIG. 4-44. MAGNETIC COUPLING.

81

THE POWER TRANSFORMER. A transformer, used to transfer AC power at power frequencies, is known as a POWER TRANSFORMER. In order for a power transformer to operate efficiently, the primary and secondary coils are wound on a laminated iron core, as illustrated in Fig. 4-45. This is known as an IRON CORE transformer, as differentiated from the AIR CORE transformer of Fig. 4-44.

Most power transformers have two or more secondary windings. The schematic symbol of a typical transformer of this type is shown in Fig. 4-46.

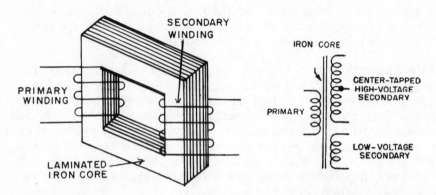

FIG. 4-45. BASIC IRON CORE POWER
TRANSFORMER.

FIG. 4-46. POWER TRANSFORMER
SYMBOL.

Power transformers can only be used on AC because an alternating magnetic field is required to induce an e.m.f. in the secondary. It is dangerous to apply DC to the power transformer primary. The primary has a low DC resistance and therefore, a high DC current will flow through it. This high current will either blow a line fuse, burn out power switch contacts or damage the transformer beyond repair. Also, it is important not to connect a transformer whose primary is rated, say, 110 volts, 60 Hz to a 110 volt, 25 Hz source; or one designed for 400 Hz to a 60 Hz source of the same or higher voltage. The inductive reactance of the primary would be reduced and this would cause a high primary current flow. The primary winding would overheat and damage to it could result.

When AC flows in the primary of a transformer, it not only induces a voltage in the secondary, it also induces a counter-emf or reactance in the primary. This is important if the secondary doesn't have a load connected to it. With the secondary unloaded, there is no secondary current and therefore, no counter-emf induced back into the primary from the secondary. In such a case, the primary current would rise and possibly damage the primary windings. However, the counter-emf due to the primary current prevents this.

VOLTAGE AND TURNS RATIO. A fundamental principle of transformer action states that the voltage ratio between the primary and secondary of a transformer varies directly as the turns ratio of the primary to secondary windings.

That is:

82

where:

(4-45) $\dfrac{E_p}{E_s} = \dfrac{T_p}{T_s}$

E_p is the primary or applied voltage.
E_s is the secondary or induced voltage.
T_p is the number of turns of the primary.
T_s is the number of turns of the secondary.

The ratio $\dfrac{T_p}{T_s}$ is called the primary to secondary TURNS RATIO of the transformer.

If there are three times as many turns on the secondary as on the primary, the voltage of the secondary will be three times the voltage that is applied to the primary. A transformer whose secondary voltage is greater than the primary voltage is called a STEP-UP transformer. See Fig. 4-47. If the primary voltage is 110 volts, the secondary voltage which appears across the load will be 330 volts. If there are ten times as many turns on the secondary as on the primary, the secondary voltage will be ten times as great as the primary voltage.

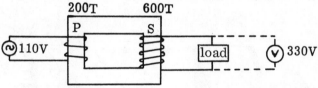

FIG. 4-47. 1 TO 3 STEP-UP TRANSFORMER.

Fig. 4-48 shows a transformer where the turns on the secondary are less than the turns on the primary. In this case, the voltage will be stepped down from the primary to the secondary. This transformer is known as a STEP-DOWN TRANSFORMER. If 100 volts were applied to the primary winding, the secondary voltage would be 50 volts. This is because the secondary winding has one half the turns of the primary winding.

When the primary and secondary have approximately the same number of turns, the unit is often called an ISOLATION transformer. This type of transformer is generally used as a safety device where it is necessary to isolate equipment from the line.

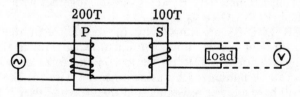

FIG. 4-48. STEP-DOWN TRANSFORMER.

4 SHIELDING. The primary and secondary windings of a transformer are actually conductors that are separated by insulation. A capacitor is therefore formed between the primary and secondary of the transformer. This makes it possible for noise and other undesirable interference to be transferred through the capacitive coupling that exists in the transformer.

An effective method of eliminating this condition is to place an electrostatic shield, made of copper or aluminum, between the windings. This reduces the capacitive coupling between windings and prevents the transfer of unwanted signals. Shielding can be used in interstage coupling transformers as well as power transformers.

TRANSFORMER LOSSES. There are three types of losses which are encountered in the operation of iron core transformers: They are: EDDY CURRENTS, HYSTERESIS LOSSES and COPPER LOSSES.

(1) EDDY CURRENTS are wasted currents induced in the iron core of the transformer by the varying magnetic field. These currents take a circular path through the core material, as shown in Fig. 4-49A. Since the resistance in the path of the eddy currents in a solid-core material is low, the eddy currents will be large. Eddy currents serve only to heat up the iron core and therefore, represent a power loss. Eddy current losses can be reduced by having the core made of LAMINATIONS (thin insulated iron sheets) instead of solid iron, as in Fig. 4-49B. The laminations limit the eddy currents by increasing the resistance in their path of flow.

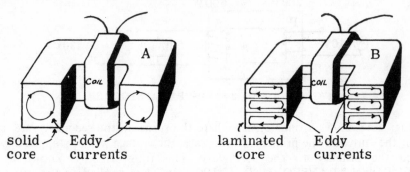

solid   Eddy   laminated   Eddy
core   currents   core   currents

FIG. 4-49A. HIGH EDDY-CURRENT FLOW IN SOLID CORE.
FIG. 4-49B. LOW EDDY-CURRENT FLOW IN LAMINATED CORE.

(2) HYSTERESIS LOSSES represent the energy that is used up in forcing the iron core to reverse the direction of its magnetic field every time the current reverses its direction. Hysteresis losses can be minimized by using cores made of special materials, Hysteresis losses, together with eddy current losses, are called IRON CORE LOSSES.

(3) COPPER LOSSES are caused by the resistance of the wire which makes up the turns of the windings. Current flowing through the resistance of the winding develops an I^2R power loss in the form of wasteful heat. Copper losses can be minimized by using a heavier wire for the windings; a thicker wire will have a lower resistance and therefore, a lower I^2R loss.

AIR CORE TRANSFORMER LOSSES. Copper losses are present in air core transformers in much the same manner as they are in iron core transformers. Current flowing through the turns of copper wire will always produce I^2R losses. There are also losses in the wire due to eddy currents and skin effect. Eddy current losses occur because the wire conductor is being cut by magnetic lines of force at varying rates. Small voltages of different values will be induced at many points along the wire conductor.

84

These different voltages produce many differences of potential which, in turn, cause many tiny currents to flow. These are wasted currents and are therefore losses. Losses due to skin effect were previously discussed. The combination of I^2R losses, eddy current losses and skin effect constitute the AC RESISTANCE encountered in an RF transformer or coil. This AC resistance increases as the frequency increases. Some other losses in an air core transformer are: losses due to radiation, shield losses and losses due to a low coefficient of coupling.

Radiation losses come about because some of the electrical energy that is transferred to magnetic energy is radiated and never returns to the circuit. Shield losses are the result of the magnetic field cutting across the shield and inducing currents in the shield. These currents go to ground and are never returned to the transformer circuit.

A low coefficient of coupling in an air core transformer means that much of the magnetic field of the primary winding does not cut the secondary winding. This represents lost energy.

CURRENT RATIO. In an ideal transformer (one with no losses), the power transferred to the secondary is equal to the power delivered to the primary.

(4-46) $P_p = P_s$ where: P_p is the primary power and
P_s is the secondary power.

Power in the primary (from Ohm's law) is: $P_p = E_p \times I_p$

and power in the secondary is: $P_s = E_s \times I_s$.

Therefore, we say $E_p \times I_p = E_s \times I_s$, which is the same as (4-46). This last expression can be rewritten as:

$$\frac{I_s}{I_p} = \frac{E_p}{E_s}$$

Since $\dfrac{E_p}{E_s}$ is the turns ratio, $\dfrac{T_p}{T_s}$, we can say by substitution that

$$\frac{I_s}{I_p} = \frac{T_p}{T_s}$$

That is, the ratio of current in the primary to the current in the secondary varies in inverse proportion to the turns ratio.

EFFICIENCY. Because there are losses in a transformer, the efficiency of a transformer must be less than 1.0. This means that power transferred to the secondary must be less than the power used in the primary of a transformer. The power in the secondary is therefore equal to the Input power multiplied by the Efficiency, or mathematically stated:

(4-47) $P_s = P_p \times Eff.$ where: P_s = secondary power
P_p = primary power

PROBLEM: A step-down power transformer has a turns ratio of 18:1 and an

85

efficiency of 80%. If the primary voltage is 110 volts and the input power is 120 watts, what is: (a) the secondary power, (b) the secondary voltage, (c) the primary current, and (d) the secondary current?

SOLUTION:

(A) (4-47) $P_S = P_p \times Eff$; $P_S = 120 \times .80$; $P_S = 96$ watts.

(B) (4-45) $E_S = \dfrac{T_s}{T_p} \times E_p$; $E_S = \dfrac{110}{18.0}$; $E_S = 6.1$ volts.

(C) $I_p = \dfrac{P_p}{E_p}$; $I_p = \dfrac{120}{110}$; $I_p = 1.09$ amps.

(D) $I_s = \dfrac{P_s}{E_s}$; $I_s = \dfrac{96}{6.1}$; $I_s = 15.74$ amps.

MAXIMUM POWER TRANSFER. In order that there be a maximum transfer of energy from a generator to a load, the impedance of the load should equal the internal impedance of the generator. This law applies to all circuits in radio and electricity.

Sometimes a load, such as a speaker voice coil, may have a very low impedance as compared to the very high internal impedance of the vacuum tube which is to energize the speaker. In order that there be a maximum energy transfer between the vacuum tube (generator) and the speaker (load), a matching transformer (output transformer) is interposed between the two. The transformer "steps up" the impedance. We say that the transformer MATCHES the load to the generator, effecting maximum power transfer.

Exact impedance matching is not always obtained. However, this is not a critical factor and exact matching is not necessary. As long as the impedances are close in value, the proper power transfer will take place.

3 **CORONA LOSS.** CORONA LOSS is an electrical discharge from a high voltage point on the surface of an electrical conductor into space. The amount of corona discharge depends upon the curvature of the conductor surface. Most corona discharge occurs from sharp points while the least corona discharge occurs from surfaces having a large ratio of curvature. Corona loss or discharge is frequently accompanied by a purplish, blue glow and an audible hiss.

A high potential generated by electrostatic fields on a moving airplane or on a moving auto radio antenna will discharge from the sharpest points of the surface into space. This discharge causes a loss of energy and will produce static in a nearby receiver.

Corona losses may be minimized by the following:

(1) Use large diameter conductors.

(2) Use the lowest required voltage.

(3) Use smooth polished surfaces.

(4) Avoid sharp points, bends or turns. The radio antenna on a car has a ball or cap at the end to prevent corona discharge.

4 **THREE-PHASE ALTERNATING CURRENT.** The AC that we have studied to this point is called single phase current. Most electronic circuits

use single phase current. However, we use POLYPHASE current in many power applications. Most large central-station electric generators are three-phase machines, and the transmission and distribution circuits to which they are connected are three-phase systems. Three-phase systems have advantages in economy and operating characteristics over single phase systems. Three phase motors are smaller and more efficient than single phase motors of the same horsepower. Also, three-phase transmission lines require smaller electrical conductors than single-phase lines of the same kilowatt rating.

In a single phase generator, there is one winding and a single sinusoidal wave is produced. In the basic three-phase generator, three coil groups are spaced 120° apart on the armature. The armature revolves at a constant speed and a separate sinewave voltage is induced in each of the three coils. The voltages are 120° out of phase with each other. This is shown in Fig. 4-50. Voltage B is 120° behind voltage A and voltage C is 120° behind voltage B.

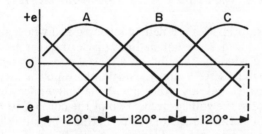

FIG. 4-50. THREE PHASE CURRENT.

The three windings of the armature can be connected to each other in one of two basic methods - the Y (wye) method or the Delta method. Fig. 4-51 shows these two basic methods of connecting a three-phase system. Note that there are three output terminals.

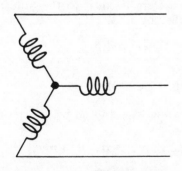 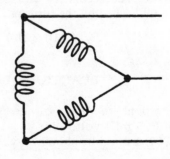

FIG. 4-51. Y-CONNECTION.   FIG. 4-51. DELTA CONNECTION.

Power may be supplied to three-phase circuits containing transformers in which the primaries and secondaries are connected in various Y and delta combinations. Fig. 4-52 shows a transformer system using a delta primary and a Y secondary. Fig. 4-52 can either represent three single phase

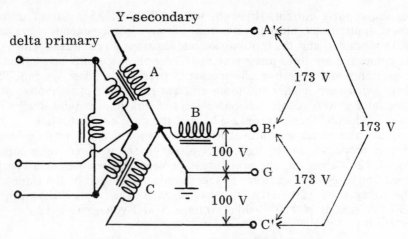

FIG. 4-52. THREE PHASE TRANSFORMER SYSTEM.

transformers whose primaries are delta connected and whose secondaries are Y connected, or it can represent a three phase transformer consisting of separated insulated windings, wound on a special core. Three-phase power is obtained from terminals A', B' and C'. Single phase power may be obtained from two terminals, G and any other one. Note that while each coil (A, B or C) provides 100 volts, the voltage across two of the coils (A' to B' or B' to C' or A' to C') is 1.73 times the voltage in one coil. This is because the voltages are 120° out of phase and must be added vectorially. The currents in each coil are the same as the line current because there is only one path for them. The delta-primary, Y-secondary system provides the maximum secondary voltage compared to other combinations.

PROBLEM: Three identical single phase transformers have step up ratios of 1 to 10. Their primaries are delta connected and their secondaries are Y-connected. If three-phase 110 volts is fed to the primaries, what is the secondary line voltage?

ANSWER: The secondary voltage in this system is equal to the primary voltage multiplied by the turns ratio, multiplied by 1.732.

$$E_S = 110 \times 10 \times 1.732 = 1905.2 \text{ volts.}$$

PRACTICE QUESTIONS - LESSON 4

1. The peak-to-peak voltage of an AC signal having an RMS voltage of 2.5 millivolts, is:
a. 7.07 mv.   b. 3.535 mv.   c. 3.25 mv.   d. 6.5 mv.

2. In Fig. 2, what is the current flow?
a. .5 A.
b. 2.22 A.
c. 2 A.
d. 3.33 A.

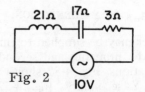

Fig. 2

88

3. In Fig. 2, if R shorted out, what is the power consumed?
a. 0 watts   b. 12.5 watts   c. 2.5 watts   d. 80 watts

4. Real power is measured by:
a. a voltmeter and ammeter
b. a voltmeter and frequency meter
c. a wattmeter
d. a power factor meter and an ammeter

5. What is the approximate power
factor in the circuit shown?
a. 2.5
b. .4
c. .6
d. .2

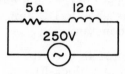

6. In a transformer, the secondary voltage:
a. always equals the primary voltage
b. is less than the primary voltage
c. equals the primary voltage times the turns ratio
d. is high

7. The inductance of a coil varies:
a. inversely with the permeability of the core
b. directly with the number of turns of wire
c. directly with the square of the core's permeability
d. directly with the square of the turns of wire

8. Inductive reactance is the:
a. opposition a coil offers to AC current flow
b. AC current flowing through the coil
c. DC resistance of the coil
d. coil inductance

9. In a power transformer, DC should not be applied to the primary because:
a. a counter-e.m.f. will be developed
b. no load will be present
c. a high DC current will flow
d. the efficiency will be poor

10. In a series resonant circuit
a. the impedance is a minimum
b. the impedance is a maximum
c. the current lags the voltage
d. the current leads the voltage

11. The frequency of a sine wave is:
a. the time in seconds for one cycle
b. the amplitude of the wave
c. the number of cycles per second
d. the angle of rotation

12. The phase angle is:
    a. always large
    b. the angle by which current leads resistance
    c. the angle by which one wave leads or lags another
    d. the angle between 0^0 and 90^0

13. Capacitive reactance is:
    a. the opposition in ohms that a capacitor builds up to AC current flow
    b. the voltage charge on a capacitor
    c. the resistance to DC current flow
    d. always constant

14. A capacitor is used to:
    a. pass DC and block AC   c. pass AC and block DC
    b. pass DC only   d. generate an AC voltage

15. The opposition that the center of a conductor offers to high frequency currents results in:
    a. Miller effect   c. skin effect
    b. low distributed capacity d. a low Q circuit

16. The resonant frequency of a tuned circuit is found by the following formula:
    a. $2\pi fLC$ b. $\dfrac{L}{2\pi fC}$ c. $2\pi LC$ d. $\dfrac{1}{2\pi\sqrt{LC}}$

17. What is the inductive reactance of a 20 millihenry choke at 3 kHz?
    a. 60 ohms   b. 377 ohms   c. 188 ohms   d. 37,700 ohms

18. At resonance:
    a. the resistance is equal to the voltage
    b. the current is zero
    c. $X_L = X_C$
    d. the voltage varies

19. In a pure capacitive circuit:
    a. the voltage leads the current by 45^0
    b. the current leads the voltage by 45^0
    c. the voltage leads the current by 90^0
    d. the current leads the voltage by 90^0

20. What is the total inductance of the circuit shown?
    a. 7.5 H.
    b. 25 H.
    c. 6 H.
    d. 4.5 H.

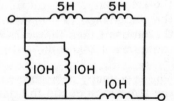

21. The ratio of resistance to impedance in an AC circuit is called:
    a. power factor   b. Q   c. apparent power   d. skin effect

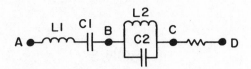

22. L2 and C2 form a parallel resonant circuit and assuming that L1 = L2 and C1 = C2, which of the following is correct?
a. minimum voltage appears across AB
b. maximum voltage appears across CD
c. maximum voltage appears across BC
d. A and C are both correct

23. What is the resonant frequency of a circuit containing a 25.6 mfd capacitor and a 10 microhenry coil?
a. 62.8 kHz   b. 1000 Hz   c. 10 kHz   d. 256 kHz

24. A discharge from a high potential sharp metal point is called: (3)
a. skin effect   c. dielectric constant
b. corona   d. induced e.m.f.

25. In using electrolytic capacitors: (3)
a. polarity must be observed
b. bleeder resistors must be used
c. hash filters must be used
d. equalizing resistors must be used

26. Capacitors in series:
a. add like resistors in series
b. add like resistors in parallel
c. are equal to the smaller capacitor
d. are equal to the larger capacitor

27. Which of the following reduces the impedance of a parallel resonant circuit?
a. increasing the internal resistance
b. reducing the internal resistance
c. increasing the skin effect
d. increasing the wire size

28. What is the total L of a 4 H coil and a 9 H coil, in series opposing, if the coefficient of coupling is .4?
a. 13 H   b. 14.4 H   c. 11.6 H   d. 8.2 H

29. If a transformer with a 95% efficiency has a primary voltage of 110 volts and a secondary of 1650 volts, what is the primary current when the secondary current is 100 ma?
a. 1.5 A.   b. 1.65 A.   c. 1.73 A.   d. 1.58 A.

30. The voltage in an AC capacitive circuit:
a. leads the current   c. lags the current by 45 degrees
b. lags the current   d. leads the current by 90 degrees

LESSON 5
MOTORS AND GENERATORS

GENERATORS. The main disadvantage of batteries is that they can only supply a limited amount of power before they must be thrown away or recharged. Electric circuits for industrial or residential use, require larger amounts of power than batteries can supply. This power must be supplied by electric generators.

A generator is a machine that converts mechanical energy into electrical energy. This conversion is accomplished by rotating conductors in a magnetic field. We have previously learned that, when this is done, an e.m.f. will be induced in the conductors. This basic generator action is completely explained in Lesson 4 and should be reviewed before continuing with this lesson.

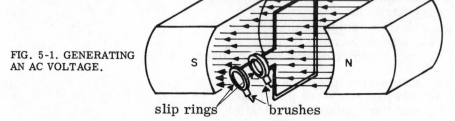

FIG. 5-1. GENERATING AN AC VOLTAGE.

slip rings   brushes

Fig. 5-1 shows a basic AC generator. A single loop of wire revolves in a magnetic field created by two field magnets. In an actual generator, there are many turns of wire. The wire is mounted on a core called the "armature." The armature is rotated by mechanical means. In practice, electro-magnets, rather than permanent magnets, are used. Also, four or six magnetic poles may be used in the field, instead of two.

The ends of the wire loop are connected to two rings that are called "slip rings." The slip rings are made of brass and are mounted at one end of the armature. They rotate with the armature. In order to receive the current developed in the armature conductors, two stationary bars, called "brushes", are placed in contact with the slip rings. This is shown in Fig. 5-1. The brushes are generally made of carbon and are held firmly against the slip rings by means of springs. The brushes, which are in continuous contact with the slip rings, lead the current from the generator to the load.

For each full revolution of the conductor in Fig. 5-1, a complete alternating current cycle is generated. If the conductor completes 60 revolutions in one second, we have a frequency of 60 Hz. If there are four poles instead of two poles, two complete cycles of current are induced in the conductor in one revolution. Thus, the frequency of an alternating current generator is equal to the product of the speed of the armature in revolutions per second and the number of pairs of magnetic poles.

The field of a generator can receive its electrical energy from an outside source or from its own output. In the former case, we refer to the generator as a separately excited generator. In the latter case, we refer to the generator as a self-excited generator.

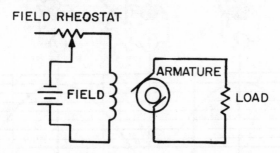

FIG. 5-2. A SEPARATELY EXCITED GENERATOR.

Fig. 5-2 shows a separately excited generator. The output of the armature is fed to the load. The field receives its energy from an external source. A field rheostat controls the amount of current flowing through the field coils. This, in turn, affects the strength of the magnetic field, which, in turn, affects the amount of the output voltage generated by the armature. The greater the current flow in the field coils, the greater is the output voltage and vice versa.

DC GENERATORS. A DC generator is similar to an AC generator, with the exception that the slip rings are replaced by a split ring, called a commutator. A simple commutator is shown in Fig. 5-3. The commutator segments are made of hard drawn copper and they are insulated from each other and from the armature by mica strips.

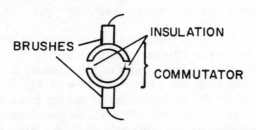

FIG. 5-3. SIDE VIEW OF A SIMPLE COMMUTATOR.

The commutator actually changes the alternating current that is generated by the armature coil into direct current. This is accomplished in the following manner (see Fig. 5-4).

When the coil moves from position 1 to position 2, the field is cut in a direction that causes current to flow out of the commutator and brush on the right hand side, through the meter and back through the brush and commutator on the left side. As the armature coil rotates from position 3 to

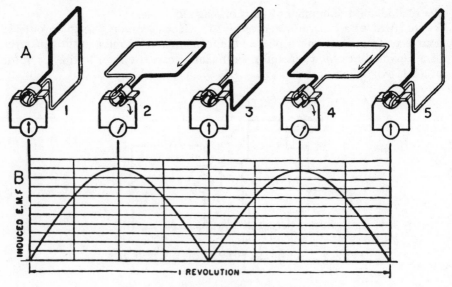

FIG. 5-4. GENERATING A DC VOLTAGE.

4, the current in the coil reverses itself. However, the segments of the commutator have rotated with the coil and they are now connected to opposite brushes. The direction of the current through the meter is therefore the same as it was before. Current still enters the meter from the brush on the right side. Thus, we have succeeded in converting the alternating current in the armature to direct current.

While the output of the generator is unidirectional, its amplitude is constantly varying. We refer to it as pulsating DC. A graph of the pulsating DC output of the generator of Fig. 5-4A is shown in Fig. 5-4B. The variations are referred to as ripple and this type of voltage is unsuitable for most applications. An actual generator has more coils and more commutator segments and produces far less ripple than shown in Fig. 5-4B. In addition to this, a filter is added and the output is practically "pure" DC.

3 BRUSHES. As the revolving commutator segments pass the stationary brushes, there are instants when the brushes short out the segments. This is shown in Fig. 5-5. We would normally expect sparking at the brushes when this occurs. However, in the simple generator of Fig. 5-4, the instant of shorting occurs when the armature coil is moving parallel with the field's magnetic lines of force. Thus, no voltage will be generated at this instant and there will be no voltage for the brushes to short out. When the brushes are in this position, we say that the brushes are in a "neutral" position. In this

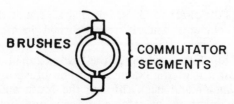

BRUSHES

COMMUTATOR
SEGMENTS

FIG. 5-5. SHORTING OUT
COMMUTATOR SEGMENTS.

position, there is no sparking at the brushes.

In actual practice, the magnetic field that is generated by the armature distorts the magnetic field produced by the field poles. The neutral position is changed somewhat and the brushes must be moved to the "real" neutral position. We can tell when the brushes are at their correct position by observing the position where there is no sparking.

Sparking, if excessive, will cause overheating, pitting and rapid wear of the brushes, with a consequent loss in power output. Sparking at the commutator will also cause radio frequency interference.

In addition to sparking being caused by the brushes being off neutral position, the following will also cause excessive sparking between the brushes and the commutator:

(1) If the commutator is not clean or if it is rough, the brushes will not make proper contact and will cause sparking. In order to clean a commutator, we first use a coarse cloth to wipe off the accumulated dirt. We then use a fine sandpaper to polish the surface of the commutator. Under no circumstances should emery cloth be used to clean a commutator. Emery cloth contains metallic particles which might short the commutator segments.

(2) Overloading the generator (drawing more current than the generator was meant to deliver) will cause sparking.

(3) Dirty or worn brushes will cause sparking.

(4) Excessive play of the brushes will cause sparking.

Brush, or commutator sparking cannot always be entirely eliminated. Therefore, when we use generators for radio transmitter power supplies, filters are used to minimize RF interference due to sparking. These filters consist of RF chokes and by-pass capacitors. Low frequency interference may be eliminated by the "ripple" filter.

A bypass capacitor is often connected between the brushes and ground to protect the armature winding from high frequency voltage surges originating in the transmitter.

3 SELF-EXCITED GENERATORS. The elementary generators described in the preceding paragraphs were "separately excited". In the self-excited generators, the armature supplies current to the field coils. Fig. 5-6 shows a self- excited generator. It is called a shunt-wound generator because the field coils are parallel to (in "shunt" with) the armature and the load.

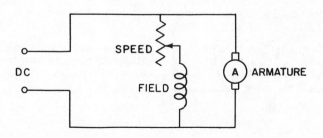

FIG. 5-6. A SHUNT-WOUND GENERATOR.

The generation of the output voltage depends on the "residual magnetism" in the field electro-magnets. By residual magnetism, we mean the small amount of magnetism that is always present in the field poles. When the armature starts revolving, the armature coil cuts the magnetic lines of force created by the residual magnetism. This causes a small current to flow in the armature. The armature current then has two paths to follow: one through the load and the other through the field. A small part of the current will pass through the field coils, resulting in an increase in the magnetic lines of force. The increased flux will cause the armature current to increase, resulting in a further increase of field flux. This building-up process, which usually takes 10 to 15 seconds, is completed when the generator reaches its rated output.

The field rheostat regulates the output voltage by controlling the amount of armature current that flows through the field. The residual magnetism of the field poles must be present in order that the generator may operate. With no flux present, the revolving armature would cut no lines of force and no current would flow in the armature coils.

The output voltage of the shunt wound generator is fairly constant even though the load varies somewhat. Thus, a shunt wound generator has good voltage regulation.

MOTORS. A motor is a device that converts electrical energy into mechanical energy. It is just the opposite of a generator. If we were to replace the load of a generator with a source of current, the generator would act as a motor.

The operation of a motor depends upon the basic principle that a current carrying conductor in a magnetic field will move at right angles to the magnetic field. The reason for this is that the conductor develops a magnetic field that reacts with the "external" magnetic field and causes motion. This motion comes about in the following manner: See Figure 5-7. The current in the conductor is flowing toward the reader. According to the left hand rule, a magnetic field, in a clockwise direction, develops around the conductor. Note that the magnetic fields of the magnets and the conductor are in the same direction on top of the conductor, and in opposite directions below the conductor. At the top of the conductor, the two fields reinforce to produce a stronger, denser field, while at the bottom of the conductor, the two fields tend to cancel each other to produce a thin weak field. Under these conditions, a force is exerted on the conductor that pushes it downward.

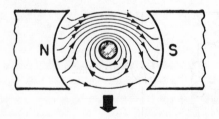

FIG. 5-7. MOTOR ACTION. CURRENT FLOWING TOWARD THE READER.

Fig. 5-8 illustrates the use of the above principles in the basic operation of a motor. In Fig. 5-8A, the current leaves the battery and enters the brush and commutator segment located near the South field pole. The current

96

direction in the dark portion of the loop is away from the reader. Applying the above principles, we see that this portion of the loop moves up. At the same time, the current in the lighter portion of the loop is moving toward the reader. This side of the loop will therefore move down. Thus we see how the loop rotates.

When the loop rotates one-half revolution to the position shown in Fig. 5-8B, the commutator segments, which are on the armature, also rotate. The current from the negative terminal of the battery enters the other commutator segment and its direction in the lighter part of the loop is now away from

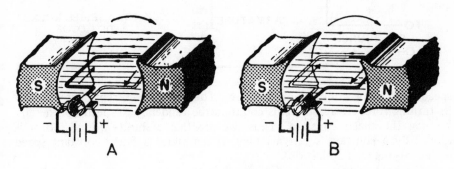

A   B

FIG. 5-8. OPERATION OF A MOTOR.

the reader. The reaction of the magnetic fields will cause this part of the loop to move up. Thus, the rotation of the loop continues in the same direction as previously.

It is apparent from the above that the purpose of the commutator in a motor is to periodically reverse the current flow in the armature so that the armature has the correct magnetic field for rotating.

4 SHUNT MOTORS. Fig. 5-9A illustrates the basic schematic of a shunt-wound DC motor. The field is parallel to the armature and both are parallel to the DC source. This is similar to the shunt-wound generator, with the exception that the DC source has replaced the load of the generator.

Current from the DC source flows through both the armature and the field coils. Magnetic fields are set up that cause the armature to rotate. As the armature rotates, an emf is induced in the armature. This occurs because the armature coils are cutting the flux of the field magnets. The induced emf opposes the armature current and is called a "counter-emf."

When there is no load on the motor, the only force necessary is that required to overcome the bearing friction. The counter-emf limits the armature current to the relatively small amount required to establish the necessary force to run the motor at no load.

When an external load is applied to the shunt motor, it tends to slow down slightly. As this happens, the armature coils cut fewer magnetic lines of force per second and the counter-emf is reduced, thereby increasing the armature current. This, in turn, increases the turning force of the motor and the original speed is maintained. If the load is removed, the motor tends to

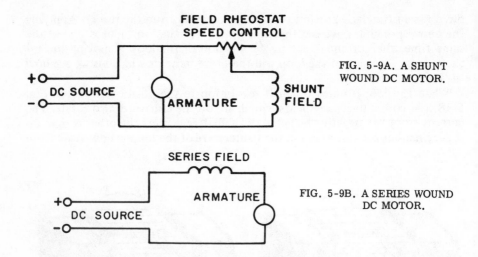

FIG. 5-9A. A SHUNT WOUND DC MOTOR.

FIG. 5-9B. A SERIES WOUND DC MOTOR.

speed up and the counter-emf increases. The armature current decreases and its turning force decreases. This counters the tendency to speed up, thereby keeping the speed constant. Thus, we see that a shunt- wound motor is essentially a constant speed machine. It maintains a fairly constant speed under varying load conditions.

If the field coils were to open up while the motor was running under no load, the results could be disastrous. In the absence of most of the field flux, the counter-emf would practically disappear. The armature current would then rise to an extremely high value. The high armature current would cause the motor to race at such high speeds that it could mechanically destroy itself. The high current could also burn out the armature coils. Large motors should be properly fused to prevent such situations.

3 **SERIES MOTORS.** Fig. 5-9B illustrates a series-wound motor. The field is in series with the armature. Therefore, the armature current is the same as the field current and the field strength is proportional to the armature current. Mechanically, it can be shown that the torque (turning force) of the armature is proportional to the square of the armature current.

If the supply voltage and the load are constant, the armature current and the field flux will also be constant. If the load on the motor were taken off, the armature would speed up to such an extent that the armature windings would be thrown from the slots and destroyed by excessive centrifugal forces. For this reason, series motors are always directly connected to their loads by gears rather than belts. The belt might come off, but a gear assembly is unlikely to come apart.

When the load on a series motor is increased, the speed and counter-emf decrease and the armature current and field strength increase. When the load on a series motor is decreased, the speed and counter-emf increase and the armature current and field strength decrease. Thus we see that the speed of a DC series motor is primarily dependent on its load.

THE AC INDUCTION MOTOR. An AC induction motor consists of a stator and a rotor. The stator has field coils in much the same manner as the

98

DC motor. However, the rotor of the induction motor is quite different. The rotor of an induction motor is not connected electrically to the source of power.

The basic operation of an induction motor can be understood by considering Fig. 5-10. It is a schematic of an elementary induction motor. The stator consists of electromagnets and the rotor is a bar magnet pivoted at its center. AC is fed to the field coils (stator) which causes their magnetic polarity to reverse periodically. Fig. 5-10A shows one alternation of the AC cycle. The North pole of the bar rotor faces the South pole of the stator. On the next alternation, the stator reverses its magnetic polarity and the bar magnet swings around. Since the field magnets continue to reverse polarity, the bar magnet continues to turn. Thus we have the basic motor action.

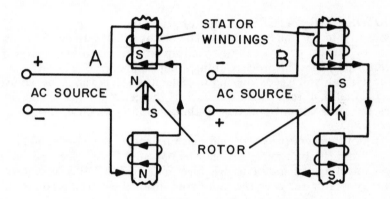

FIG. 5-10. AN INDUCTION MOTOR.

In an actual induction motor, the stator consists of two or more electromagnetic field poles. The field coils are energized by single phase or polyphase AC which produces a rotating magnetic field.

In Fig. 5-10, the rotor was assumed to be a bar magnet for explanatory purposes only. In actual practice, the rotor consists of a cylindrical core with parallel slots in the outside circumference to hold coil windings in place. The rotor is not physically connected to the stator. As the stator's magnetic field rotates, it induces an emf in the rotor conductors, which, in turn, develop a magnetic field around the rotor. (This induction process is where the term "induction motor" originates). The two magnetic fields react and cause the rotor to turn.

The number of revolutions per second of the rotating magnetic field depends upon the frequency of the AC supply and the number of field poles. Therefore, the speed of the induction motor depends primarily upon the frequency of the supply voltage and the number of field poles. To a slighter extent, the speed of the induction motor depends upon the size of the load.

The formula for the speed of an induction motor is:

Syn. speed (RPM) $= \dfrac{120\ f}{N}$ where f is equal to the line frequency and N is equal to the number of poles.

EXAMPLE: Find the speed of a 220 volt, 60 cycle, 6 pole, 3 phase induction motor.

$$\text{Syn. speed} = \frac{120 \times 60}{6} = \frac{7200}{6} = 1200 \text{ RPM}$$

SYNCHRONOUS AC MOTORS. The synchronous motor, though similar in general principle to the induction motor, differs from it in several aspects. The synchronous motor requires a source of DC for the rotor. It also requires a special starting winding. However, the stators of both motors are essentially the same.

The speed of the synchronous motor depends primarily on the frequency of the applied current and the number of field poles, as does the induction motor described above.

3 **MOTOR-GENERATORS.** A motor-generator is a power supply that consists of a motor and a generator. The motor which is fed with an available source of power, is physically hooked up to a generator and drives it. The generator produces the proper output voltage and current.

The output voltage of the motor-generator set is varied by adjusting a rheostat that is in series with the field of the generator part of the set. This varies the field current and flux in the generator, which in turn, varies the output voltage.

The motor-generator is a rugged machine and may be operated at a point remote from the transmitter. It may be operated from either AC or DC by simply adapting the motor to whatever is available. Other advantages of a motor- generator set over the more conventional electronic power supplies are as follows: It does not require rectifier tubes, and so the need for changing tubes does not exist. It has a high ripple frequency and consequently, does not require a large filter to smooth out the ripple. The voltage regulation of the motor-generator is excellent at the full rated voltage.

The motor-generator is not without its disadvantages when comparing it to electronic power supplies. Its output voltage regulation is poor when it is not operating at its full rated output voltage. It has a high initial cost and occupies a large amount of space. Because it has moving parts, it requires frequent service, inspection and repair. Other disadvantages are: Sparking is generally present, which in turn, causes RF interference. Noise and vibration are present. Very high DC voltage cannot be obtained with motor generator sets.

A motor-generator requires bearings and care should be taken to see to it that the bearings do not become overheated. There should be sufficient lubrication of the bearings and the line feeding the lubrication to the bearings should be free of dirt or other obstruction. The machine should not be overloaded for any length of time since this will cause the bearings to overheat. All foreign matter except the lubricant, should be kept from the bearing area.

3 **DYNAMOTORS.** A dynamotor is a combination of a motor and a generator housed in a single frame. It appears to be a single machine. Actually, it contains two armature windings on a single shaft. The dyna-

motor has a single field that produces magnetic flux for both generator action and motor action.

A practical application for a dynamotor would be at a portable location where we wish to step up the low voltage DC of a battery to high voltage DC for plate circuits. A 12 volt battery is fed through brushes and a commutator to the motor windings of the armature. The armature reacts with the field and rotates. The high voltage generator windings on the same armature cut the field flux and a high voltage is induced. This high voltage is fed through another commutator and another set of brushes to the output terminals of the dynamotor. By using slip rings on the generator section, we can develop AC at the output. We can also use slip rings at the motor section of the armature if AC is the available source. By the use of slip rings or commutators, dynamotors can be designed to take AC or DC and deliver AC or DC.

The dynamotor is a highly efficient, compact machine. However, it does have an important drawback; its output voltage is not easily varied. Since its field is common to both the motor part and the generator part, any change in field current will affect both parts.

There are two ways in which the output voltage of the dynamotor can be varied. One way is to vary the speed of the motor. This will vary the speed of the generator, which in turn, will vary the output voltage of the generator. The other method is to place a rheostat in series with the output of the generator. Both methods are unsatisfactory, since they waste power and degrade the voltage regulation of the dynamotor. (Voltage regulation is a term that will be discussed in the lesson on Power Supplies.)

PRACTICE QUESTIONS - LESSON 5

1. A shunt-wound generator using field coil magnets depends upon what factor for its operation? (3)
a. frequency   c. load
b. speed of rotation   d. residual magnetism

(3)
2. By-pass capacitors across the brushes of a generator are used:
a. to increase output   c. to increase ripple frequency
b. to minimize RF interference   d. none of the above

3. A motor-generator bearing will overheat because of: (3)
a. insufficient speed   c. overloading
b. an open load   d. an open field rheostat

4. Which of the following should not be used to clean a commutator? (3)
a. sandpaper   c. cheese cloth
b. a commutator polishing agent   d. emory cloth

5. Simple control of output voltage characterizes a:
a. motor-generator   c. synchronous generator
b. dynamotor   d. shunt-fed motor

6. A motor-generator power supply: (3)
a. is not rugged
b. is inexpensive
c. has good regulation at its full rated output
d. has a low ripple frequency

7. In a DC generator, the commutator:
a. changes DC to AC   c. changes AC to DC
b. filters out the DC   d. reduces the line frequency

8. Excessive sparking at the brushes of a DC motor is caused by:
a. RF feedback   c. motor underload   (3)
b. brushes in neutral position   d. dirty commutator

9. The speed of a DC series motor is determined chiefly by: (3)
a. the number of the pairs of poles
b. the frequency stability of the line
c. the line frequency
d. the load

10. The output voltage of a generator is controlled by a:
a. field rheostat   c. pair of slip rings
b. commutator   d. starting rheostat

11. Excessive sparking between the brushes and a commutator of
a generator will not cause: (3)
a. pitting   c. RF interference
b. overheating   d. increased output voltage

12. A combination motor and generator, using a common shaft, is
called a: (3)
a. regulator   c. dynamotor
b. generator   d. powerstat

13. Compared to a transformer-rectifier power supply, a motor-
generator set has a: (3)
a. higher ripple frequency   c. less frequent need for service
b. lower initial cost   d. less rugged construction

LESSON 6
THE DIODE

THE DEVELOPMENT OF THE VACUUM TUBE. Thomas A. Edison was one of the great pioneers in the development of the vacuum tube. Edison invented the incandescent light bulb whose basic principles were later put to use by Fleming and DeForest, in the development of the modern vacuum tube.

Edison's incandescent electric lamp consisted of a resistance wire called a filament, enclosed within a glass envelope. The air within the glass envelope had been removed to create a vacuum. The ends of the resistance wire protruded through the glass, as illustrated in Fig. 6-1. If a current was passed through the resistance wire, it heated up and glowed. We can then say that the filament was heated to INCANDESCENCE.

While working with his electric light, Edison discovered that the incandescent wire emitted, or boiled off, electrons. These electrons remained

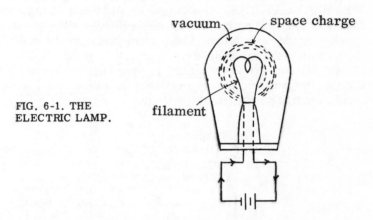

vacuum   space charge

FIG. 6-1. THE
ELECTRIC LAMP.   filament

around the wire in the form of an electron cloud or SPACE CHARGE. This phenomenon of electron emission is known as the EDISON EFFECT, and is the basis for the operation of all vacuum tubes.

ELECTRON EMISSION. Many metallic substances will emit electrons when heated to incandescence. For instance, the resistance wire in the light bulb emits electrons. These emitted electrons are wasted since they serve no useful purpose.

The vacuum tube is similar to the light bulb in that it also contains a resistance wire which emits electrons when heated. The vacuum tube, however, is designed to make use of the emitted electrons. In addition to the

103

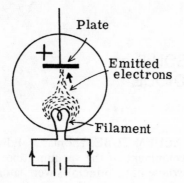

Plate

Emitted electrons

Filament

FIG. 6-2. POSITIVE PLATE ATTRACTING ELECTRONS.

resistance wire, the vacuum tube has a positively charged collector of electrons called the PLATE. The positive plate attracts the emitted electrons. This is illustrated in Fig. 6-2.

THE CATHODE. The element in the vacuum tube which supplies the electrons is called the CATHODE. The cathode emits or boils off electrons when energy, in the form of heat, is supplied to it. There are two common types of cathodes used in vacuum tubes. They are: (1) the directly heated cathode, and (2) the indirectly heated cathode.

(1) The directly heated cathode. This type is also known by the name FILAMENT-CATHODE. An example of a filament- cathode is illustrated in Fig. 6-3. The heating current is passed directly through the cathode wire which is made of tungsten. The current heats up the cathode wire which then emits electrons from its surface. Directly heated filament- cathodes usually require very little heating power. They are therefore used in tubes designed for portable battery operation because it is necessary to impose as small a drain as possible on the batteries.

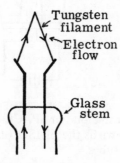

Tungsten filament

Electron flow

Glass stem

FIG. 6-3. DIRECTLY-HEATED CATHODE.

Examples of filament-cathode tubes are the 1K3, the 3DG4 and the 5AU4. Filaments are made of tungsten or thoriated tungsten. Directly heated filament-cathodes are also designed to handle large amounts of power and therefore find use in high power rectifier and transmitting tubes.

(2) The indirectly-heated cathode. This type is also known as the HEATER-CATHODE and is illustrated in Fig. 6-4A. The heater-cathode consists of two parts:

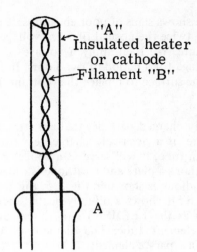

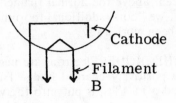

"A"
Insulated heater
or cathode
Filament "B"

A

FIG. 6-4. INDIRECTLY-
HEATED CATHODE.

(A) A thin metal sleeve or cylinder coated with an electron emitting material (usually nickel, coated with barium oxide or thorium oxide). We refer to this cylinder as the cathode. (B) A heater wire within the cylinder. The heater wire or filament is usually made of tungsten and is insulated electrically from the cylinder or cathode.

Current is passed through the heater, causing it to heat up. The heater, in turn, heats up the cylinder or cathode. Since the cathode has an electron emitting surface, the heat will cause it to emit electrons. Note that the heater function in this case is not to emit electrons, but merely to heat the cathode. Fig. 6-4B shows the schematic symbol for the heater-cathode. Almost all present day receiving tubes designed for AC operation are of the indirectly-heated cathode type.

The directly heated filament can be designed to be heavier and more rugged than the indirectly heated type. As such, the directly heated cathode can handle large amounts of power and can withstand high operating temperatures without melting.

A major disadvantage of the directly-heated filament is that AC hum will get into the signal if we use AC current to heat the filament. Other disadvantages are low emission efficiency and greater possibility of filament burnout compared to indirectly heated tubes.

The indirectly-heated cathode has a high emission efficiency, low operating temperature and relative freedom from filament burnout. Its chief disadvantages are that it requires a longer warm-up time and it must be used in a low current circuit.

3 **THORIATED TUNGSTEN FILAMENTS.** The thoriated tungsten filament is a directly-heated filament that is made of tungsten, to which a small amount of thorium oxide is added. During the manufacturing process, the filament is activated. This is done by heating the filament to a high temperature. Some of the thorium is boiled to the surface and forms a thin layer around the tungsten. This thin layer of thorium improves the emission efficiency of the filament, compared to the pure tungsten filament.

105

When the thoriated tungsten filament shows signs of poor emissions, it can be reactivated. This is done by applying twice the normal filament voltage to the filament for a period of one minute. We then apply a voltage of 25 percent above the normal filament voltage for a period of two hours. In this way, we "boil" additional thorium to the surface to replace the thorium that has been worn away.

THE DIODE. Electrons are negatively charged particles that are attracted to a positively charged body. Therefore, if a positively charged electrode, called a PLATE, is put into the vacuum tube, it will serve as a collector of the electrons. A vacuum tube which contains a plate and a cathode is called a DIODE. The schematic symbol for the diode is shown in Fig. 6-5. Fig. 6-5A is an indirectly-heated diode and Fig. 6-5B shows a directly-heated diode. The plate and the cathode are known as the ELEMENTS of the vacuum tube. The diode is therefore a two-element tube. The filament of the indirectly-heated tube is not counted as a separate element.

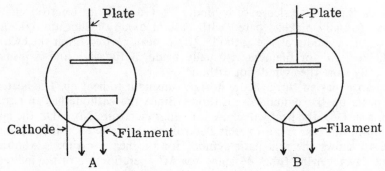

FIG. 6-5A. INDIRECTLY-HEATED DIODE. FIG. 6-5B. DIRECTLY-HEATED DIODE.

THE DIODE AS A CONDUCTOR. The schematic diagram of Fig. 6-6 shows a diode connected to a voltage source. This voltage source is called a "B" supply. The top terminal is B+ and the bottom terminal is B−. Note that the heater is NOT connected to a voltage source. Whenever a schematic shows a heater left hanging in this manner, it is ASSUMED to have a supply voltage connected to it.

The instant the switch is closed, the milliammeter in the curcuit will register a current flow indicating that electrons are flowing from the cathode to the plate. The diode is said to be CONDUCTING. The diode conducts because the plate is positive with respect to the cathode. The plate therefore attracts the negatively charged electrons emitted by the cathode. The electrons flow from the plate to the positive terminal of the battery. They then flow through the battery and back to the cathode where they once more can be emitted to the plate. If the battery voltage is increased, the plate will become more positive and will attract more electrons. The ammeter will consequently register a larger current flow. Conversely, if the plate battery voltage is decreased, the plate will attract less electrons and the ammeter will register a smaller current flow.

When the diode conducts, it represents a very low resistance path between

106

the cathode and plate.

THE DIODE AS A NON-CONDUCTOR. If we reverse the battery connections, as shown in Fig. 6-7, the plate becomes negative and the cathode positive. Since the negative plate will not attract electrons, the diode will NOT CONDUCT. The diode, therefore, acts like an open circuit and no current will flow. The meter will read zero current. The emitted negatively-charged electrons are repelled by the negative plate and remain close to the cathode where they form an ELECTRON CLOUD. The cloud of electrons around the cathode is also known as a SPACE CHARGE. If the plate were to become positive once again, the space charge would be rapidly reduced since its electrons would be attracted to the plate.

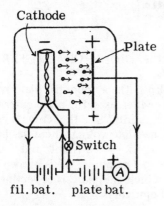

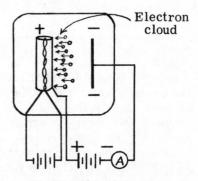

FIG. 6-6. DIODE ACTION
WHEN PLATE IS POSITIVE.

FIG. 6-7. DIODE ACTION
WHEN PLATE IS NEGATIVE.

Let us now summarize the operation of the diode.

(1) Electrons flow in one direction only - from cathode to plate. We refer to this electron flow as the PLATE CURRENT.

(2) Electron flow to the plate will take place only when the plate is positive with respect to the cathode. The voltage on the plate is referred to as the PLATE VOLTAGE.

(3) The current flow will vary with the amount of plate voltage.

(4) The diode acts as a conductor when the plate is positive.

(5) The diode acts as a non-conductor (open circuit) when the plate is negative.

THE DIODE CHARACTERISTIC CURVE. Fig. 6-8 illustrates a diode connected to a source of variable voltage. The heater circuit has been omitted for the purpose of simplicity. "A" is a milliammeter connected in series with the tube. It measures the plate current. The voltage applied to the plate of the diode can be varied by changing the position of the plate tap from #1 to #8. As the tap is moved from position #1 to position #8, the plate voltage increases. For every value of plate voltage, there will be a different value of plate current. The table in Fig. 6-8 shows a tablulation of plate current readings for various values of plate voltage. If we plot these readings on the graph of Fig. 6-8, and then draw a line through the different

107

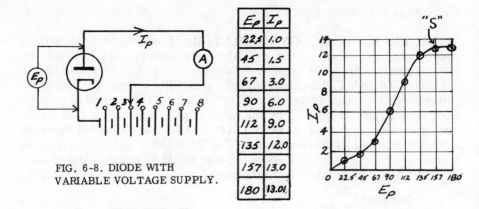

E_p	I_p
22.5	1.0
45	1.5
67	3.0
90	6.0
112	9.0
135	12.0
157	13.0
180	13.01

FIG. 6-8. DIODE WITH VARIABLE VOLTAGE SUPPLY.

points, we obtain a curve known as the DIODE CHARACTERISTIC CURVE.

Ip is the symbol for plate current and Ep is the symbol for plate voltage. The curve indicates that, as the plate voltage increases, the plate current also increases, up to the point "S". Beyond point "S", the curve becomes practically horizontal. In other words, as the plate voltage increases beyond point "S", the plate current remains essentially constant and will not increase, regardless of plate voltage increases. The point "S" is known as the SATURATION POINT. It is the point at which the plate is collecting all of the electrons that the cathode is capable of emitting.

The characteristic curve is important because it tells us at a glance what the plate current will be for any particular plate voltage. This information is useful if we are designing a circuit for a certain diode application.

SOLID-STATE DIODES. Not all diodes have their electrodes separated by a vacuum, or a conductive gas as in some special tubes. There are diodes that use oxide layers or metallic alloys. These diodes are called SEMICONDUCTORS. Semiconductors pass current freely in one direction and allow little or no current to flow in the opposite direction. Almost all semiconductor diodes are indicated by the symbol in Fig. 6-9. Variations of this symbol are used to indicate special purpose diodes.

Solid-state diodes are not a recent development. Copper oxide rectifiers were used in battery chargers when the vacuum tube was first being added to the crystal set as an amplifier. Copper oxide rectifiers are still being used as meter rectifiers to convert AC to DC.

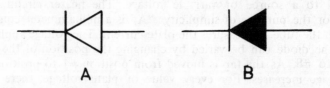

FIG. 6-9. SEMI-CONDUCTOR DIODE SYMBOLS.

108

Selenium rectifiers became popular in the 1950's but were soon replaced by germanium and silicon diodes that were physically smaller and easier to mount in the more compact TV receiver chassis. Silicon diodes have become more or less standard in power supplies since they can operate at higher temperatures with less possibilities of breakdown.

3 INSULATORS AND DOPING. Certain elements are good conductors; others are good insulators. Copper wire is a good conductor, while other elements, such as pure germanium, selenium or pure silicon, are insulators. We can modify the characteristics of any element by mixing in other elements. For example, we can add boron, antimony or arsenic to pure germanium or pure silicon and change these elements from non-conductors into conductors.

The addition of an element, such as antimony, to either germanium or silicon, is known as doping. Since the germanium or silicon, at the start, is as pure as it can be made, the added element is referred to as an impurity. It takes just a very small amount of impurity to modify the germanium or silicon so that they are no longer insulators.

By diffusing certain elements, such as antimony, into pure germanium or silicon, we increase the total number of electrons in the germanium or silicon. These "doped" elements now have more electrons than they originally had. Since electrons are negatively charged, we refer to them as negative germanium or negative silicon. We abbreviate negative germanium as n-germanium or n-type germanium.

We can diffuse other substances, such as boron, into germanium or silicon, and create a deficiency of electrons. When a substance or an element has a deficiency of electrons, it is no longer neutral. It becomes positive. Germanium or silicon, doped with boron, is referred to as positive germanium or positive silicon. We abbreviate this as p-germanium or p-silicon or p-type. We can represent n-type or p-type pictorially, as shown in Fig. 6-10. An atom that has an electron missing is positively charged and is sometimes referred to as a "hole". The term "hole" stands for the hole that was left by the missing electron.

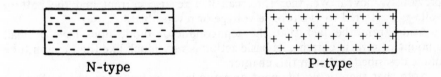

N-type   P-type

FIG. 6-10. N-TYPE AND P-TYPE GERMANIUM OR SILICON.

When the n-type material is hooked up to a battery, the negatively charged electrons, which are the "majority" carriers, flow from the negative terminal of the battery, through the n-type material and back to the positive terminal. In the p-type circuit, the positively charged "holes", which are the majority carriers, flow from the positive terminal of the battery, through the material and back to the negative terminal of the battery.

The internal resistance of both p-type and n-type material is low in the direction of the flow of majority current carriers.

109

3 THE SEMICONDUCTOR DIODE. If we take a block of p-type germanium and a block of n-type germanium (or silicon) and put them together, we will have a semiconductor diode. The semiconductor diode is referred to as a solid-state device.

In Figure 6-11, a battery is connected across two blocks of doped germanium or silicon. The negative terminal of the battery is connected to the n-type material, while the positive terminal is connected to the p-type material. Connecting a voltage in this manner is known as biasing. Electrons will now flow from the battery, through the n-type material, into the p-type material and back to the battery. The reason for the current flow is that the battery urges or forces electrons into the n-type block, which already has more electrons than normal. The electrons migrate over to the p-type block since this region is more positive and attracts them. However, as electrons leave the p-type block to the battery, more electrons from the n-type block cross the junction between the two blocks, and so the process is a continuous one. The current that flows is referred to as a forward current. The voltage producing this current is called a forward voltage or forward bias.

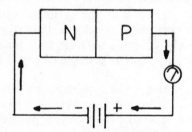
FIG. 6-11. FORWARD BIASING.

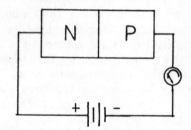
FIG. 6-12. REVERSE BIASING.

Now examine Fig. 6-12. The only difference is that we have reversed the polarity of the battery. As a result, very little current flows. The small current that does flow moves in an opposite direction to the way it previously moved. We, therefore, call it a reverse current and the battery voltage is referred to as a reverse voltage or reverse bias.

Aside from the fact that the semiconductor diode does have a small amount of reverse current, its basic action is very much like the vacuum tube diode described earlier in this chapter.

Note that there is no filament or cathode to be heated and so, unlike the tube, the semiconductor diode does not get warm or hot when operating. Therefore, since we do not need to wait for the filament or cathode to get hot enough to emit electrons, the semiconductor diode acts at once.

PRACTICE QUESTIONS - LESSON 6

1. Which of the following creates N-type material when diffused into germanium? (3)
a. antimony   c. selenium
b. boron   d. copper oxide

2. The point when the plate is collecting all the electrons that the cathode is emitting, is called:
a. saturation point
b. cut-off point
c. maximum usable current
d. maximum plate dissipation

3. An advantage of a filament-type tube is:
a. uneven wear of the filament
b. redistribution of hum
c. can handle high power
d. does not require electrolytic capacitors

4. The indirectly-heated cathode type tube:
a. has the heating current pass directly through the cathode
b. has a separate filament and cathode
c. does not require heater current
d. has no cathode

5. When the plate of a diode is positive, relative to the cathode:
a. current will flow from plate to cathode
b. the cathode stops emitting
c. the tube conducts
d. an electron cloud forms

6. Electron emission:
a. is undesirable in vacuum tubes
b. is necessary for the operation of a light bulb
c. can only take place when the filament is cold
d. is the giving off of electrons by a metal when heated

7. What are the majority carriers in N-type material? (3)
a. holes   b. electrons   c. protons   d. neutrons

8. The directly-heated cathode type tube:
a. has the heating current pass directly through the cathode
b. has a separate filament and cathode
c. does not require heater current
d. is the same as the indirectly-heated cathode type tube

9. In semiconductor conduction, a "flow of holes" refers to:
a. a flow of positive carriers
b. a flow of electrons
c. a flow of protons
d. a flow of neutrons

10. The diode tube has:
a. one element
b. two elements
c. three elements
d. four elements

11. Hum can be a problem when using:
a. transistors
b. directly-heated tubes
c. indirectly-heated tubes
d. diodes

111

12. The diode acts as an open-circuit:
a. when the tube conducts
b. when the plate is negative with respect to the cathode
c. when the plate emits electrons
d. when the cathode is negative with respect to the plate

13. When the plate of a diode is negative, relative to the cathode:
a. the cathode stops emitting
b. the tube conducts
c. current will flow from cathode to plate
d. the tube acts as an open-circuit

14. The plate is:
a. a positively charged collector of electrons
b. a positively charged emitter of electrons
c. not necessary for the operation of a diode
d. none of the above

15. A diode tube allows current to flow:
a. only from cathode to plate   c. in either direction
b. only from cathode to heaters   d. straight up

16. The cathode:
a. is not necessary for the operation of a diode
b. is a positively charged collector of electrons
c. repels electrons
d. emits electrons for tube operation

LESSON 7
POWER SUPPLIES

INTRODUCTION. There are very few electronic devices that make actual "use" of the 117V. AC that is supplied in homes throughout the United States. The internal circuits of most receivers, transmitters and TV sets require DC. They also require AC voltages that are higher and/or lower than the 117 volts available at the wall outlet. The section of the equipment that supplies these varied AC and DC voltages is called the POWER SUPPLY. The major components in a power supply are: The power transformer, the rectifier and the filter system. The power transformer supplies the various AC voltages. The rectifier and the filter system combine to supply the various DC voltages.

THE DIODE AS A HALF WAVE RECTIFIER. The component in a power supply which converts the alternating current into direct current is called the RECTIFIER. It may be either a vacuum tube or a semiconductor device. The process of converting AC to DC is called RECTIFICATION.

The ability of the diode to pass current in only one direction makes it possible to convert alternating current into pulsating direct current. Let us see how this is done. Fig. 7-1 illustrates a simple diode rectifier circuit. When terminal B of the transformer is positive with respect to terminal A, the diode plate becomes positive with respect to its cathode. The diode therefore conducts current in the direction indicated by the arrows. The DC milliammeter will deflect to the value of the current flow.

On the next half of the alternating current cycle, the polarity of the transformer will be reversed, making the plate negative with respect to the cathode. The diode will stop conducting because a negative plate will repel the electron flow. In the case of a semiconductor, the high reverse resistance of the semiconductor material will allow very few electrons to flow. The current in the circuit will, therefore, cease flowing during the negative half of

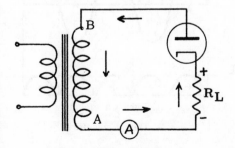

FIG. 7-1. DIODE USED
AS HALF-WAVE RECTIFIER.

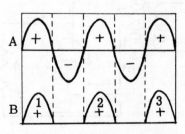

FIG. 7-2. HALF-WAVE
RECTIFIER WAVEFORMS.

113

the cycle. When the polarity of the transformer again reverses itself and makes the plate positive, current will again flow through the circuit. Fig. 7-2 is a graphic explanation of what is happening. Fig. 7-2A shows the sine wave which is generated across terminals A-B of the transformer. Fig. 7-2B shows the voltage which is obtained across the load resistor RL. In Fig. 7-2B, we see the positive halves of the cycle when the plate is positive with respect to the cathode. At that time, the diode conducts. The positive half cycles are, therefore, impressed directly across the resistor RL. During the negative half of each AC cycle, the diode does not conduct and is effectively an open circuit. During these times, there is no voltage developed across the resistor since there is no current flow. The current through the resistor is therefore a pulsating direct current, and the voltage across the resistor is a pulsating direct voltage. Even though the current flows in spurts or pulses through the resistor, the current is still DC because it flows in ONE direction only. This action of the diode, in passing only one-half of the AC input wave to the load resistor, is known as HALF-WAVE RECTIFICATION.

The ends of the load resistance have been marked as to polarity because electrons are entering and emerging from it. The end at which they enter is more negative than the end from which they emerge.

THE DIODE AS A FULL-WAVE RECTIFIER. In half-wave rectification, only the positive half of the AC input is used. The negative alternations are completely cut off and wasted. If we could somehow utilize the negative as well as the positive alternations, we would be operating our rectifier system more efficiently. This is accomplished in full-wave rectification.

Fig. 7-3 illustrates a full-wave rectifier. Another diode and a transformer secondary center-tap have been added to Fig. 7-1.

The operation of a full-wave rectifier is as follows: When point "A" is positive with respect to point "B", the plate of diode #1 is positive and the tube conducts. The electrons flow through the transformer, from A to C, out of C, into the load resistance RL. From RL, the electrons flow to the cathode of diode #1. Since the tube is conducting, the current flows to the plate and back to point A to complete its circuit. During all this time, the plate of diode #2 is negative and does not conduct.

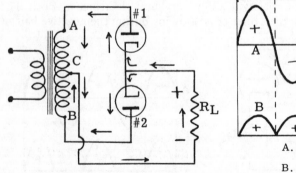

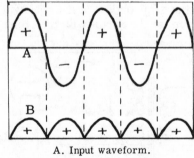

A. Input waveform.

B. Output waveform.

FIG. 7-3.
FULL-WAVE RECTIFIER.

FIG. 7-4.
FULL-WAVE RECTIFIER WAVEFORMS.

114

On the next half of the AC cycle, the bottom of the transformer, point "B", is positive, while the top, point "A", is negative. The plate of diode #2 is now positive and the plate of diode #1 is negative. Diode #2 will now conduct, and diode #1 will not. The electrons flow through the transformer from B to C, into the load resistor R_L, and back to the cathode of diode #2. They then flow to the plate and back to point B. Note that the current flows through the resistor in the same direction during both the positive and negative halves of the input cycle. We have very definitely used both halves of the AC input cycle, and have accomplished full-wave rectification. Fig. 7-4A shows the AC across the transformer secondary. Fig. 7-4B shows the pulsating DC flowing through the load.

There are several advantages in using a full-wave rectifier system rather than the half-wave system. They are:

(1) The full-wave system is twice as efficient as the half-wave system.

(2) The current flowing in the half-wave system is only in one direction, which tends to saturate the transformer core with residual magnetism.

(3) Each diode in the full-wave system needs only half the total load current rating of the diode used in a half-wave system.

(4) The output of a full wave rectifier has a higher AC ripple frequency than a half wave rectifier. We will see in a later section of this lesson, that this results in a purer DC output for the full wave system.

3 COPPER-OXIDE. The full wave rectifier circuit of Fig. 7-3 uses high vacuum diode tubes as the actual rectifiers. There are a number of "dry-metal" or "junction" type rectifiers that can function in a manner similar to the diode rectifier tube. One such type is the COPPER-OXIDE RECTIFIER. See Fig. 7-5A. It consists of a copper disc in contact with copper oxide. It is found that electrons will flow from the copper to the copper oxide, but not the other way. This unidirectional characteristic allows it to be used as a rectifier.

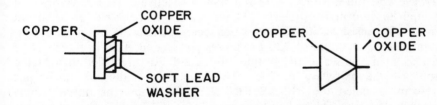

FIG. 7-5A. COPPER OXIDE RECTIFIER.   FIG. 7-5B. SYMBOL FOR COPPER OXIDE RECTIFIER.

Copper oxide rectifiers are used in small current applications such as AC meters. The AC must be changed to DC because the DC meter movement requires DC. Copper oxide rectifiers occupy much less space than a rectifier tube and cost less to use since they don't require a tube socket with its additional wiring.

Copper oxide rectifiers have a low breakdown voltage rating (11 volts peak) and therefore, must be connected in series and in parallel to increase their voltage and current handling capabilities. The copper oxide rectifiers have a high shunt capacity and can only be used in low frequency applications.

3 SELENIUM RECTIFIERS. The selenium rectifier is a more popular type of "junction" rectifier than the copper-oxide type. It consists of steel and selenium or aluminum and selenium. The electron flow is from the steel or the aluminum to the selenium. There is a high impedance to electron flow in the opposite direction.

Compared to high vacuum tubes, the selenium rectifier is smaller, runs cooler and is less fragile. It has a longer life span and has a lower initial cost. The selenium rectifier has a low voltage drop and consequently, better voltage regulation.*Compared to the copper oxide rectifier, the selenium rectifier is more rugged and has a larger current handling capability. It is used in high power circuits.

The selenium rectifier has a high shunt capacity. This limits its use in high frequency circuits. It is good only up to approximately 1000 cycles. When a selenium rectifier is used with a capacitor input filter, it should have a small resistor in series with it to limit the charging current due to the capacitor.

3 SILICON RECTIFIERS. Of all the dry-type rectifiers, the silicon diodes have become the most popular. They are extremely compact and have a high current rating. They provide for good voltage regulation because of their low voltage drop. Silicon rectifiers can operate on a broad temperature range. While silicon rectifiers can handle high currents, their peak current ratings are critical and should not be exceeded. It is necessary to use series resistors to protect them against peak-capacitor charging surges. Another disadvantage of silicon rectifiers is its low peak inverse voltage rating. *

The advantages of silicon rectifiers far outweigh the disadvantages and they are used almost everywhere in electronic equipment.

RIPPLE FREQUENCY. Fig. 7-6 illustrates the input waveforms of the half-wave and full-wave rectifiers and their respective output waveforms. If the input waveform is 60 Hertz AC, we can see that the half-wave output current will consist of 60 DC pulses per second, while the full-wave output current will be made up of 120 DC pulses per second. That is, there will be twice as many pulses in the output of the full-wave rectifier than in the output of the half-wave rectifier. The number of pulses in the output waveform is called the RIPPLE FREQUENCY. Thus, the output ripple frequency of a single phase half-wave rectifier is 60 Hz, while that of a single phase full-wave rectifier is 120 Hz. Since a three-phase system produces three times as many pulses per Hertz as a single-phase system produces, the output ripple frequency of a rectifier using three-phase current as its source would be 180 Hz for a half-wave system and 360 Hz for a full-wave system.

THE FILTERING SYSTEM. It is obvious that the rectifier output is not pure DC. It is actually a pulsating DC, or DC with a superimposed AC ripple. If we could somehow remove, or filter out the AC ripple from the pulsating DC, we would end up with pure DC.

* Voltage regulation and peak inverse voltage are discussed later in this chapter.

116

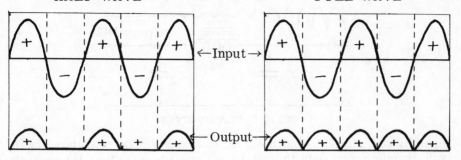

HALF-WAVE   FULL-WAVE

FIG. 7-6. INPUT VERSUS OUTPUT WAVEFORMS.

The method of removing the ripple from the DC output is known as FILTERING. The device which does the filtering is called a FILTER. It generally consists of capacitors and inductors. The capacitors are called filter capacitors and the inductors are known as filter chokes.

There are two different types of filter arrangements that are most commonly used in power supplies. One is the CAPACITOR INPUT type and the other is the CHOKE INPUT type.

THE CAPACITOR INPUT FILTER. Fig. 7-7 shows a capacitor input filter system connected to the output of a full-wave rectifier. The filter is enclosed within the dotted line and is recognizable as a capacitor input type because the filter component nearest to the rectifier is a capacitor (C1). The complete filter is called a "pi" filter because its component arrangement resembles the Greek letter Π (pronounced "pi").

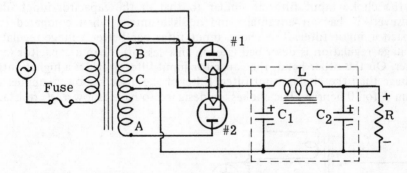

FIG. 7-7. FULL-WAVE RECTIFIER WITH CAPACITOR INPUT FILTER.

Fig. 7-8 illustrates how the filter removes the AC ripple from the output of the rectifier. At A we see the rectifier waveform at the input to the filter. It is pulsating DC. C1 is a large capacitor of about 20 mf. A 20 mf. capacitor has a very low reactance to the 120 Hertz ripple component. It will, therefore, short out or by-pass most of the ripple component. The capacitor acts like an open circuit to the DC component and will therefore prevent DC from being shorted out. At B we see the resulting wave shape after it is acted

117

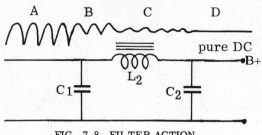

FIG. 7-8. FILTER ACTION.

upon by capacitor C1. The choke, L1, has a very low DC resistance. The DC will, therefore, pass right through L1 without any oppostion. However, the choke will generate a very strong counter-emf to oppose the AC ripple. The result is that practically all of the remaining ripple will be prevented from passing through the choke. The waveform appearing on the other side of the choke is shown at C. The wave shape is practically pure DC with just a very slight ripple remaining. Capacitor C2 acts in the same manner as C1. It shorts out the remaining ripple, leaving just the pure DC, as illustrated at D. The pure DC voltage can now be applied to the vacuum tube elements for their proper operation.

It is easier to filter out the 120 Hz ripple from a full-wave rectifier than the 60 Hz ripple from a half-wave rectifier. This is because the capacitors that short out the ripple have a lower capacitive reactance to 120 Hz than they do to 60 Hz. Also, the choke has a higher inductive reactance to 120 Hz than to 60 Hz. (See Lesson 4).

THE CHOKE INPUT FILTER. Fig. 7-9 shows a CHOKE INPUT FILTER, hooked up to a full wave rectifier. The filter is called a choke input filter because the first component after the rectifier is a choke. The filtering action of the choke input filter is similar to that of the capacitor input filter. However, it has an advantage and a disadvantage when compared to a capacitor input filter. The choke input filter has better voltage regulation (voltage regulation is described later in this lesson) than a capacitor input filter. On the other hand, the capacitor input filter provides a higher output voltage than the choke input filter. Filter chokes used in power supplies run from 4 to 30 henries. The chokes are designed to have as low a DC resistance

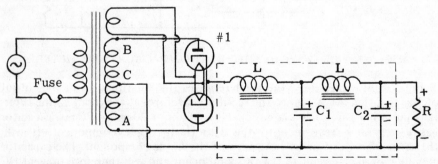

FIG. 7-9. FULL-WAVE RECTIFIER WITH CHOKE-INPUT FILTER.

118

as possible. As a result, the DC voltage drop across the choke will be low and the remaining B+ voltage will be high.

Chokes are designed to carry a maximum amount of current for optimum performance. If this current is exceeded in operation, magnetic saturation will occur. Magnetic saturation is the point in a magnetic circuit where increases in current produce little or no increase in flux density. As the choke becomes saturated, its permeability decreases. This reduces the inductance of the choke which, in turn, reduces its filtering ability. If the current is too large, it may burn out the choke.

A SHORT-CIRCUITED FILTER CAPACITOR. If capacitor C1 of Fig. 7-7 shorts, the rectifier tubes will draw excessive current. As a result, the fuse in series with the primary of the power transformer, will blow. The fuse acts as a protective device for the transformer in the power supply. If there is no fuse, the plates of the rectifier tube will become red hot due to the large electron flow. Any time that there is an excessive current flow of current in a tube, its plates will become red hot. The tube may become damaged and will have to be replaced. The primary or secondary windings of the transformer may also burn out due to the excessive current. Before replacing the damaged tube, the cause of the high current should be found and corrected.

If capacitor C2 in Fig. 7-7 were to short, a heavy current would flow through the choke coil. The choke coil might burn out, in addition to the other components. It is important, therefore, that the primary of a power transformer always be protected by a proper size fuse. If either C1 or C2 shorts, there obviously will be no B+ voltage, and the equipment would not function.

VOLTAGE REGULATION. The load current is the current that is drawn from the power supply by the vacuum tubes that it supplies. If the load current varies, the B+ voltage will also vary. The B+ voltage is at a maximum when the load current is zero. As the load on the power supply increases, the B+ voltage drops. At full load current, the B+ voltage is at a minimum. A good power supply is one whose B+ voltage varies very little under varying load conditions. We say that such a power supply has good VOLTAGE REGULATION. A power supply with poor voltage regulation is one whose B+ voltage varies considerably with changes in load conditions. Voltage regulation tells us, in percentage, how much the output voltage of the power supply has dropped from no load to full load.

The vacuum tubes in a radio receiver draw a constant load current from the power supply. A receiver power supply is therefore, not required to have good voltage regulation characteristics. A transmitter, on the other hand, presents a varying load to the power supply. The transmitter power supply should therefore have good voltage regulation characteristics.

In general, it is easier to obtain good regulation of a power supply when the load requirements are small. If the load requirements are large, more current is drawn from the power supply. This means that the voltage drops in the rectifier tubes, the filter chokes and other circuit elements will be greater. Greater internal voltage drops mean that less voltage will be available at the output under full load. This means that the regulation will be poorer.

The formula for percentage regulation is:

$$(7\text{-}1) \quad \% \text{ Reg} = \frac{E_{nl} - E_{fl}}{E_{fl}} \times 100 \quad \text{where: } E_{nl} = \text{no load voltage} \quad E_{fl} = \text{full load voltage}$$

PROBLEM: What is the percentage regulation of a power supply with a no-load output voltage of 1500 volts and a full-load voltage output of 1400 volts?

SOLUTION: Use (7-1) $\% \text{ Reg} = \dfrac{E_{nl} - E_{fl}}{E_{fl}} \times 100$

$$\% \text{ Reg} = \frac{1500 - 1400}{1400} \times 100; \quad \% \text{ Reg} = \frac{100}{1400} \times 100 ;$$

$$\% \text{ Reg} = \frac{100}{14} ; \quad \% \text{ Regulation} = 7.14\%$$

PROBLEM: If a power supply has an output voltage of 150 volts at no load and the regulation at full load is 20%, what is the output voltage at full load?

SOLUTION: By algebraically solving formula (7-1) for E_{fl}, we arrive at the following formula:

$$E_{\text{full load}} = \frac{100 \, E_{nl}}{100 + \% \text{ Reg}}$$

We then substitute and solve.

$$E_{fl} = \frac{100 \, E_{nl}}{100 + \% \text{ Reg}} \qquad E_{fl} = \frac{100 \times 150}{100 + 20} ;$$

$$E_{fl} = \frac{15,000}{120} ; \qquad E_{fl} = 125 \text{ volts}.$$

In order to improve the voltage regulation of a power supply, a resistor is often bridged across the output capacitor (resistor R in Fig. 7-9). This resistor is called a BLEEDER RESISTOR. A bleeder resistor improves the voltage regulation by providing a minimum load on the power supply. It also discharges the filter capacitors after the power is turned off, thus serving as a safety device.

The exact value of a bleeder resistor is a compromise. If we make the bleeder resistor too high, it will draw very little current and have no "bleeder" effect. If we make the bleeder's resistance too low, it will draw too much current from the power supply. It will also allow the filter capacitor to reach peak charge, thereby increasing the ripple voltage. We choose a value that gives us minimum output ripple and sufficient loading to improve the voltage regulation of the power supply.

The bleeder resistor may also be used as a voltage divider to supply different voltages for use in receivers and transmitters. This can be seen in Fig. 7-10.

PROBLEM: In a power supply designed to furnish 800 volts at 200 ma. and 200 volts at 35 ma., a tapped bleeder resistor carrying 15 ma. is used as a

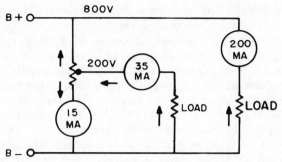

FIG. 7-10. A BLEEDER USED TO SUPPLY
TWO DIFFERENT VOLTAGES.

voltage divider. What is the resistance of that part of the bleeder between the 800 volt point and the 200 volt tap? See Fig. 7-10.

SOLUTION: The resistance between the 200 volt tap and the 800 volt point must carry the 15 ma. bleeder current plus the 35 ma. used by the 200 volt load. Also, this part of the bleeder must drop 600 volts. Therefore:

$$R = \frac{E}{I}, \qquad R = \frac{600}{.050}, \qquad R = 12,000 \text{ ohms}.$$

THE MERCURY VAPOR RECTIFIER TUBE. When a high vacuum tube contains some gas which is not supposed to be in the tube, we say the tube is SOFT. A soft tube usually shows a blue or purple haze between the cathode and the plate. If the tube is soft, it will not function properly and the plate may become red hot. There are, however, tubes in which gas is deliberately introduced and a blue haze in these tubes is normal.

When the ordinary high vacuum rectifier tube conducts, it has a fairly constant internal resistance of 100 ohms or so. This internal resistance remains constant; it does not change with fluctuations in load current. The voltage drop across the tube, however, does change with a varying load. As the load current increases, the voltage drop across the tube increases; as the load current decreases, the voltage drop across the tube decreases. This varying voltage drop will, in turn, cause the B+ voltage to vary. The result is that a high vacuum rectifier system, under varying load conditions, will have poor regulation. It is, therefore, desirable to use a rectifier tube with a constant internal voltage drop. A MERCURY VAPOR RECTIFIER TUBE fulfills this requirement. It differs from a high vacuum rectifier tube in that it has mercury vapor or gas enclosed in the glass envelope.

An electron traveling at high speed in a mercury vapor tube, will hit a mercury atom with great force. The tremendous impact causes an electron to be knocked out of the structure of the mercury atom. This electron is attracted to the positive plate, just as if it had been emitted by the cathode. The result is that for every emitted electron that crashes into a mercury atom, two electrons end up at the plate. As the load current increases, the cathode current of the mercury vapor tube increases. The increased cathode current produces many more electrons by atom bombardment of the mercury gas. The resulting large increase in the number of electrons flowing to the plate causes the internal resistance of the tube to drop. We say that

121

the CONDUCTIVITY of the tube has increased. The product of an increasing current and a decreasing resistance is a constant voltage drop across the tube. This will produce a constant B+ voltage, regardless of load current changes. The voltage drop across most mercury vapor tubes is a constant, low 15 volts. This constant voltage characteristic of the mercury vapor rectifier tube greatly improves the regulation of the rectifier system.

When a mercury atom loses an electron by bombardment, it becomes IONIZED. The atom is now a POSITIVE ION. Ionization is accompanied by a characteristic bright blue glow of the mercury vapor. The filaments of a mercury vapor tube must be heated for at least one minute before the plate voltage is turned on. If the filament and plate voltages are turned on at the same time, the heavy positive mercury ions will bombard and possibly ruin the cathode. If the filament is turned on before the plate voltage, there will be a sufficient number of space charge electrons emitted to neutralize the positive ions. A time delay relay or a separate switch is used in the primary of the high voltage plate transformer which cannot be activated until the filament power has been on for some time.

It is also important to maintain proper operating temperatures in a mercury vapor rectifier system. A high filament voltage increases the temperature, which increases ionization and reduces tube life. It may also cause arc-back. A low voltage produces incomplete ionization, overloading, possible damage and reduced efficiency.

A mercury vapor rectifier power supply should use a choke input filter. For one thing, we use a mercury vapor rectifier because we want good voltage regulation. There is no point in losing this advantage by using a capacitor input filter, which gives poor voltage regulation. A second reason for using a choke input filter is that the first capacitor of a capacitor input filter may discharge through the mercury vapor tube and cause a damaging flash back. Later on in this lesson, we will see that a mercury vapor rectifier cannot handle as much reverse (inverse) voltage as a high vacuum tube can.

The mercury vapor tube is used in transmitter power supplies because of its high current load capabilities and excellent voltage regulation.

When mercury vapor tubes are connected in parallel in a rectifier system to handle higher current demands, small resistors (between 50 and 100 ohms) are placed in series with the plate leads of the tubes. These resistors act to equalize the voltage and hence, the ionization of the tubes. Without the resistors, one tube may ionize first and take almost the entire load current.

THE SWINGING CHOKE. Transmitter power supplies provide a varying load current to the transmitter tubes. If an ordinary choke is used in a transmitter power supply, the B+ voltage will be found to vary as the load current varies. This results in poor voltage regulation, which is highly undesirable. The use of a special choke can improve the voltage regulation of the transmitter power supply. This special choke is called a SWINGING CHOKE. A swinging choke has a very small air gap in the core. The air gap causes the inductance of the choke to vary with the load current. As the load current increases, the inductance decreases; as the load current decreases, the inductance increases. This variable inductance characteristic improves the voltage regulation of the power supply by keeping the B+ voltage constant.

Swinging chokes are used only where large load current changes take place, such as in transmitters.

Filter chokes, when used in a transmitter power supply, may be placed in the negative lead or ground side of the filter (Fig. 7-11). If this is not done, the insulation between the choke windings and the core of the choke may break down because the full DC output voltage appears between the windings (B+) and the core (ground).

THE FILTER CAPACITOR IN A TRANSMITTER POWER SUPPLY. A transmitter power supply requires a capacitor with a high DC working

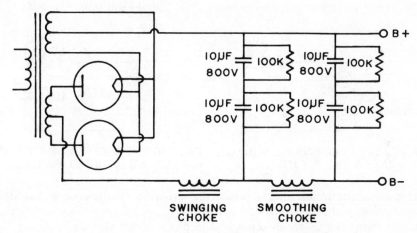

FIG. 7-11. HIGH VOLTAGE POWER SUPPLY FOR TRANSMITTER.

voltage. For example, a 1600 volt supply uses a capacitor with a DC working voltage of about 2400 volts. Oil filled dielectric capacitors can be used for this purpose because of their low leakage. However, they are not too popular due to their large physical size and cost. Electrolytic capacitors are small and inexpensive, but usually, they do not have a DC working voltage much higher than 800 volts. To increase the working voltage of a filter capacitor system, two or more capacitors are connected in series. For example, two electrolytics, each rated at 800 DC working volts, when connected in series (Fig. 7-11) will have a total DC working voltage of 1600 volts.

When connected in series, EQUALIZING RESISTORS are connected across each capacitor. Their purpose is to equalize the DC voltage drop across the capacitors. If there are no equalizing resistors, there will be unequal voltage drops across the series connected capacitors. This is due to unequal capacitances or unequal leakage resistances of the individual capacitors, or both. This may result in too great a voltage stress across one of the capacitors, causing it to break down and short out. The equalizing resistors also serve to discharge the filter capacitors when the power is removed from the supply.

The capacitors used in transmitting power supplies are generally in the range of 2 to 10 mf. If they are in series, the combination will be less than the smaller value of the two capacitors used.

PEAK INVERSE VOLTAGE. A rectifier tube does not conduct during one-half of the input AC cycle. This is when the plate is negative with respect to the cathode. During this non-conducting time, there will be a high negative voltage on the plate, especially at the peak point of the alternation. Fig. 7-12A illustrates this condition. The voltage across the transformer secondary is 300 volts rms or 424 peak volts (peak voltage = 1.414 x rms voltage). The 424 peak volts appear across the tube and is referred to as the PEAK INVERSE VOLTAGE, or the PEAK NEGATIVE VOLTAGE. The PEAK INVERSE VOLTAGE RATING is the maximum voltage that a rectifier tube can safely withstand between its plate and cathode when the tube is not conducting. Therefore, in the case of a half-wave rectifier, the peak inverse voltage is equal to the secondary voltage multiplied by 1.414.

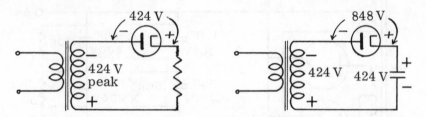

FIG. 7-12A. PEAK INVERSE VOLTAGE OF A HALF-WAVE RECTIFIER.

FIG. 7-12B. PEAK INVERSE VOLTAGE WITH CAPACITOR INPUT FILTER.

If a capacitor input filter is used, the situation changes somewhat. The input capacitor charges up to 424 volts from the previous alternation. Notice that the two voltages are in series and in phase across the rectifier. See Fig. 7-12B. The maximum voltage between plate and cathode during non-conduction is now 848 volts. The peak inverse voltage under this condition is therefore equal to the RMS secondary voltage, multiplied by 2.8.

If the peak inverse voltage exceeds the rating given by the manufacturer, there is a great danger of damage from arc-back between the plate and cathode of the rectifier tube. Arc-back is a current flow that could ruin the tube.

Fig. 7-13 illustrates an elementary schematic of a full wave rectifier. When

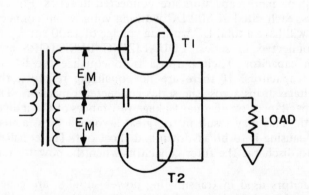

FIG. 7-13. PEAK INVERSE VOLTAGE USING A FULL WAVE RECTIFIER.

T2 is conducting, T1 is cut off. The full peak voltage across the secondary (2Em), less the small voltage drop across T2, now appears across T1. This is the peak inverse voltage of a full wave rectifier and it is equal to the RMS voltage of the full secondary times 1.414. The peak inverse voltage rating of the tube must be at least this high in order to prevent arc back and possible damage to the tube.

The peak inverse voltage rating of a mercury vapor rectifier is low compared to that of a high vacuum rectifier tube.

3 **VOLTAGE REGULATOR TUBES.** Fig. 7-14 is a diagram of a power supply with a voltage regulator tube to stabilize the output voltage. This supply is not conventional. The rectifier filament, which is normally positive with respect to ground, is now grounded. The center tap, which is normally grounded, is not grounded. It now has the filter in its line. The filter is a single section type. This power supply is used where a negative voltage with

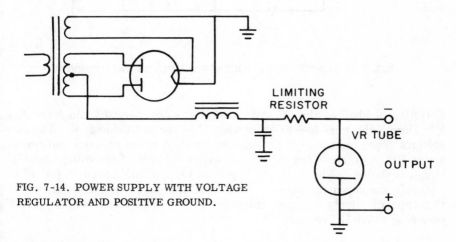

FIG. 7-14. POWER SUPPLY WITH VOLTAGE REGULATOR AND POSITIVE GROUND.

respect to ground is required.

The voltage regulator (VR) tube is a gas filled tube capable of keeping the output voltage constant, regardless of power supply or load variations. It operates in the following manner: When the operating voltage across the VR tube reaches a certain point, the gas ionizes and the VR tube conducts. A fixed, known voltage develops across the regulator tube and the remainder of the voltage appears across the limiting resistor. Let us assume that the output voltage suddenly rises. The voltage across the limiting resistor and the VR tube, as well as the current through both, tend to rise. However, the increased current in the VR tube increases its ionization. This decreases the resistance of the VR tube. Since the voltage across the tube is the product of the tube's current and the tube's resistance (E = IR), the voltage across the tube, which is also the output voltage, remains constant.

If the output voltage of the power supply tends to decrease, the opposite occurs. The current through the VR tube decreases, and its ionization decreases. This causes the resistance of the VR tube to increase and the voltage (IR) drop or output remains the same.

THE VOLTAGE DOUBLER POWER SUPPLY. It is sometimes necessary to have a higher DC output voltage than is possible with a simple rectifier system. A voltage doubler power supply is one that uses two capacitors in parallel with the input voltage and in series for the output voltage, with rectifiers switching between them. Such a supply is shown in Fig. 7-15.

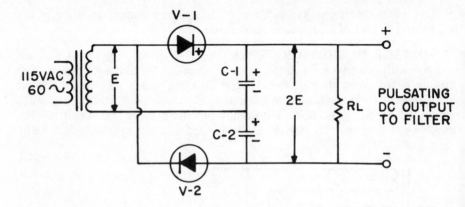

FIG. 7-15. A FULL-WAVE VOLTAGE DOUBLER POWER SUPPLY.

During one-half of the AC cycle, capacitor C1 is charged through rectifier V1. During the next half of the cycle, C2 is charged through V2. The two voltages appearing across the capacitors are then added in series and appear across R_L. A graph of the input and output voltages of the voltage doubler circuit is shown in Fig. 7-16. The larger the value of the capacitors (50 mf to 150 mf), the closer the output voltage will approach 2E. The regulation of this type of supply is poor. However, it is a cheap and simple way of obtaining a high DC voltage.

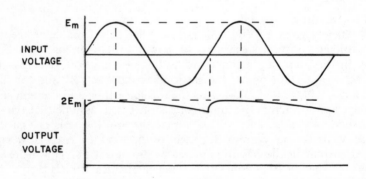

FIG. 7-16. VOLTAGE GRAPHS IN A VOLTAGE DOUBLER POWER SUPPLY.

THE FULL-WAVE BRIDGE RECTIFIER SYSTEM. The full-wave bridge rectifier system delivers an output voltage that is twice that available using the ordinary center-tapped high voltage system previously described. It also

126

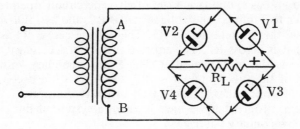

FIG. 7-17. A FULL-WAVE BRIDGE RECTIFIER SYSTEM.

has good voltage regulation. Two rectifiers operate in series during each half of the AC cycle. Such an arrangement is shown in Fig. 7-17. The filter is not shown since we are not concerned about it in the explanation of the rectifier.

During the first half of the AC cycle when point A of the transformer secondary is positive and point B negative, current flows from point B through V4, then through the load, through V1 and back to point A to complete the circuit. During the second half of the cycle, when point B is positive and point A is negative, the current flows from point A through V2, through the load, through V3 and back to point B. Note that the current flows through the load in the same direction (DC) during both halves of the cycle. Thus the current is changed from AC to DC. Also note that the full secondary voltage is used during both alternations. This gives us twice the voltage that we obtain from a center-tapped full wave rectifier where only one-half of the secondary is used during each alternation.

4 BRIDGE AND FULL WAVE RECTIFIER COMBINATION. Fig. 7-18 illustrates an interesting power supply combination. It is a method of

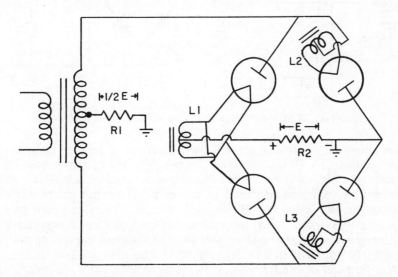

FIG. 7-18. A COMBINATION BRIDGE AND FULL -WAVE RECTIFIER.

obtaining two voltages, one twice the other. The circuit operates both as a bridge rectifier to produce one voltage across R2, and as a full-wave rectifier to produce another voltage across R1. The voltage across R1 is one-half of the voltage that is across R2. The entire transformer secondary and the four tubes, behave as the bridge rectifier. The entire secondary voltage, less the voltage drops of the tubes, are across R2. One-half of the secondary voltage and two of the four tubes, make up an ordinary full-wave, center-tapped rectifier system. From what we have learned, a system of this type provides one-half of the secondary voltage.

3 **VIBRATOR POWER SUPPLIES.** A vibrator power supply converts low voltage DC to high voltage DC. It consists of a vibrating or "interrupting" device, a step-up transformer and a rectifier. The low voltage DC from a battery is fed to the vibrator which chops it up, making it suitable for a transformer. A transformer will not operate on pure DC. The step-up transformer produces a high voltage AC at its secondary. This is then fed to a rectifier, which changes it to high voltage DC.

There are two general types of vibrator supplies. One is called the non-synchronous type. The other is the synchronous type. The non-synchronous vibrator supply is shown in Fig. 7-19. The vibrator is shown within the dotted lines. Before the switch is turned on, a vibrating reed, R, is halfway between contacts D and C. It touches neither one of them. As soon as the switch is turned on, current flows from the negative terminal of the battery, through the vibrator's electromagnet, M, up through the bottom half of the transformer's primary and back to the positive terminal of the battery.

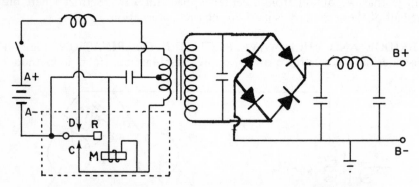

FIG. 7-19. A NON-SYNCHRONOUS-VIBRATOR POWER SUPPLY.

The energized electromagnet will pull the vibrating reed down and it will touch contact "C". When the reed touches "C", the electromagnet "M" is shorted out. "M" will no longer be magnetic and the reed "R" will be released from "C" and will tend to return to its former position midway between the two contacts. However, inertia will carry the reed past the midway position and over to contact "D". Current will now leave the negative terminal of the battery and flow to the reed, up to contact "D", through the top half of the primary of the transformer and back to the positive terminal of the battery. At the same time that this happens, current once again flows through the vibrator's electromagnet "M" and the vibrating reed "R" once again returns to contact "C" to start the cycle all over again. This continues as long as the switch is closed. You will note that the current flows through the primary, first in one direction and then in the other. This is similar to what happens when AC is impressed upon the primary. The turns ratio of the transformer is such that high voltage AC appears across the secondary. The AC is changed to DC by the bridge rectifier in the manner previously discussed. A Pi-type capacitor input filter is used to smooth out the pulsating DC to make it pure DC.

The vibrator power supply shown in Fig. 7-20 is a synchronous type. The action of the vibrating reed is similar to that in the non-synchronous type of vibrator. However, an extra set of contacts (E and F) has been added. The purpose of these contacts is to change the AC output of the transformer secondary to pulsating DC without the use of a separate rectifier. In other words, the extra contacts take the place of the rectifier. Note that the output of the transformer is fed back to contacts E and F. As the reed vibrates, the top and bottom of the transformer secondary is alternately grounded. The center is always positive with respect to the ends. This causes the output to be pulsating DC. The pulsating DC is then fed to the pi-type filter, to be filtered in the usual manner.

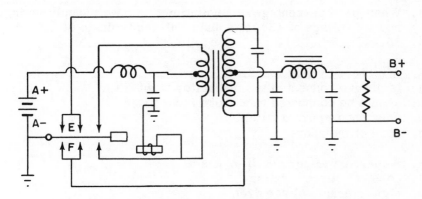

FIG. 7-20. A SYNCHRONOUS-VIBRATOR POWER SUPPLY.

PRACTICE QUESTIONS - LESSON 7

1. As compared to a choke-input system, a capacitor-input filter system has:
a. lower DC output voltage   c. better voltage regulation
b. higher peak surge currents   d. no important advantages

2. Full-wave rectification is better than half-wave rectification because:
a. its output is easier to filter
b. its output contains a lower ripple frequency
c. a choke input filter may be used
d. a swinging choke may be used

129

3. A full-wave, bridge rectifier system, using the same power transformer as a full-wave center-tapped rectifier system, would have:
a. one-half the output voltage   c. triple the output voltage
b. double the output voltage   d. the same output voltage

4. The principal function of a swinging choke in a filter system is:
a. to improve the regulation of the power supply under varying loads
b. to provide pure, constant AC input to the power supply
c. to prevent harmonic radiation
d. to cause air circulation around the rectifiers

5. Which of the following will not cause the plates of a rectifier to suddenly become red hot?
a. a shorted filter capacitor
b. a shorted filter choke
c. a short between B+ and ground
d. a short between the filter choke and ground

6. What is the percentage of regulation of a power supply having a no load voltage of 150 volts and a full load voltage of 130 volts?
a. 15.4%   b. 20%   c. 13.3%   d. 120%

7. A mercury vapor rectifier:
a. is always connected to a capacitor input filter
b. should be connected to a choke input filter
c. does not require a filter
d. none of the above

8. A mercury vapor rectifier has a:
a. constant current rating
b. high internal voltage drop
c. high inverse peak voltage rating
d. relatively high current rating

9. A bleeder resistor:
a. improves voltage regulation   c. should be replaced
b. improves ripple frequency   d. is very critical

10. A mercury vapor tube in operation exhibits:
a. white spot on the cathode   c. red plate
b. drops of mercury on the plate   d. a bluish-green glow

11. The purpose of equalizing resistors is to:
a. improve the voltage regulation
b. equalize the DC drop across the different filter capacitors connected in series
c. limit the ripple voltage
d. prevent an arc-back

12. Which of the following is not a feature of a silicon voltage rectifier? (3)
a. compactness
b. high current rating
c. high peak inverse voltage rating
d. good voltage regulation

13. The ripple frequency of a full-wave rectifier using a 3-phase, 60 Hz source is:
a. 60 Hz
b. 120 Hz
c. 180 Hz
d. 360 Hz

14. A filter choke with a low DC resistance is desirable in a power supply because:
a. the ripple frequency is decreased
b. the voltage regulation is made worse
c. the output voltage is increased
d. the peak inverse voltage is increased

15. What is the peak inverse voltage across the tubes of a full-wave rectifier?
a. the RMS secondary voltage
b. 1/2 the secondary x 1.414
c. the full secondary x 1.414
d. twice the secondary x 1.414

16. The peak voltage across the input filter capacitor of a full-wave rectifier is:
a. the full secondary x 1.414
b. the full secondary x 2.828
c. 1/2 of the secondary x 1
d. 1/2 of the secondary x 1.414

17. The advantages of a mercury-vapor rectifier over a high-vacuum type rectifier do not include:
a. greater efficiency and economy
b. cooler operation
c. better filament efficiency
d. high internal drop of voltage

18. Connecting the primary of a power transformer to the DC line:
a. burns out the primary winding
b. burns out the secondary winding
c. burns out the rectifier tube
d. blows the filter capacitors

19. In a mercury vapor rectifier system, the:
a. filament and plate voltages may be applied simultaneously
b. plate voltage must always be turned on first
c. filament voltage must always be turned on first
d. filament voltage is turned on 10 seconds after the plate voltage

20. The approximate values of the filter capacitors in a transmitter power supply are between:
a. 20 to 40 mf
b. 100 to 200 mf
c. 2 to 4 mf
d. 200 to 400 mf

21. If the high voltage secondary of a transformer was changed from a full-wave, center-tapped connection to a bridge rectifier connection, the output voltage rating would:
a. remain the same   c. be halved
b. be doubled   d. be tripled

22. The filament is always allowed to warm up before applying plate voltage with a:
a. mercury vapor tube   c. cold-cathode, gas-filled rectifier
b. high vacuum rectifier   d. beam power pentode

23. If a filter capacitor shorts:
a. the ripple frequency is increased
b. the rectifier tube will probably burn out
c. the output current will vary
d. B+ voltage will tend to increase

24. A copper oxide rectifier has: (3)
a. a high breakdown voltage rating
b. a large current handling ability
c. a high shunt capacity
d. high usage in high frequency equipment

25. A mercury-vapor rectifier does not have:
a. low internal resistance
b. high current rating
c. high inverse peak voltage rating
d. constant internal voltage drop

26. A filter circuit in a power supply does not:
a. filter out the AC   c. use electrolytic capacitors
b. filter out the DC   d. provide a DC voltage

LESSON 8
VACUUM TUBES

INTRODUCTION. In Lesson 6, we studied the construction and electrical characteristics of the diode vacuum tube. In Lesson 7, we studied the action of a diode as a rectifier. We will now examine the operation of the vacuum tube when used as an amplifier. An amplifier increases the amplitude of small AC voltages. The vacuum tubes associated with amplification are three, four and five element tubes. The three element tube is called a TRIODE: four and five element tubes are called TETRODES and PENTODES, respectively.

THE TRIODE. The TRIODE is different from the diode in that it contains an additional element. This new element is called the CONTROL GRID. The control grid is a thin piece of wire, wound in a spiral. It surrounds the cathode. Electrons emitted by the cathode pass through the grid structure and continue on to the plate. Fig. 8-1A shows the physical arrangement of the cathode, grid and plate structure in a typical triode. Note that the grid is placed much closer to the cathode than to the plate. Fig. 8-1B illustrates the schematic symbol of the triode. The grid is shown by a dotted line between the cathode and plate.

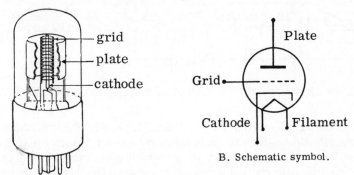

A. Cut away section of a triode.

B. Schematic symbol.

FIG. 8-1. THE TRIODE.

OPERATION OF A TRIODE. Fig. 8-2 shows a triode circuit which is used to study the effect of grid voltage variations upon the plate current. The plate current is measured by placing an ammeter in series with the plate circuit. All tube voltage measurements are taken with the cathode as a reference point.

Letters A, B and C in Fig. 8-2 indicate the voltages that are applied to the different elements in the tube. The "A" voltage is applied to the heater, or

133

filament. The "B" voltage is applied to the plate; the "C" voltage is applied to the grid. "S" is a three-position switch in the control grid circuit. With the switch in position #1, the control grid is connected directly to the cathode. With the switch in position #2, the control grid is connected to the negative terminal of a battery. With the switch in position #3, the control grid is connected to the positive terminal of a battery. Let us see how changes in the control grid voltage affect the operation of the triode.

When the switch is in position #1, electrons will flow from the cathode through the grid structure to the positive plate. Since the grid is connected directly to the cathode, it will not affect or influence the flow of electrons to the plate, and normal plate current flow will result.

If the switch is in position #2, the grid becomes negative with respect to the cathode. The negatively charged grid will repel many of the negatively charged electrons back into the area surrounding the cathode. Hence, the number of electrons which are able to reach the plate is reduced. The milliammeter in the plate circuits will show a reduction in plate current.

When the switch is thrown to position #3, the grid becomes positive with respect to the cathode. The plate current will increase since the positive control grid attracts the negative electrons and allows many more electrons to be drawn to the plate than it did in switch positions #1 or #2. Thus, we see that the control grid acts as a control valve for plate current flow. As we vary the voltage on the grid, the plate current varies. THE CONTROL GRID THEREFORE, CONTROLS THE FLOW OF ELECTRONS TO THE PLATE.

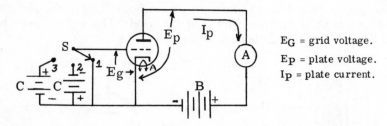

E_G = grid voltage.
E_P = plate voltage.
I_P = plate current.

FIG. 8-2. EFFECT OF GRID VOLTAGE ON PLATE CURRENT FLOW.

PLATE CURRENT - GRID VOLTAGE CURVE. Fig. 8-3 is a schematic of a triode circuit whose grid voltage is varied by a potentiometer placed across the "C" battery. Fig. 8-4 is a graph on which plate current readings have been plotted for different values of grid voltage. The horizontal direction represents the grid voltage, and the vertical direction represents the plate current. The plate voltage is kept constant. If we draw a line through the points that represent the various plate current readings, we obtain a curve known as the Eg-Ip characteristic curve. Notice that if the grid is made sufficiently negative (minus 10 volts), the plate current drops to zero. At this point, the highly negative grid repels all the electrons back to the cathode area. As the grid voltage is made less negative (more positive), the electrons begin to flow to the plate. If we continue to make the grid voltage less negative, the plate current will continue to increase. If we reverse the C battery and make the grid positive with respect to the cathode, the plate

134

current keeps on increasing. As the grid voltage is made more positive, the plate current continues to rise. A point is soon reached (not shown in Fig. 8-4), where the plate current can no longer increase, regardless of further increases in positive grid voltage. This point is called the SATURATION POINT.

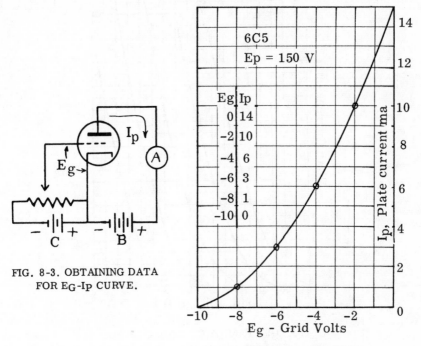

FIG. 8-3. OBTAINING DATA
FOR E_G-I_P CURVE.

FIG. 8-4. E_G-I_P CURVE.

The voltage that is applied to the grid is called GRID BIAS VOLTAGE, or simply BIAS. The BIAS that cuts the plate current to zero is called the CUT-OFF BIAS. In Fig. 8-4, the cut-off bias is -10 volts. Whenever the voltage on the grid prevents current from flowing, we say that the tube is CUT OFF or that we have a BLOCKED GRID.

The curve of Fig. 8-4 was obtained with the plate voltage held constant. We can also take grid voltage and plate current readings for different values of plate voltage. The result of plotting all these points is a series of curves called a FAMILY OF CURVES. See Fig. 8-5. Notice that for a given grid voltage, the plate current increases with an increase in plate voltage. This is to be expected, since an increase in plate voltage should result in an increase in plate current.

THE TRIODE AS AN AMPLIFIER. Since the control grid is physically much closer to the cathode than the plate, the grid voltage will have a greater effect on the plate current than will the plate voltage. A small change in grid voltage will cause a large change in plate current; whereas, a small change in plate voltage causes a small change in plate current. Let us see how a changing voltage (such as an AC signal) on the grid, causes the plate current

135

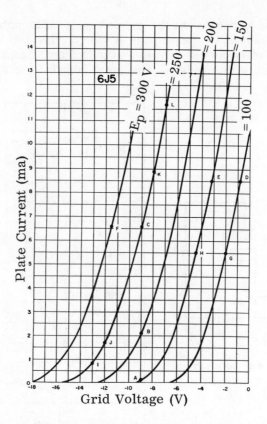

FIG. 8-5. FAMILY OF Eg-Ip CURVES.

to vary. Fig. 8-6 is a triode circuit whose plate is connected to a fixed B+ voltage. The grid is in series with an AC generator and a fixed bias voltage. The total voltage between the grid and cathode will always be the sum of the signal voltage and the bias voltage.

We will assume that the signal voltage is 1 volt peak or 2 volts peak to peak, and that the battery bias voltage is 3 volts. From the Ip-Eg curve of

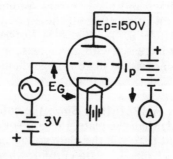

FIG. 8-6. TRIODE WITH AN AC SIGNAL ON THE GRID.

136

Fig. 8-7, it can be seen that when the AC signal applied to the grid is zero, the plate current will be 8 ma. This is due to the −3 volts of bias supplied by the battery. The value of 8 ma. is obtained from the graph by working vertically from the −3 volt point on the grid voltage line until the curve is reached. From this point we go straight across until we hit the vertical plate current line. In this case, we reach the vertical line at 8 ma.

Let us see what happens on the positive half of the AC signal when its peak is +1 volt. Since the signal voltage of +1 volt and −3 volts of bias are in series, the resultant voltage between the grid and cathode will be −2 volts (the sum of +1 and −3 is −2). Looking at Fig. 8-7, we see that −2 volts on the grid results in a plate current of 10 ma.

On the negative half of the incoming signal, −4 volts will appear between the grid and cathode. By looking at the curve, it can be seen that −4 volts on the grid causes a plate current of 6 ma. Thus, when the incoming signal reaches its negative peak value of −1 volt, the plate current drops to 6 ma.

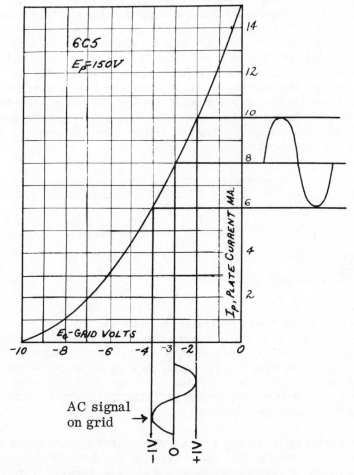

FIG. 8-7. PLATE CURRENT WAVEFORM
RESULTING FROM AN AC SIGNAL ON THE GRID.
137

From the above, we can see that the plate current rises and falls in step with the signal on the grid. As a matter of fact, the waveform of the plate current variation is an exact reproduction of the signal that is applied to the grid.

Thus far, we have converted grid voltage variations into plate current variations. In order to make use of these plate current variations, some device must be placed in the plate circuit to act as a load across which the varying plate current will develop a varying voltage. The plate load may be a resistor, an inductor, or a tuned circuit. Fig.8-8 shows a resistor used as a plate load in a triode amplifier circuit. Except for the plate load resistor, this circuit is the same as that in Fig. 8-6.

From Fig. 8-7, we see that a 2 volt peak-to-peak signal causes a total plate current variation of 4 milliamperes (from 6 to 10 ma.). This 4 ma variation will cause a total voltage variation of 40 volts to be produced across a 10K ohm load resistor. This can be proven by Ohm's Law: $E = IR$, $E = .004 \times 10,000$, $E = 40$ volts. Thus it can be seen that a 2-volt signal variation at the grid, (from -2 volts to -4 volts) can produce a 40-volt variation in the plate circuit. In other words, the original signal has been AMPLIFIED twenty times.

The relationship that exists between the voltage and current in the plate circuit is important. The plate voltage is the voltage measured between the plate and the cathode. This is different from the load voltage or from the supply voltage. The load voltage is measured across the load and the supply voltage is measured across the B supply. A series circuit exists between the tube, the plate load and the battery (see Fig. 8-8). The battery voltage is equal to the plate voltage plus the load voltage. The plate current is the same in all three components because they are in series.

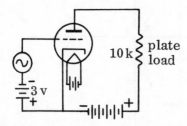

FIG. 8-8. TRIODE USING A RESISTOR AS A PLATE LOAD.

3 **TRIODE Ep-Ip CHARACTERISTIC CURVE.** In Fig. 8-4, the plate voltage was kept constant and plate current readings were plotted as we varied the grid voltage. Another popular characteristic curve is the Ep-Ip curves of Fig. 8-9. Here, the grid voltage is kept constant and plate current readings are plotted as we vary the plate voltage. Notice that the plate current rises as the plate voltage increases. The Ep-Ip curves are the ones that are usually found in tube manuals.

3 **THE LOAD LINE.** In Fig. 8-9, we have plotted a family of plate current, plate voltage curves for different values of grid bias. We have super-imposed on this family of curves, two lines, AB and AC. These lines are known as LOAD LINES. A different load line is drawn for a different amount of plate

138

load. Line AB represents the load line for one value of plate load resistance·
and line AC represents the load line for another value of plate resistance.
Any point on a line represents the plate current and plate voltage for a
particular grid voltage. As the grid voltage varies, we move up and down the
load line to determine the plate current and plate voltage.

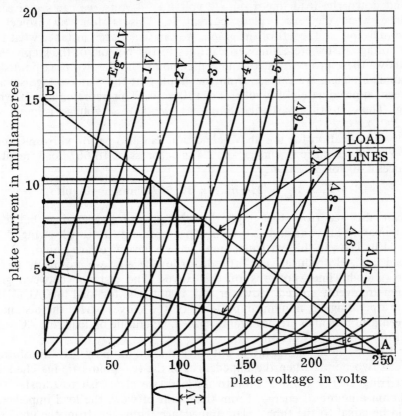

FIG. 8-9. FAMILY OF Ep-Ip CURVES.

Some actual values will illustrate the significance of the load lines. Let us
take load line AB. It is formed when a resistance of 16,667 ohms is used in
the load and a voltage of 250 volts is used as the B supply. Point A is plotted
for the B supply (250 volts). In order to find point B, we use Ohm's law:

$$I = \frac{E_p}{R_L} = \frac{250}{16,667} = 15 \text{ ma}$$

We therefore place point B at the 15 ma. point on the graph. The load line is
formed by connecting points A and B. AC represents the load line that we
would have with a plate load of 50,000 ohms. This can be seen from Ohm's
law:

$$R_L = \frac{E_B}{I_p} = \frac{250}{.005} = 50,000 \text{ ohms}$$

Note that the lower load line (AC) is for the higher plate resistance and the
upper load line (AB) is for the lower plate resistance. This is obvious since

139

we know that the higher the resistance, the lower is the current.

Let us return to load line AB and see what happens when a 1 V. AC signal (2 volts peak to peak), is fed to the grid of an amplifier with a −3 volt bias. We can see from the graph that the plate current will vary from approximately 7.8 ma. to 10.2 ma., a change of 2.4 ma. By moving the operating point up and down the load line, from −2 volts to −4 volts, we can see at each instance what the exact plate current is. This is done by projecting horizontal lines to the left of the graph. We can see at each instance what the plate voltage is, by projecting vertical lines to the bottom of the graph. Fig. 8-9 shows these projections for the center point and the two peak points of the applied signal. We can see from the graph that the plate voltage swings between approximately 80 volts and 120 volts. This represents a 40 volt swing. Thus, in this particular amplifier, we have a voltage gain of 20 (40÷2=20).

The amplification for the above condition can also be found from Ohm's law. The plate current change of 2.4 ma across a 16,667 load resistor produces a 40 volt variation.

$$E = I_p \times R_L = 2.4 \text{ ma.} \times 16,667 \text{ ohms} = 40 \text{ volts.}$$

We can also see from the graph that the plate voltage swings between approximately 80 volts and 120 volts. This represents a 40 volt swing (120 −80 = 40). Thus, in this particular amplifier, we have a voltage gain of 20.

Load line AB produces very little distortion because we are operating on linear (straight line) portions of the curves. The distance between grid voltages are evenly spaced. However, this is not true for load line AC. Here we are operating on non-linear portions of the curves where the distances between grid bias lines are not evenly spaced. Operating on load line AC will, therefore, produce distortion.

In Lesson 4, it was pointed out that maximum power is transferred between two points when the impedances of the two points are matched. In transferring energy from a tube to its load, we also wish to transfer the maximum amount of energy. From this point of view, the load impedance should be equal to the tube's plate impedance. However, from the previous paragraph, we can see that some load values produce distortion and others do not. In actual practice, the load value that gives the maximum transfer of power is not the same as the load value that produces the maximum DISTORTIONLESS transfer of power. In the case of an audio power amplifier, the load impedance is not equal to the tube's plate impedance since we do not want to distort the signal.

VACUUM TUBE CHARACTERISTICS. Since many different types of vacuum tubes are used in radio and television circuits, it is important to classify tubes according to the performance which may be expected of them. The three most important factors by which tubes are classified are: the AMPLIFICATION FACTOR, the TRANSCONDUCTANCE and the PLATE RESISTANCE.

The AMPLIFICATION FACTOR of a tube is the maximum voltage amplification which can be expected from the tube. It is a theoretical value never reached in actual circuit use. Stated mathematically, it is the ratio of the change in plate voltage to the change in grid voltage that produces the

140

same change in plate current. For example, let us assume that a certain tube is operating with a plate voltage of 250 volts, a grid voltage of −10 volts and a plate current of 18 ma. Let us further assume that if we should change the plate voltage to 280 volts and leave the grid voltage constant, the plate current would go up to 23 ma. This means that a plate voltage change of 30 volts results in a plate current change of 5 ma. Suppose that a grid voltage change from −10 volts to −13 volts returns the plate current from 23 ma. back to 18 ma. We can say that a grid voltage change of 3 volts has the same effect on the plate current as a plate voltage change of 30 volts. The amplification factor would therefore be the plate voltage change (30 volts) divided by the grid voltage change (3 volts) or 10.

The amplification factor is commonly designated by the Greek letter μ. The formula for the μ, or mu, of a tube is:

$$(8\text{-}1) \quad \text{Amplification factor } (\mu) = \frac{\Delta E_p}{\Delta E_g}$$

where: ΔE_p and ΔE_g mean a small change in plate voltage and a small change in grid voltage, respectively.

The TRANSCONDUCTANCE, or MUTUAL CONDUCTANCE, of a tube is the figure of merit of the tube. It tells us how much of a plate current change we can get for a certain amount of grid voltage change. Transconductance is defined as the ratio of a small change in plate current to the small change in grid voltage that produced it. The formula for transconductance is:

$$(8\text{-}2) \quad G_m = \frac{\Delta I_p}{\Delta E_g}$$

where:
ΔI_p is a small change in plate current
ΔE_g is the small change in grid voltage that caused ΔI_p
G_m is the symbol for transconductance

The basic unit of transconductance is the MHO. The mho was previously mentioned in Lesson 1 as the unit of conductance. We use the same unit because the transconductance of a tube is similar to the conductance of a circuit. They are both equal to current divided by voltage.

The PLATE RESISTANCE of a tube is the internal resistance between the cathode and plate to the flow of varying plate current. Mathematically speaking, it is the ratio of a small change in plate voltage to the change in plate current that this voltage change produces. The formula for plate resistance is:

$$(8\text{-}3) \quad \text{Plate resistance} = \frac{\Delta E_p}{\Delta I_p}$$

where: R_p = the plate resistance
ΔE_p = a small change in plate voltage, and
ΔI_p = a small change in plate current caused by ΔE_p

EFFICIENCY OF VACUUM TUBES. We often use the term EFFICIENCY when we speak about the performance of a certain device or machine. Efficiency refers to the amount of power that can be taken out of a device, as compared to the amount of power that has been put into it. For instance, if 100 watts of electrical power is used up in a light bulb and only 2 watts of

141

equivalent light power is produced, we can say that the electric bulb is a low-efficiency device. The bulb converts into light only 2% of the power that is put into it. The other 98 watts are dissipated inside the bulb in the form of heat. On the other hand, an electric motor may draw 100 watts of electric power and produce 75 watts of equivalent mechanical power. We can say that the motor is a high efficiency device. The motor produces, in the form of useful work, 75% of the power put into it.

In radio, we classify vacuum tubes according to their efficiency in delivering useful power to a load. The plate efficiency of a vacuum tube is defined as the ratio of the AC plate power output to the DC plate power input. It is given in a percentage, and its mathematical formula is:

$$(8\text{-}4) \quad \text{Plate efficiency} = \frac{\text{AC output power}}{\text{DC input power}} \times 100.$$

For example, if the AC power output of a vacuum tube is 150 watts, and the DC power input is 200 watts, the efficiency is 150 divided by 200 or 75%.

The AC power output of a tube is the power in watts that the tube delivers to its load. The load may be a loudspeaker, the coupling circuit to the grid of a following tube or an antenna. The DC power input, on the other hand, is the product of the DC plate voltage applied to the tube and the DC plate current. For example, if the plate voltage is 750 volts and the plate current is 150 milliamperes, then the power input is 112.5 watts. We arrive at this in the following manner:

$$\text{Power input in watts} = E_p \times I_p = 750 \times .15 = 112 \text{ watts}.$$

MAXIMUM PLATE DISSIPATION. In the above problem concerning the plate efficiency of a vacuum tube, it is apparent that only a certain percentage of the applied power (input power) appears as output power. What happened to the remainder of the input power? The remainder of the input power is wasted in the form of heat within the tube, exactly as in a light bulb. Remember that the tube represents a resistance between the cathode and plate. Power loss applies to the resistance of a tube, as well as any ordinary resistor. The plate current, in flowing through the plate resistance, dissipates heat. The power dissipated on the plate in the form of heat is equal to $I_p^2 R_p$, where Ip is the plate current and Rp is the plate resistance.

There is a limit to the amount of power that a tube can dissipate in the form of heat without damaging itself. This limit is known as the MAXIMUM PLATE DISSIPATION, and it is expressed in watts. To find the maximum plate dissipation for any particular tube, we simply look it up in the tube manual.

In order to keep the plate dissipation within safe limits, the maximum plate voltage and maximum DC plate (or cathode) current must not be exceeded. The maximum DC plate voltage and maximum DC plate current are both given in the tube manuals.

Exceeding the maximum plate voltage for a period of time will cause excessive dissipation within the tube, as well as possible arcing between the tube elements. We can, however, exceed the maximum specified voltages for

142

a small instant of time or for a small pulse of high voltage. In other words, if the maximum DC plate voltage for a tube is given as 500 volts, it is possible to apply 3,000 volts to the tube without causing damage, provided that the 3,000 volts is on for only a tiny fraction of a second. Thus, if one looks at a tube manual, he will find, in addition to the normal maximum ratings, peak voltage and peak current ratings. He may also find "peak positive pulse voltage" or "peak negative pulse voltage"

LIMITATIONS OF A TRIODE. In the early days of radio, triodes were used exclusively in radio receivers and transmitters. Later on the tetrodes and pentodes made their appearance and replaced the triode in many applications. The reason for this change was that the triode had certain characteristics that limited its application in radio work. Before we discuss the tetrode and pentode, we shall first examine in detail the limitations of the triode.

In Lesson 4, we learned that two conducting surfaces, separated by an insulator, form a capacitor. Since the plate and grid of a tube are two conducting surfaces separated by a vacuum dielectric, a capacitance exists between them. By the same reasoning, a capacitor is formed between the grid and cathode and between the plate and cathode. These internal tube capacitances are called INTERELECTRODE CAPACITANCES. The inter-electrode capacitance between the plate and the grid of a triode limits the useful frequency range over which the tube can be used as an amplifier. This capacitance gives rise to a condition known as OSCILLATION, which is extremely undesirable in an amplifier circuit. In Lesson 12, we will discuss this condition of oscillation in greater detail.

Another limiting effect of a triode used as an amplifier, is that the plate current depends, not only on the grid voltage, but also upon the plate voltage. This limits its gain. For example, a positive-going grid signal will cause the plate current to go up. This increases the voltage drop across the load resistor. The voltage drop across the load resistor and the voltage between the plate and cathode are in series and therefore, must always add up to the fixed B+ voltage. If the voltage drop across the load resistor goes up, the plate voltage must go down. The decreased plate voltage will cause the plate current to decrease somewhat, counteracting the effect of the grid signal on the plate current. Thus, the amplification is kept down. The way to circumvent this defect would be to make the plate current independent of the plate voltage. Variations in plate voltage would then have no effect on the plate current. This is achieved in the tetrode and pentode vacuum tubes.

THE TETRODE. In an effort to reduce the grid-plate capacitance within the tube, a fourth element was added to the triode. This fourth element is called a SCREEN GRID and the tube is called a TETRODE. The screen grid is placed between the control grid and the plate. The top view of a tetrode is shown in Fig. 8-10A. The schematic symbol of a tetrode is shown in Fig. 8-10B. The screen is wound in the form of a spiral grid, similar to the control grid. The screen shields the control grid from the plate and thereby reduces the grid-plate capacitance.

In order for the screen grid to act as an effective shield, it must be
143

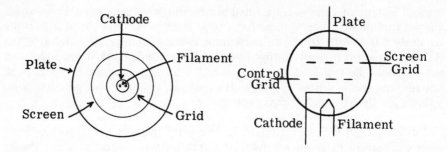

FIG. 8-10A. TOP VIEW OF A TETRODE.   FIG. 8-10B. SCHEMATIC SYMBOL

grounded for AC. But, as we shall soon see, the screen grid must also be kept at a high positive DC potential. The way to satisfy both conditions is to ground or by-pass the screen grid through a capacitor (C in Fig. 8-11).

A typical screen grid tube, connected in an amplifier circuit, is shown in Fig. 8-11. The screen grid is operated at a high DC potential and acts like the plate of a triode in attracting electrons emitted by the cathode. A few of the electrons will hit the screen grid, resulting in screen current flow. The screen current flows through resistor R1, the screen voltage-dropping resistor. The screen current that flows through R1 causes a voltage drop across it. The screen-grid voltage is therefore the B+ voltage minus the voltage drop across R1. The screen voltage is measured from the screen grid to the cathode.

The higher the screen grid voltage, the greater is the current flow through the screen grid. If we increase the screen grid voltage too high, the heating effect on the screen grid will be more than it can safely dissipate. The tube manual gives the maximum screen grid voltage and current that a particular tube can handle. The maximum power that the screen grid can safely dissipate is called the MAXIMUM SCREEN GRID DISSIPATION. This is also given in the tube manual.

INCREASED AMPLIFICATION OF THE TETRODE. Capacitor C keeps the screen grid voltage constant by by-passing any screen variations to ground. At the same time, the effect of the plate voltage on the plate current is reduced considerably because the screen grid is closer to the cathode than

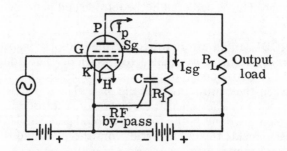

FIG. 8-11. TETRODE AMPLIFIER CIRCUIT.

144

the plate. The screen voltage and the grid voltage determine how much plate current can flow. Small variations of voltage on the control grid will cause the plate current to vary without any counter-action from a varying plate voltage. As a result, the plate resistance and the amplification factor of the tetrode are much greater than they are in a triode.

Generally speaking, tetrodes are capable of higher plate currents than triodes. This is because a high current in a triode circuit results in a lower plate voltage which, in turn, tends to cut the plate current down. As we have seen above, the plate voltage in a tetrode has very little effect on the plate current and will not counteract it.

THE PENTODE. The introduction of the screen grid in the tetrode successfully reduced the plate-grid capacitance and increased the amplification factor. The tetrode, however, suffers from one important defect. This defect is known as SECONDARY EMISSION. The PENTODE (five-element tube) was developed to overcome the effects of secondary emission.

Secondary emission is a condition that arises when high velocity electrons strike the plate of a vacuum tube. The force of the impact causes additional electrons to be knocked out of the atomic structure of the plate. For every electron that strikes the plate, two or three electrons will be knocked out of the plate. In a triode, these secondary emission electrons normally find their way back to the highly positive plate and cause no interference in the operation of the tube. In the tetrode, as long as the plate voltage is much higher than the screen voltage, the secondary emission electrons fall back to the plate, and tube operation will be normal. However, if a large signal voltage is applied to the control grid, the plate voltage will drop below the screen voltage at the positive peak of the input signal. The result of this lowered plate voltage is that secondary emission electrons flow to the positive screen grid instead of returning to the plate. Thus, the number of electrons reaching the plate drops, while at the same time, the screen current is increased. This results in a reduction in the amplification of the tube and distortion in its output.

In the pentode, a third grid (Fig. 8-12) is placed between the screen grid and the plate. The third grid is similar in physical construction to the screen grid and the control grid. This third grid is connected to the cathode (See Fig. 8-12) so that it will be highly negative with respect to the plate, and will force the secondary emission electrons back to the plate. Because it suppresses secondary emission, the third grid is called the SUPPRESSOR GRID. The negative suppressor grid will not interfere with the flow of electrons from the cathode to the plate, even though it does suppress the secondary electrons coming from the plate. The reason for this is that the electrons from the cathode are traveling at such a high velocity when they reach the vicinity of the suppressor grid, that they go right on through to the highly positive plate. On the other hand, the secondary electrons coming from the plate are moving at a rather low velocity and are easily pushed back to the plate.

In determining the input power to a tetrode or pentode, the plate current used in the calculations is only the plate current and should not contain any screen grid or control grid current.

145

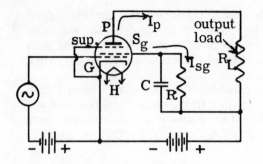

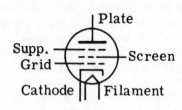

FIG. 8-12. PENTODE AMPLIFIER CIRCUIT.   FIG. 8-13. SCHEMATIC SYMBOL
FOR PENTODE.

3 THE BEAM POWER TUBE. A beam power tube is a pentode with special construction features that give it a greater power-handling ability than the ordinary tetrode or pentode. With very small grid voltages, a beam power tube can develop large amounts of power in its plate circuit. The tube is therefore said to have high power sensitivity.

The beam power tube is constructed so that the wire turns of the control grid and screen grid line up with each other horizontally. This means that every turn of the screen grid mesh is directly behind a turn of the control grid mesh. Thus, electrons flowing from the cathode, travel through the control grid to the plate, without striking the screen grid. The screen grid current is, therefore, very low and, since the plate gets the electrons which would normally have gone to the screen grid, the plate power output is increased. Because of the physical alignment of the control grid and the screen grid, the electrons flow to the plate in sheets, or beams. This is illustrated in Fig. 8-14. To further concentrate and form the heavy beams of plate current, deflecting plates are incorporated into the tube structure. These deflecting plates are placed between the screen grid and the plate, and extend partway around the tube. The beam forming deflecting plates are internally connected to the cathode and therefore, have a negative charge with respect to the plate. As a result, the deflecting plates repel the electrons into concentrated heavy beams of plate current.

No actual suppressor grid is necessary because secondary emission from the plate is suppressed by the space charge which forms between the plate and screen grid. This space charge has been indicated by the heavier dashes in Fig. 8-14. The space charge of the electron beam is caused by the slowing up of electrons in the area between the screen grid and the plate. By operating the plate of the beam power tube at a lower potential than the screen grid, the plate is made negative with respect to the screen. The electrons are therefore slowed down when they pass through the screen on their way to the plate. Stray secondary emission electrons cannot return to the screen grid outside of the beam area because of the beam-forming plates. Some beam power tubes use an actual suppressor grid in place of the space charge effect.

To summarize, we can say that the beam power tube has high power sensitivity, high power output and high plate efficiency.

146

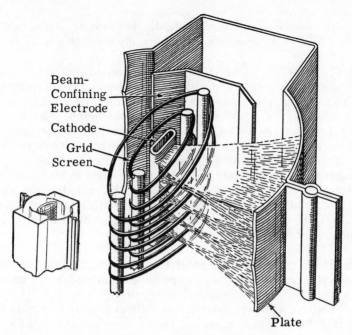

Beam-
Confining
Electrode

Cathode

Grid

Screen

Plate

FIG. 8-14. THE BEAM POWER TUBE (COURTESY RCA).

GAIN OF A STAGE. The gain of a stage is the amplification that the stage gives to a signal that is fed to the input of the stage. The formula that is used to calculate the gain of a stage is:

$$A = \frac{\mu R_L}{R_p + R_L}$$

where: A is the gain of the stage,
μ is the amplification factor of the tube,
R_L is the load resistance and
R_p is the plate resistance.

An example will clarify the use of the formula: Let us assume that the amplification factor of a triode tube is 30, its plate resistance is 10,000 ohms and the load resistance is 20,000 ohms. Find the gain of the stage.

$$A = \frac{\mu R_L}{R_p + R_L} = \frac{30 \times 20,000}{10,000 + 20,000} = \frac{600,000}{30,000} = 20$$

It can be seen from the formula that the stage gain is always less than the amplification factor. However, as the load impedance gets larger and larger, the stage gain begins to approach the amplification factor. We can see from the formula that as the load resistance becomes very large, the plate resistance becomes insignificant in the denominator of the fraction. The formula then becomes:

$$A = \frac{\mu R_L}{R_L}$$

147

The R_L in the numerator cancels the R_L in the denominator and we have only the μ left. In other words, A is practically equal to μ if R_L is very large.

3 MULTI-PURPOSE TUBES. For reasons of economy or convenience, several tubes may be mounted within a single envelope. For instance, we can have a twin triode, also known as a duo-triode, which contains two entirely distinct triodes in a single envelope. The two heaters may be connected together; however, the rest of the elements are completely separate.

Another example is a tube that consists of a diode, a triode and a pentode, all in one envelope. The 3A8-GT is an example of such a tube.

Another type of multi-purpose tube may contain as many as five grids, a cathode and a plate. Two of the grids and the cathode serve as one tube, while the cathode and the other grids act as another tube. In this particular type, the plate current passes through all elements. This type of tube is explained in detail in the section on receivers.

3 GAS-FILLED TUBES. In general, the tubes used in electronics are vacuum-types. As much of the air as possible is pumped out of them. Any air left in a tube may ionize and cause damage to the tube.

Gases such as neon or argon are sometimes purposely put into specially constructed tubes. These tubes are then known as GAS TUBES. Fig. 8-15 shows a circuit using a gas tube. This circuit is placed across the output of a power supply to keep its output voltage constant. Note that the tube does not have a filament. Because of this, it is called a cold-cathode, gaseous diode. It contains a plate and a "cold cathode". When a positive voltage is applied to the plate, a few stray electrons migrate toward the plate. These electrons collide with the gas atoms in the tube and strip one or more electrons from their outer rings, converting them into positive ions. These ions are attracted to the negative cathode and bombard it. This striking action warms up the cathode and it starts to release a few electrons, which are promptly attracted to the plate. Further ionization takes place, with the result that there is continued bombardment of the cathode and a steady flow of current toward the plate.

The cold-cathode, gaseous diode is used as a voltage regulator across power supplies because it maintains a constant or regulated DC output voltage. The explanation of how it maintains a constant voltage is given in Lesson 7. These circuits are found in transmitter power supplies and in test equipment because of the need for good voltage regulation. They are not used in receivers because the ordinary receiver has no need for them.

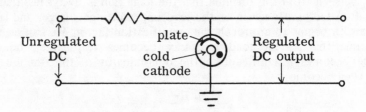

FIG. 8-15. COLD CATHODE GASEOUS VOLTAGE REGULATOR.

148

3 **THE THYRATRON.** A THYRATRON is a gas-filled triode or tetrode tube. The thyratron is used to control large amount of electron flow by means of signals on the control grid. When the grid of a thyratron is sufficiently negative, no plate current flows. However, if the negative bias is reduced to, the point where plate current begins, the gas in the tube immediately ionizes and a heavy plate current will flow. At this point, the control grid loses control over the plate current; varying the bias voltage will have no effect on the plate current. The only way to stop the flow of plate current is to remove the plate voltage or lower it below the ionization potential of the gas. The thyratron grid, therefore, acts as a trigger to turn on relatively large currents in the plate circuit. Thyratrons also function as high voltage rectifiers.

3 **THE CATHODE-RAY TUBE.** A CATHODE-RAY TUBE, abbreviated CRT, is a vacuum tube designed to give a graphical display of electrical signals. The CRT (Fig. 8-16) is the heart of the oscilloscope, radar screen and early television set.

The face or screen of the CRT used in oscilloscopes and radar sets is round. Most television sets use tubes that have a rectangular face. The diameter of the tube face varies from one inch in size to twenty-four inches. Small screens (one to ten inches) are used in test equipment and radar, while the larger size screens are mainly used in television sets.

The inside surface of the screen is coated with a powder called a phosphor. When electrons strike the screen, the phosphor gives off light. The color and length of time (persistance) that the phosphor is capable of displaying depends on the material used to make up the phosphor coating.

3 **OPERATION OF A CRT.** See Fig. 8-16. Electrons are emitted by the cathode and are attracted to the positive anodes. The anodes have large positive voltages on them and cause the electrons to travel at very high velocities. The control grid, which partially surrounds the cathode, is operated at a potential more negative than the cathode, and is used to control the amount of electron flow.

The anodes are constructed so that electrons attracted to them can pass through holes in them and travel towards the screen. The beam of electrons that emerges from the anodes will form a rather large spot on the screen,

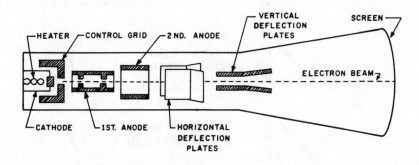

FIG. 8-16. A CATHODE RAY TUBE.

149

unless this beam is narrowed down and brought to a point of focus at the screen. To accomplish this, the focus anode has a potential less than that of the accelerating anode. Because of this potential difference, an electrostatic field exists between the two anodes. This electrostatic field, along with the action of the accelerating anode, causes the electron beam to focus on the screen. A potentiometer, called the Focus Control, controls the potential of the focus anode.

Before the electron beam strikes the phosphor screen, it must pass through two sets of plates which are at right angles to each other. The potential applied to one set of plates causes the beam to move in a vertical direction. These plates are called the vertical deflection plates. The potential on the other set of plates (the horizontal deflection plates) causes the beam to move in a horizontal direction. Thus, the focused beam of electrons can be moved anywhere on the screen's surface. The potentiometer used to adjust the potential on the vertical plates is called the VERTICAL CENTERING control, while the potentiometer used to control the potential on the horizontal plates is called the HORIZONTAL CENTERING control.

By applying varying voltages to the horizontal and vertical deflection plates, the electron beam is deflected so that a trace appears on the screen of the CRT tube.

When the oscilloscope is utilized to display waveforms, a signal is applied to the horizontal plates to create a horizontal trace (also called a time base). The purpose of the horizontal trace is to create a horizontal time scale so the varying voltages can be displayed on the face of the CRT tube. The signal that is applied to the horizontal plates to create the horizontal trace is a SAW-TOOTH VOLTAGE. This saw-tooth voltage is developed by a sweep generator, which is an integral part of the oscilloscope. See Fig. 8-17.

TRACE — STEP BY STEP ANALYSIS

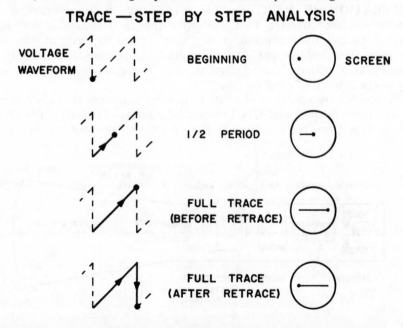

FIG. 8-17. DEVELOPMENT OF THE OSCILLOSCOPE HORIZONTAL SWEEP.

150

The saw-tooth voltage varies in a regular linear manner, as shown in Fig. 8-17. At the beginning, the saw-tooth voltage is at a minimum and the beam is at the extreme left of the CRT screen. As the voltage increases to its maximum value, it moves the electron beam across the screen to the extreme right. When the beam has completed its maximum excursion to the right, the saw-tooth voltage falls, almost instantaneously, to its minimum value. This returns the beam to the left in preparation for the next sweep. The beam's gradual movement from left to right is called the "trace". Its quick movement back to the left is called the "retrace". Fig. 8-17 illustrates how the horizontal trace is developed. Note that although the electron beam is continuously sweeping left to right, the trace appears as a solid horizontal line (rather than as a moving spot). This is due to the "persistance" of the screen which allows the screen to remain illuminated for a short time after the electron beam has swept by.

If a varying voltage, such as an AC sine wave, is applied to the vertical plates of the CRT tube, it will cause the beam to be deflected up and down, in accordance with the sine wave. Therefore, a sine wave will be displayed on the screen. This is shown in Fig. 8-18.

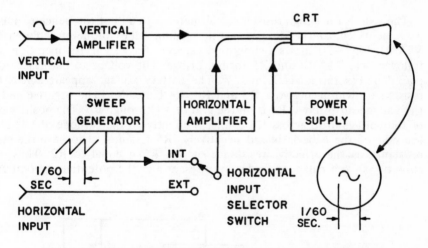

FIG. 8-18. SIMPLIFIED BLOCK DIAGRAM OF AN OSCILLOSCOPE.

THE VACUUM TUBE VOLTMETER. The chief disadvantage of a D'Arsonval type voltmeter is that it draws current from the device under measurement and thereby gives an inaccurate reading. Fig. 8-19 illustrates this. An ordinary voltmeter is placed across the plate and cathode in order to measure the plate voltage. However, the voltmeter draws current from the circuit and this increases the current through R_L. The voltage across R_L increases and the voltage between the plate and cathode decreases. Thus, the meter reads a lower voltage than the one that existed before the meter was connected.

The only way to overcome this fault is to use a voltmeter whose resistance is so high that it does NOT draw a significant amount of current from the circuit. However, if we use a D'Arsonval type voltmeter with a high input resistance, the meter movement must be extremely sensitive. Such meters are very expensive and delicate.

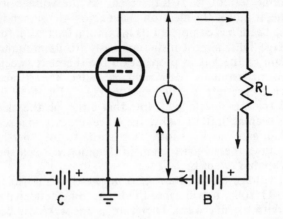

FIG. 8-19. READING PLATE VOLTAGE WITH A D'ARSONVAL METER.

The search for a high resistance voltmeter with a "not-too-delicate" meter movement led to the design of the vacuum tube voltmeter (abbreviated VTVM). Fig. 8-20 shows a simplified version of a VTVM. Its operation is as follows: V1, R1, R2 and R5 form a bridge. The voltage to be measured is placed across terminals X and Y. The battery voltage appears across the resistance dividing network R3 and R4. R4 biases V1. The negative end of the voltage drop across R4 is on the grid of V1 through R6. The positive end of the voltage drop across R4 connects directly to the cathode of V1. Thus the grid of the tube is biased negatively. R5 is adjusted to have the same resistance as the effective resistance of V1. R1 is equal to R2. Thus, the conditions for a balanced bridge are present and the potential at point A is

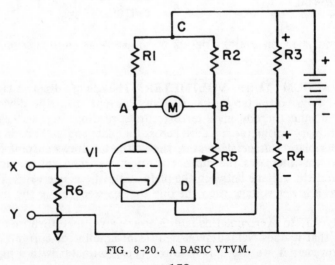

FIG. 8-20. A BASIC VTVM.

152

equal to the potential at point B. No current will flow through M and we will have zero reading.

As soon as the voltage to be read is placed across X and Y, there is a change in the current flow through the tube. The potential at point A changes and the meter indicates this. Even though current flows through the meter, it is calibrated to read voltage. R6 is a high value and the resistance of the grid circuit of V1 is also high. Thus, the vacuum tube voltmeter draws a negligible amount of current from the circuit and gives an accurate reading. In practical circuits, a second vacuum tube replaces R5.

PRACTICE QUESTIONS – LESSON 8

1. An amplifier stage is one which:
a. increases the DC component of the signal
b. extracts audio from an RF carrier
c. boosts the low frequency components of an audio signal
d. increases the strength of the signal that is applied to the control grid

2. What is the DC power input to a tube having a plate voltage of 250 V. and a plate current of 40 ma?
a. 10 W.   b. 100 W.   c. 1 W.   d. 6.25 W.

3. The screen grid reduces:
a. secondary emission   c. interelectrode capacitance
b. plate resistance   d. transconductance

4. What is the gain of a stage having a triode tube with an amplification factor of 20, a plate resistance of 5,000 ohms and a load resistance of 10,000 ohms?
a. 40   b. 20   c. 13   d. 8

5. A gaseous tube that controls large amounts of power, is the:
a. cathode ray tube   c. mercury vapor rectifier
b. beam power tube   d. thyratron

6. A single tube containing two tetrodes:
a. is used extensively in oscillator circuits
b. can only be used in parallel or push-pull
c. is called a duo-tetrode
d. is called a hexode

7. The life of a vacuum tube will not be shortened by:
a. excessive screen current   c. excessive plate voltage
b. insufficient filament voltage   d. insufficient grid bias

8. A tetrode has:
a. one grid   b. two grids   c. three grids   d. four grids

9. A cathode ray oscilloscope uses a sawtooth oscillator in its: (3)
a. horizontal deflection circuit   c. brightness circuit
b. damping circuit   d. low voltage power supply

10. Increasing the negative voltage on the control grid will:
a. decrease the plate voltage   c. decrease the plate current
b. increase the plate current   d. not affect the plate current

11. In a CRT, the beam moves: (3)
a. "rapidly" to the right and "slowly" to the left
b. "slowly" to the right and "rapidly" to the left
c. "rapidly" to the right and "rapidly" to the left
d. "slowly" to the right and "slowly" to the left

12. With reference to the figure shown, what is the grid bias?
a. 6 V
b. 7 V
c. 1 V
d. 3 V

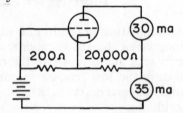

13. With reference to the above figure, what is the plate voltage?
a. 500 V   b. 700 V   c. 100 V   d. 600 V

14. With reference to the above figure, what is the supply voltage?
a. 107 V   b. 706 V   c. 106 V   d. 607 V

15. A type of voltmeter that absorbs no power from the circuit under test is a:
a. hot wire meter   c. thermocouple meter
b. vacuum tube voltmeter   d. high frequency ammeter

16. A small value of grid-to-plate capacitance is characteristic of:
a. tetrodes and pentodes   c. triodes
b. all vacuum tubes   d. diodes

17. The grid voltage of an indirectly heated tube is the voltage between the:
a. grid and cathode   c. grid and filament
b. grid and plate   d. grid and B+

18. The DC plate power input to a tube having a plate voltage of 800 volts and a plate current of 85 ma is:
a. 6,800 W   b. 68,000 W   c. 680 W   d. 68 W

19. A tube is said to have a blocked grid when the grid:
a. is negative enough to cut off plate current
b. is positive enough to saturate the plate
c. cuts off grid current   d. cuts off filament current

20. The tube that cannot amplify is the:
a. pentode   b. tetrode   c. triode   d. diode

154

LESSON 9
AUDIO AMPLIFICATION

SOUND. An audio amplifier is used to amplify the small signal output of a microphone. The action of a microphone depends upon certain characteristics of a sound wave. It is important, therefore, to understand the nature of sound.

SOUND is defined as a disturbance in a material medium caused by the vibration of a body. A sound wave travels through a medium, such as air or steel, in the form of a compressional wave. This compressional wave travels out from the region of disturbance in exactly the same manner as ripples do when a pebble is dropped into a pool of water. Vibrating objects, such as vocal cords, cause regions of compressed air, followed by rarefied air, to move outward in the form of concentric spheres. These vibrations or disturbances reach the ear and cause the eardrum to move inward and outward, in accordance with the pressure exerted by the compressions and rarefactions. The human ear is capable of hearing such disturbances only if they occur within the range from 16 to 20,000 cycles per second or Hertz. The FREQUENCY RESPONSE of the ear is, therefore, said to be from 16 to 20,000 Hz. This range of frequencies is designated by the term AUDIO FREQUENCIES.

AMPLIFIER APPLICATION. At this point, we understand that when a small amplitude signal is applied to the grid of a triode or pentode, it will be amplified and will appear many times larger in the plate circuit. This property of grid-controlled vacuum tubes makes possible their use as AMPLIFIERS. An amplifier may be defined as a device which transforms a small signal into a large signal.

Amplifiers find many practical applications. For example, the signal that is developed in the crystal pickup of a record player is much too weak to be applied directly to a speaker. This weak signal must first be amplified before it can properly drive the speaker. A lecturer addressing an audience in a large auditorium must have his voice amplified in order for him to be heard by everyone in the hall. The amplifier that accomplishes this is called a PUBLIC ADDRESS SYSTEM. Amplifiers are also used extensively in fields such as motion pictures, electrical recording and photo-electronics. Since amplifiers find such a wide application, it is important that we thoroughly understand their operation.

AMPLIFIERS USED IN RADIO RECEIVERS. The modern radio receiver uses two types of amplifiers in its operation. They are:

(1) The Radio-Frequency (RF) Amplifier. This amplifier amplifies the weak radio-frequency signals picked up by the antenna of the receiver. A radio frequency signal is a high frequency radio wave (usually above 400

kHz), which is sent out into space by the radio transmitter. RF amplifiers will be discussed in a later chapter.

(2) The Audio Frequency (AF) Amplifier. This amplifier amplifies the sound frequencies or audio frequencies before they are applied to the speaker. This chapter will concern itself primarily with audio amplifiers.

A BASIC AMPLIFIER. Fig. 9-1 illustrates a simple amplifier circuit. The output of the microphone is a weak, audio signal. It is impressed on the grid of the tube and amplified. The output of the tube appears across the primary of the transformer. From here it is coupled to the secondary and then travels to the speaker.

This is actually a one-stage amplifier. If additional amplification is required, a second tube can follow the first tube. The amplifier then becomes a two-stage amplifier.

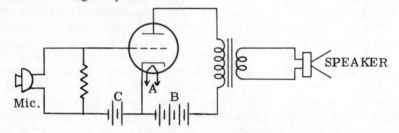

FIG. 9-1. SIMPLE ONE-STAGE AMPLIFIER CIRCUIT.

CLASSIFICATION OF AMPLIFIERS. Amplifiers are classified into general categories (Class A, Class B, Class C), according to the work they are intended to perform and the manner in which they are operated. The classification is determined by the bias of the amplifier, which, in turn, determines the manner in which the amplifier will operate. The audio amplifier is invariably operated either Class A, Class AB or Class B, while Class C amplifiers are usually associated with the radio- frequencies(RF).

CLASS A AMPLIFICATION. A graphical illustration of Class A amplification is given in Fig. 9-2. This graph is actually a plate current-grid voltage characteristic curve of the Class A amplifier. The bias voltage or operating point is at the mid- point of the straight line portion of the curve. Because the tube is operated on the straight or linear portion of the curve, the PLATE CURRENT VARIATIONS ARE AN EXACT REPRODUCTION OF THE INPUT SIGNAL. Thus we see that a Class A amplifier gives us excellent fidelity or minimum distortion. If we were to operate on the curved portion of the tube, distortion would be introduced.

The plate current flows for the entire cycle of the input signal. This means that there is plate dissipation all the time, which results in a loss of power and a decrease in efficiency. The Class A amplifier has the lowest efficiency of the various classes of amplifiers. It runs approximately 25% to 35%.

Other characteristics of a Class A amplifier are:

(1) The signal never drives the grid negative enough to cut the tube off. If the signal were too large, it would drive the grid negative and the tube would

156

not conduct current during portions of the signal. This would result in serious distortion. The fact that a large signal causes the tube to operate over curved sections of the characteristic curve, would also add to the distortion.

(2) The signal never drives the grid positive with respect to the cathode. A positive grid would result in grid current flow, which causes distortion. There is no grid current flow in a properly operated Class A amplifier.

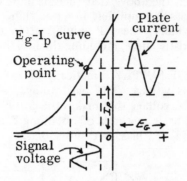

FIG. 9-2. CLASS A OPERATION.

CLASS B AMPLIFICATION. In a Class B amplifier, the grid is biased at approximately the cut-off point. This is shown in Fig. 9-3. With no signal, there is very little plate current flow. The Class B amplifier characteristics are as follows:

(1) Plate current flows only during the positive half of the signal. The negative half of the signal cuts off the tube. This amplifier operates in a manner similar to that of a rectifier in that it conducts only when the signal is positive.

(2) The amplifier is operated over the entire length of its characteristic curve so that large plate current swings can be obtained. The large plate current swing is necessary if large power output is to be realized.

(3) The efficiency for Class B operation is between 40% and 60%. It is

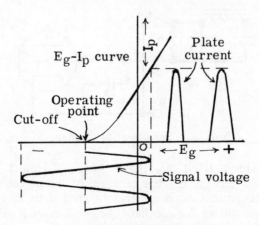

FIG. 9-3. CLASS B OPERATION.

157

much higher than that for Class A, for two reasons:

(a) Plate current flows for half a cycle, so that the power wasted in heating the plate is very much reduced.

(b) Efficiency of operation increases when a greater portion of the length of the characteristic curve is utilized. The Class B amplifier uses a greater portion of the characteristic curve than a Class A amplifier.

(4) It is obvious from the above that there is more distortion in a Class B amplifier than in a Class A amplifier. For one thing, half the signal is not even reproduced. Secondly, Class B amplification operates over a large section of the characteristic curve, including the non-linear sections.

THE BIAS VOLTAGE SUPPLY. Practically all amplifiers operate with a certain amount of bias voltage. The bias voltage, as we have previously learned, is a constant DC voltage that makes the grid negative with respect to the cathode. The two basic methods of obtaining bias for an AF amplifier are: (1) fixed bias and (2) self-bias, or cathode bias.

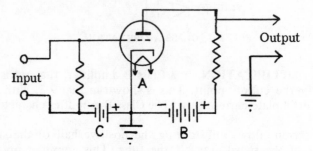

FIG. 9-4. AMPLIFIER STAGE USING FIXED BIAS.

Fig. 9-4 illustrates an amplifier stage with fixed bias. The fixed bias in this case is obtained from a bias supply or "C" battery. The negative end of the battery is connected to the control grid through R1 and the positive end is connected to the cathode.

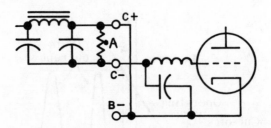

FIG. 9-5. POWER SUPPLY BIAS.

Fig. 9-5 illustrates a fixed bias that is obtained from a separate small power supply. Note that the negative terminal of the power supply goes to the grid, while the positive terminal goes to ground or B−. If we wish to obtain another bias voltage for another tube, we can tap it off at the proper point on the bleeder. (Terminal A in Fig. 9-5).

Fig. 9-6 illustrates an interesting method of obtaining fixed bias. Instead of grounding the most negative point of the bleeder, we ground and set all our cathodes to tap F. Thus, point A is negative with respect to the cathodes and may be used as grid bias.

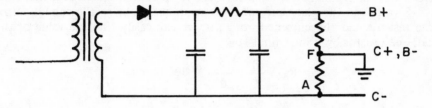

FIG. 9-6. POWER SUPPLY BIAS.

It has been pointed out that as we increase the negative voltage on the grid, less and less plate current flows. A point is reached where plate current stops flowing. The grid bias voltage that just about cuts off the plate current is called the "cut-off bias." The cut-off bias for a particular tube can be found by the following formula:

(9-1) $\quad E_{co} = -\dfrac{E_b}{\mu} \quad$ where: E_{co} is the cut-off bias, E_b is the plate supply voltage and μ is the amplification factor.

Fig. 9-7 is the schematic diagram of an amplifier using cathode bias. The biasing circuit consists of the resistor, R, and the capacitor, C. The bias voltage is developed by the plate current flowing from ground through the resistor to the cathode. Since the current flows into the resistor from ground, this side of the resistor is negative with respect to the cathode side. The negative side of the resistor is effectively connected to the grid through the input circuit. The positive side is connected to the cathode.

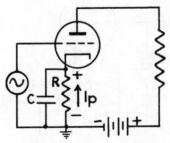

FIG. 9-7. CATHODE-BIAS.

The purpose of the capacitor, C, is to by-pass the AC component of the plate current around the resistor. If the AC component were allowed to flow through the biasing resistor, a varying bias voltage would be developed. Under normal amplifier operation, the bias voltage must be constant. The AC component therefore flows through the by-pass capacitor, C, while the DC component of the plate current flows through the biasing resistor, R,

159

establishing a source of constant bias voltage.

It may sometimes be necessary to compute the values of the cathode bias resistor and capacitor. For example: Suppose we wish to operate a certain tube as a Class A amplifier and the lowest frequency to be amplified is 100 Hz. The tube manual states that for Class A operation, the bias for that tube is −3 volts and the plate current is 10 ma. Since we know the voltage across the resistor and the current through it, we can easily find the value of the cathode resistor by using Ohm's law:

$$R_k = \frac{E}{I} = \frac{3}{.01} = 300 \text{ ohms}.$$

In order to calculate the value of capacitor C, we must assume that its reactance should be approximately 10% of the resistance of the cathode biasing resistor at the lowest audio frequency to be passed. Thus, X_c must be 10% of 300 or 30. Once we know the reactance, it is a simple matter to find the capacitance from formula (4-22A). We then substitute values and solve.

$$C = \frac{1,000,000}{2 \pi f X_c} = \frac{1,000,000}{6.28 \times 100 \times 30} = \frac{1,000,000}{18,840} = 53 \text{ mf}$$

The advantage of cathode bias is that it eliminates the need for a separate source of bias voltage. Most receiver circuits use this self-biasing principle.

Fig. 9-8 illustrates a method of obtaining cathode bias when a filament-type tube is used. Note that the plate current flows through resistor R and a voltage drop is formed across R. The negative point of the voltage drop goes to the grid through the RF choke and the positive point is connected to the center tap of the filament resistor. Thus the filament is positive with respect to the grid, or the grid is negative with respect to the cathode.

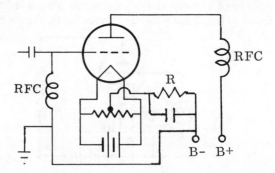

FIG. 9-8. OBTAINING CATHODE BIAS WITH FILAMENT TYPE TUBE.

PHASE RELATIONSHIPS IN AMPLIFIERS. Fig. 9-9 illustrates a simple, conventional one-stage amplifier using cathode bias. The input signal is applied between the grid and ground. The output signal is taken from between the plate and the ground. Graphs of the input and output signals are shown. Note that the output is an amplified, but not exact version of the input. In the input signal, the first alternation, A, is positive. In the output,

160

the same alternation, A', is negative. In the input, the second alternation of the cycle, B, is negative; in the output, it is positive. In other words, the output is 180° out of phase with the input. Let us see why this occurs:

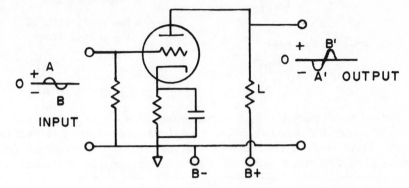

FIG. 9-9. PHASE RELATIONSHIPS IN AN AMPLIFIER.

When the signal on the grid is going positive, the plate current rises. This causes the voltage drop across the load resistor L to increase. Since the B supply voltage is fixed, the output voltage (plate to cathode) must decrease. This is because the plate circuit is a series circuit and the instantaneous plate voltage and instantaneous load voltage must add up to the B supply voltage.

When the input signal is negative "going", the grid goes in a negative direction and the plate current falls. The voltage across the load decreases and the voltage between the plate and ground (which does represent the output signal) increases. Thus we see how the ordinary amplifier stage reverses the phase of a signal by 180°.

Reversing the phase of a signal does NOT distort the signal in a way that the ear can hear. The ear cannot hear phase reversals. The amplitude, the frequency and the variations in the wave form do not change, and thus, the fidelity of the amplifier is not affected by the phase shift.

COUPLING SYSTEMS IN AMPLIFIERS. Audio amplifiers are also classified according to the method of coupling the signal from one stage to another. There are two common types of AF coupling used in receivers and transmitters. They are: TRANSFORMER COUPLING and RESISTANCE-CAPACITANCE COUPLING.

TRANSFORMER COUPLING. A simple transformer coupled audio-amplifier is shown in Fig. 9-10. V1 and V2 are the voltage amplifiers. T1 is a special type of matching transformer, known as an audio interstage transformer. For maximum power transfer from the plate of V1 to the grid of V2, the transformer is so designed that its primary impedance approximately matches the plate circuit impedance of V1, and its secondary impedance matches the grid circuit impedance of V2.

The ratio of input impedance to output impedance of an audio interstage transformer varies as the square of the turns ratio of the transformer. That is:

161

$$(9\text{-}2) \quad \frac{Z_p}{Z_s} = \left(\frac{N_p}{N_s}\right)^2$$

where: Z_s = secondary
impedance ,
Z_p = primary
impedance and
$\dfrac{N_p}{N_s}$ = the turns ratio of
the transformer.

From (9-2) we can say:

$$(9\text{-}3) \quad Z_p = Z_s \left(\frac{N_p}{N_s}\right)^2 \qquad \text{and} \qquad (9\text{-}4) \quad Z_s = Z_p \left(\frac{N_s}{N_p}\right)^2$$

A typical audio interstage transformer might have a 1 to 3 step-up turns ratio. The secondary would therefore have three times as many turns as the primary. From (9-4) it can be seen that the secondary impedance (grid impedance) is nine times higher than the plate impedance of the previous stage.

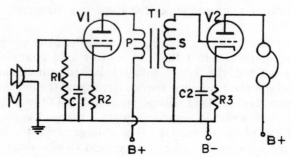

FIG. 9-10. TWO-STAGE TRANSFORMER-COUPLED AMPLIFIER.

Coupling the audio signal from V1 to V2 is accomplished in the following manner: The varying plate current of V1 (which is a replica of the audio signal) generates a varying magnetic field about the primary of transformer T1. This varying magnetic field, in turn, induces a voltage in the secondary of T1 which is applied as a signal voltage to the grid of V2. This signal is then amplified by V2 and applied to the headphones.

R1 is the grid resistor which serves two purposes:

(a) Microphone current flowing through the resistor establishes an AC voltage drop between the grid and ground which is the audio signal to be amplified.

(b) Any electrons which collect on the grid can leak off to ground through the resistor. These electrons might otherwise accumulate sufficiently on the grid to cause the tube to cut-off, a condition known as a "blocked grid."

The value of R1 must not be too high. The reason for this is as follows: The grid is normally negative. It therefore attracts positive ions to itself. These positive ions flow to the grid and through the resistance, causing a voltage drop across the resistor. Because the ions are positively charged, the grid will be positive with respect to the cathode. If the resistance is too high, this positive voltage will be high. This might cancel out the bias voltage, causing a high plate current, which might damage the tube.

162

ADVANTAGES AND DISADVANTAGES OF TRANSFORMER COUPLING. The advantages of transformer coupling are:

(1) High gain due to step-up ratio of transformer.

(2) Low DC resistance of transformer primary permits the use of lower B+ voltages.

The disadvantages of transformer coupling are:

(1) Distortion of the signal due to the transformer characteristics. An amplifier which reproduces faithfully and amplifies equally the band of audio frequencies which is applied to its input, is said to have low distortion, or HIGH FIDELITY. The average transformer used in a transformer-coupled amplifier introduces some frequency distortion into the signal. As a result, the amplifier is said to have POOR FIDELITY. High fidelity transformer-coupled amplifiers are very difficult to design and therefore, are quite expensive.

(2) The transformers are physically large.

(3) The transformers must be magnetically shielded to prevent the pickup of hum.

(4) Transformer coupling is usually limited to triode amplifiers with the result that the high gain of pentodes cannot be realized.

RESISTANCE-CAPACITANCE COUPLED AMPLIFIER. The disadvantages of the transformer-coupled amplifier are overcome in the resistance-capacitance coupled amplifier (commonly referred to as resistance-coupled or R-C coupled). The major difference between the two amplifiers is that the interstage coupling transformer is replaced with a resistance-capacitance coupling network. The elimination of the transformer allows the use of pentode tubes, with a consequent increase in the overall gain of the amplifier. The elimination of the audio-coupling transformer also does away with the distortion associated with its use. Generally speaking, the RC amplifier is the superior of the two amplifiers because of its simplicity, compactness, lower cost and higher fidelity.

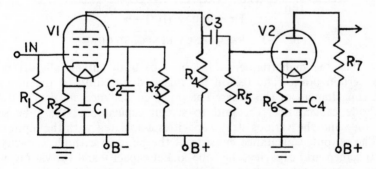

FIG. 9-11. TWO-STAGE RESISTANCE-COUPLED AMPLIFIER.

Fig. 9-11 illustrates a two-stage, resistance-coupled amplifier. The coupling between the plate of V1 and the grid of V2 consists of an R-C network (R4, C3 and R5). Capacitor C3 is the COUPLING capacitor. Its function is to pass the audio from the plate of V1 to the grid of V2, while at the same time,

163

blocking the positive plate voltage of V1 from being applied to the grid of V2. C3 must offer a low reactance to the lowest audio frequency that is being amplified.

If the coupling capacitor becomes shorted, the positive DC plate voltage of V1 would be applied directly to the grid of V2. This would result in excessive grid and plate current flow, and would cause the audio signal to become distorted.

If we were to replace R4 with a choke, we would have a system of coupling that is known as impedance coupling. A choke has a low DC drop and a high AC drop across itself. This means that more DC voltage will be available for the plate and a greater audio voltage can be developed across the output. Impedance coupling has many of the disadvantages of transformer coupling and is rarely ever used.

FREQUENCY RESPONSE. An amplifier is said to have a FLAT FREQUENCY RESPONSE if it amplifies equally all frequencies applied to its input. A frequency response curve is a graph which plots the amplifier voltage output in either volts or similar units over a frequency range. Fig. 9-12 gives the frequency response curves for a transformer-coupled audio amplifier and an R-C coupled audio amplifier. The R-C amplifier has the flatter curve and has, therefore, a flatter frequency response. A flatter response means better fidelity.

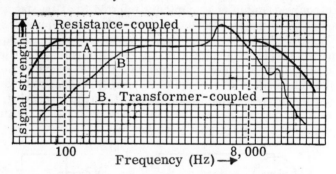

FIG. 9-12. FREQUENCY RESPONSE CURVE.

Note that the high frequency response of both curves falls off rapidly after a certain point. The reason for this is due mainly to the input and output capacitances of the tubes. The input capacitance consists of the grid to cathode capacitance, the grid to screen capacitance, the tube socket capacitance and the various stray capacities associated with the input of the tube. The output capacitance consists of the plate to cathode capacity, the plate to screen-grid capacity, the tube socket capacity and the various wiring and stray capacities associated with the output circuit of the tube. The input and output capacitances are in parallel with the path of the signal. As the frequency goes up, the capacitive reactances of the input and output capacitances go down and effectively shunt the loads of the tubes. A low impedance load will cause a reduction in output signal. We can therefore see that it is important to have low input and output capacitances in order to have good high frequency response.

164

DISTORTION IN A CLASS A AMPLIFIER. The ideal audio amplifier is one which will amplify a sine wave signal without changing its waveshape. The amplified plate signal must therefore be an exact duplicate of the signal applied to the grid. Fig. 9-13A shows a pure sine wave voltage.

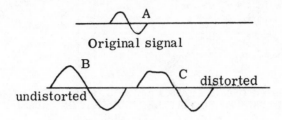

Original signal

FIG. 9-13. DISTORTION IN CLASS A AMPLIFIER.

Fig. 9-13B shows an amplified version of this sine wave. It has the exact same waveshape as that in Fig. 9-13A and therefore, is still considered a pure undistorted signal. Fig. 9-13C illustrates a distorted sine wave. The top of the positive portion of the wave is flattened out.

CAUSES OF DISTORTION IN CLASS A AMPLIFIERS. The causes of distortion in a Class A amplifier are as follows:

(1) Too high an input signal (signal overloading): Excessive excitation voltage will drive the grid positive with respect to the cathode on the positive peaks of the signal. A positive grid draws grid current, which results in distortion of the signal. The negative peaks of the signal may drive the grid so negative that the tube will be driven into cutoff and distort the signal. See Fig. 9-14. Compare this graph with Fig. 9-2.

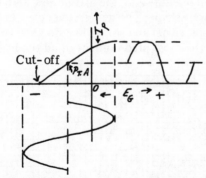

FIG. 9-14. DISTORTION DUE TO EXCESSIVE SIGNAL VOLTAGE.

(2) Improper grid bias. The result of operating the amplifier with too little grid bias is shown in Fig. 9-15. The low bias places the operating point of the tube at the top of the curve instead of the middle of the curve. This causes the positive peaks of the signal voltage to drive the grid positive and draw grid current. The resulting distortion is a flattening or clipping of the positive peaks of the output signal.

165

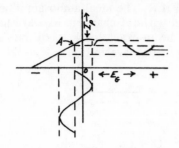 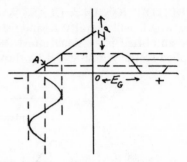

FIG. 9-15. DISTORTION IN CLASS A
OPERATION CAUSED BY TOO LITTLE
BIAS.

FIG. 9-16. DISTORTION IN CLASS A
OPERATION CAUSED BY EXCESSIVE
BIAS.

The result of operating the amplifier with an excessive negative grid bias is shown in Fig. 9-16. The negative peaks of the signal drive the tube into cutoff. This results in a clipping of the negative peaks of the output signal.

The distorted signal is converted by the speaker into a distorted sound which is unpleasant to a listener. It is therefore necessary to eliminate distortion before it reaches the speaker.

SECOND HARMONIC DISTORTION. Any distorted waveform may be analyzed and found to consist of a fundamental frequency plus a number of harmonics. Harmonic frequencies are multiples of the fundamental frequency. For example: Suppose the original undistorted signal is a 1000 Hz wave. The second harmonic would be 2000 Hz. The third harmonic would be 3000 Hz, etc. During the process of amplification, the signal becomes distorted due to the addition of harmonic frequencies to the original waveform. The fundamental and the harmonics add together to give us a resulting distorted waveshape. The new frequencies that are created were not present in the original signal and sound like noise to the listener. The second harmonic is usually the most predominant of all the harmonics present.

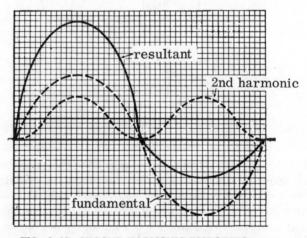

FIG. 9-17. SECOND HARMONIC DISTORTION.

166

Fig. 9-17 shows the effects of second harmonic distortion on a signal. The resultant signal comes about by adding each point of the fundamental wave to its "vertical counterpart" on the second harmonic wave. The resultant wave is not symmetrical above and below the center line and is therefore distorted.

THE CLASS A POWER AMPLIFIER. A Class A voltage amplifier serves only to amplify weak voltage variations. A voltage amplifier is not required to supply a large power output. The average plate current of a voltage amplifier is therefore comparatively low in value. A representative value would be about 5 ma. A loudspeaker, however, needs a large current variation in order to operate properly. The tube, which is to drive the loudspeaker, must be capable of handling a large amount of power. Such a tube is known as a POWER AMPLIFIER. The plate current of an audio power amplifier tube is about 50 ma.

The characteristics of an audio power amplifier tube are as follows:

(1) Low plate resistance. Since a power tube must be able to handle a relatively high power, it must be capable of conducting a large plate current. A low plate resistance will enable a large plate current to flow. For example: The plate resistance of a typical voltage amplifier may be as high as 700,000 ohms, and the plate current is 3.0 ma; whereas, the plate resistance of a power amplifier is around 78,000 ohms, with a plate current of about 45 ma.

(2) Large signal handling ability: A large signal on the grid means a large plate current variation. The tube must be capable of handling a large signal without going into cutoff or drawing grid current. This means that the grid will normally operate with a comparatively large bias voltage. The bias voltage for a power amplifier is as high as −16 volts, compared to −3 volts for the voltage amplifier.

(3) A low amplification factor: The amplification factor is directly related to the plate resistance. If the plate resistance is low, the amplification factor will be low. The 2A3 triode power amplifier has an amplification factor of only 4.2.

(4) Large cathode and plate structures: These elements must be large in order to be able to handle the large plate current requirements.

THE CLASS B POWER AMPLIFIER. A power amplifier operated Class A has a comparatively poor operating efficiency. The reason for this is that the tube conducts plate current for the entire cycle of the input signal; this results in a continuous dissipation of heat by the plate.

The modulator stages of radio-telephone transmitters require power audio amplifiers capable of delivering large amounts of power. Class A power amplifiers would not be practical for such an application because of their poor operating efficiency. The Class B power amplifier is, therefore, used because of its higher operating efficiency. A Class B amplifier is biased to cutoff so that plate current is practically zero without a signal.

A Class B a-f amplifier stage requires a greater driving power than a Class A stage because the Class B input signal drives the grid positive and causes grid current to flow. This power dissipated in the grid circuit must come from the preceding stage (driver stage). In the case of a Class A power amplifier, the grid is never driven positive and therefore, does not require any power from the driver stage.

PARALLEL OPERATION OF TUBES If the power output of a single tube is too small to produce a certain volume, two similar tubes may be connected in parallel in order to increase the power output of a single tube.

Fig. 9-18 illustrates two Class A amplifier tubes in parallel. The plates, cathodes and grids of the two tubes are connected together. The circuit operates in the same manner as that of a single Class A amplifier. However, the power and distortion will be double that of a single tube. The percentage of distortion will remain the same.

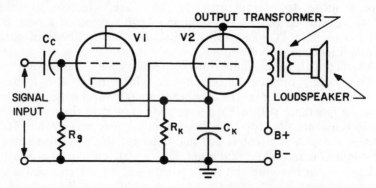

FIG. 9-18. TWO TRIODE VACUUM TUBES OPERATED IN PARALLEL.

Since the plate impedances of the two tubes are in parallel, the total output impedance will be cut in half. The design of the circuit components must take this into consideration. Twice the plate current will flow through the cathode resistor and the output transformer. The resistance of R_k must be cut in half to maintain the same bias. The transformer windings must be heavier to handle more current.

The input and output interelectrode capacitances, which are in parallel, will double. This will reduce the gain of the amplifier at high frequencies.

The efficiency of two Class A amplifiers is still low, and this fact limits the use of this type of amplifier. Current usage favors other types of amplifiers which are more efficient and reduce distortion.

POWER OUTPUT OF AN AMPLIFIER. Determining the power output of an amplifier is a simple matter. We measure the voltage across the load, and knowing the load resistance, we can use the basic power formula to find the wattage. For example, let us assume that 6 volts develops across a load resistance of 20 ohms. We use the power formula containing voltage and resistance and solve for power.

$$P = \frac{6^2}{20} = \frac{36}{20} = 1.8 \text{ watts}.$$

CLASS B PUSH-PULL POWER AMPLIFIER. A Class B amplifier tube, when used alone, will distort the signal because only one-half of the input

168

cycle is amplified. Two tubes are therefore necessary, one to amplify the positive half of the input signal and the other to amplify the negative half. The plate output of each tube is combined with the other to form one continuous wave. This system of amplification is called PUSH-PULL amplification.

A transformer usually feeds the grid circuit of a Class B push-pull stage. The secondary of this transformer has a low impedance to match the low impedance grid circuit, and to be able to handle heavy grid current swings. The grid bias supply should be well regulated.

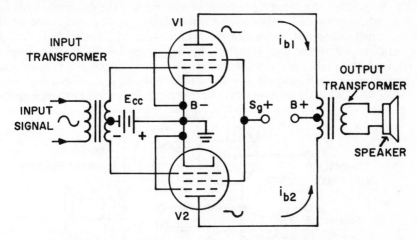

FIG. 9-19. A CLASS B PUSH-PULL PENTODE AMPLIFIER.

Fig. 9-19 illustrates a basic Class B push-pull amplifier. Before the signal is applied, the grid bias cuts off the plate current flow for both tubes. Once the signal is applied, its operation is as follows: During the positive half of the input cycle, the grid of V1 goes positive and the grid of V2 goes negative. V1 will conduct current, while V2 will be cut off. V1 will therefore amplify the positive half of the signal.

During the negative half of the input signal, the grid of V1 goes negative, while the grid of V2 goes positive. V1 will cutoff and V2 will conduct. V2, therefore, amplifies the negative half of the input signal. The negative plate signal of V2 and the positive plate signal of V1 combine in the output to form a complete amplifier cycle. This is illustrated in Fig. 9-20.

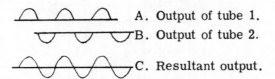

A. Output of tube 1.

B. Output of tube 2.

C. Resultant output.

FIG. 9-20. OUTPUT OF A CLASS B PUSH-PULL AMPLIFIER.

Push-pull operation has enabled us to utilize the high efficiency of a Class B amplifier, while at the same time, eliminating the distortion inherent in Class B operation.

169

CLASS A PUSH-PULL AMPLIFIER. Fig. 9-21A illustrates two tubes in push-pull Class A operation. Fig. 9-21B illustrates, graphically, the undistorted output of this arrangement. A Class A push-pull amplifier differs from a Class B push-pull amplifier in that both tubes in the Class A system conduct current continuously. Both tubes combine their outputs during the positive as well as the negative cycles of the signal. In Fig. 9-21B, wave 1 and wave 2 represent the distorted outputs of V1 and V2 respectively. They are unsymmetrical (recall Fig. 9-17). These two distorted curves combine together, point by point, to produce wave 3, an undistorted output wave form. In reality, the second harmonics (which cause the distortion) are 180° out of phase with each other in the transformer primary and consequently, cancel each other out. Push-pull operation eliminates even (2nd, 4th, 6th, etc.) harmonic distortion, thereby improving the fidelity of the amplifier over that obtainable from one tube (single-ended) operation. A good audio system always uses push-pull amplifiers in its last stage.

Since the DC plate currents flow in opposite directions in their respective

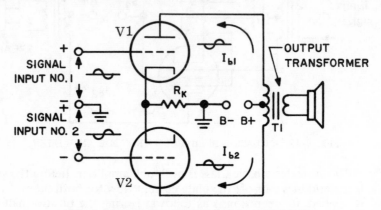

FIG. 9-21A. CLASS A PUSH-PULL AMPLIFIER.

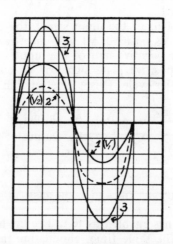

FIG. 9-21B. PUSH-PULL OPERATION ELIMINATING SECOND HARMONIC.

170

halves of the transformer primary, their magnetizing effect on the iron core cancels out. Therefore, it is almost impossible to saturate the core. The reason we are concerned with core saturation is that it causes distortion. Core saturation reduces the inductance of the transformer and places varying output loads across the tubes. This will cause amplitude variations that depend on the saturation of the core and not on the signal. This results in distortion. A push-pull system eliminates core saturation and reduces distortion.

Push-pull also eliminates AC hum from a signal. Any AC hum voltage that may be present in the power supply will be balanced out in the primary windings of the output transformer. The AC hum output of a push-pull amplifier is therefore greatly reduced.

If one tube goes bad or is removed from a push-pull Class A a-f amplifier, the result will be a great reduction of power and an increase in distortion and hum. Other causes of distortion may be: operating with incorrect grid bias, a shorted or leaky coupling capacitor, improper plate or filament voltages, and incorrect load impedance.

3 **PHASE INVERTERS.** A basic requirement of a push-pull amplifier is that each grid is fed a signal that is equal and 180 degrees out of phase with the signal being fed to the other grid. In Fig. 9-19, this requirement is met with the input transformer. The transformer is center-tapped so that equal signals are applied to the grids of V1 and V2. The voltages fed to the two grids are 180 degrees out of phase because the polarities at opposite ends of a transformer are 180 degrees out of phase.

The problem with using transformers in an audio circuit is that the frequency response of ordinary transformers is poor. A high fidelity transformer is costly. The input transformer can be eliminated in a push-pull stage by means of phase inverter circuits.

Fig. 9-22 illustrates a simple inverter circuit that can take the place of a transformer. Two outputs are taken from V1; one is from the plate and one is from the cathode. Rk is made equal to Rp. Since the same plate current

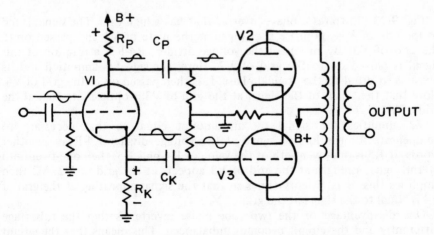

FIG. 9-22. CATHODE-RESISTOR PHASE INVERTER.
171

flows through Rk and Rp, the voltages across them will be equal. Thus, the grids of the push-pull tubes, V2 and V3 will receive equal signals. This satisfies the first of the two requirements for signals feeding a push-pull stage. An examination of the polarities of voltage drops across Rk and Rp indicates that the grid of V2 is connected (through Cp) to the negative end of Rp and the grid of V3 is connected to the positive end of Rk. Thus, the second requirement (that of the grids receiving opposite polarity signals) is also satisfied.

The gain of the phase inverter of Fig. 9-22 is very low because the cathode is unbypassed and a degenerative type of feedback (see next section) occurs. However, it is a simple circuit with good fidelity.

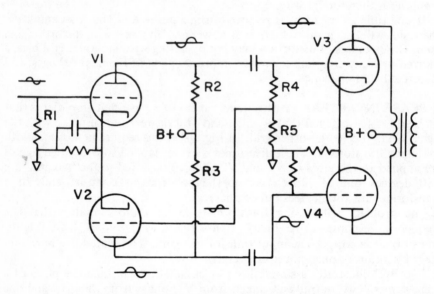

FIG. 9-23. PHASE INVERTER WITH HIGH GAIN.

Fig. 9-23 illustrates a phase inverter that has a high gain. The signal is fed to the grid of V1. Its phase is changed at the plate of V1 and passed on to the grid of V3. By means of the voltage divider, R4-R5, a fraction of this signal is passed on to the grid of V2. Here, the signal is amplified and its phase is inverted to the original phase. It is then passed on to the grid of V4. Note that the phase of the signal at the grid of V3 is opposite to that at the grid of V4.

V2 amplifies the signal by an amount equal to that necessary to compensate for the loss of signal at the voltage divider R4-R5. In other words, if R5 is one-twentieth of the value of R4 plus R5, then one-twentieth of the signal strength at the grid of V3 appears at the grid of V2. V2 then amplifies this signal twenty times so that the signal appearing at the grid of V4 is equal to the signal at the grid of V3.

One disadvantage of the two tube phase inverter is that the tubes age differently and the circuit becomes unbalanced. This means that the circuit balance should be checked frequently if perfect balance is required.

172

NEGATIVE FEEDBACK. Negative feedback is used to reduce distortion and improve frequency response in an audio amplifier. In a negative feedback circuit, some of the output voltage (or current) is fed back to the input of the circuit 180 degrees out of phase with the input voltage. This means that the voltage fed back will oppose and cancel some of the input voltage. Some of the distortion, as well as some of the desired signal, will be cancelled. However, there is no problem in adding additional amplification to bring the desired signal up to the proper level.

If the voltage fed back from the output is proportional to the current through the load, we refer to the feedback as CURRENT FEEDBACK. If the voltage fed back is proportional to the voltage across the load, we refer to the feedback as VOLTAGE FEEDBACK. Fig. 9-24 illustrates current feedback and Fig. 9-25 illustrates voltage feedback.

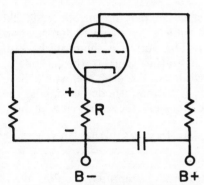

FIG. 9-24. NEGATIVE CURRENT FEEDBACK.

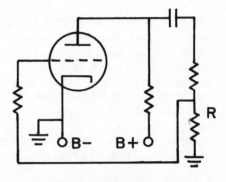

FIG. 9-25. NEGATIVE VOLTAGE FEEDBACK.

The unbypassed resistor, R, of Fig. 9-24 provides the current feedback in the circuit. The output current flows through R, causing a voltage drop across it which is 180 degrees out of phase with the input signal. The explanation for this is as follows: If the signal on the grid is increasing in a positive direction, the plate current increases. This causes the voltage drop across R to increase. The polarity of the voltage drop is such that the cathode becomes more positive with respect to the grid. This is the same as saying that the grid becomes more negative with respect to the cathode. This is in opposition to the signal on the grid which is "positive-going." When the incoming signal on the grid is "negative going", the plate current decreases and the voltage drop across the cathode resistor decreases. The cathode becomes less positive or more negative. This is the same as saying that the grid becomes more positive. This is in opposition to the negative signal on the grid. Thus we see how an unbypassed cathode resistor provides the negative feedback necessary to reduce distortion.

In Fig. 9-25, a portion of the output voltage (the voltage across R) is fed back to the input of the circuit. Since the tube changes the phase of the signal by 180 degrees, the voltage fed back to the grid opposes the input signal by a pre-determined amount and the condition for negative feedback is accomplished.

173

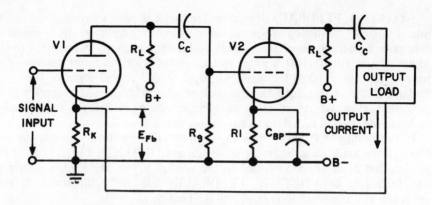

FIG. 9-26. TWO CLASS A STAGES IN CASCADE.

Fig. 9-26 shows two Class A cascaded stages employing current feedback. Feedback over two stages is perfectly feasible. The signal undergoes two phase reversals in the two-stage amplifier. The output is therefore back in phase with the input. However, we feed the output signal to the cathode of V1, not to the grid. If we were to feed it to the grid, we would have regeneration, not degeneration. By feeding it to the cathode, we oppose the incoming signal (see explanation above on current feedback) and thereby reduce distortion.

Other names for negative feedback are INVERSE FEEDBACK and DEGENERATIVE FEEDBACK.

3 **TONE CONTROL CIRCUITS.** The ideal audio amplifier should have a response that is linear and level over the entire audio frequency range. There are times, however, when it is desirable to control the frequency response so as to compensate for certain non-linear components such as pickups or loudspeakers, or to enable the listener to suit his taste. Such methods of frequency controls are known as tone controls, base boosting, treble control, etc.

Fig. 9-27 illustrates a simple tone control circuit that is found in many receivers. Capacitor C1, in series with potentiometer R1, represents a bass-boost tone control. C1 shunts the high frequencies to ground directly or

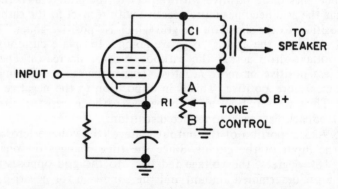

FIG. 9-27. A SIMPLE METHOD OF TONE CONTROL.

174

through R1. When the center arm of the potentiometer is at point A, C1 is connected directly to ground. The high frequencies are shunted to ground and are not heard in the speaker. The tone of the signal appears bassy.

When the center arm of the tone control is at point B, R1 prevents the high frequencies from being shunted to ground. They will, therefore, appear in the speaker. By varying R1, we control the tone of the output signal. We call it a bass-boost tone control because we are, in effect, "boosting" the bass frequencies when we cut out the high frequencies.

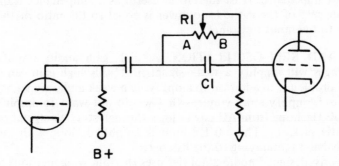

FIG. 9-28. A SERIES TONE CONTROL.

Fig. 9-28 illustrates another form of tone control. C1 and R1 are the tone control components. They are in series with the signal. When the control arm is at point A, the tone control circuit is shorted out and has no effect on the circuit. When the control arm is at point B, voltage drops for the lower frequencies appear across C1 and are not passed on to the following stage. As the control arm slides across to point A, more and more of the low frequencies appear in the output. By replacing C1 with a choke, we can control the amount of high frequencies that appear in the output.

3 CATHODE FOLLOWER AMPLIFIER. A circuit of a cathode follower amplifier is shown in Fig. 9-29. The significant feature of the cathode follower is that the output is obtained at the cathode of the tube. The term "cathode follower" comes from the fact that the output follows the input voltage. There is no phase difference between the output and input as there is in the conventional amplifier. The reason for this is as follows: When the signal applied to the input goes positive, the plate current, which flows through the cathode resistor, increases. This increases the voltage across R_k

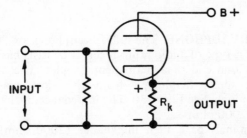

FIG. 9-29. A CATHODE FOLLOWER AMPLIFIER.

175

and consequently, the output increases. This means that the output is in phase with the input voltage.

The voltage gain of the cathode follower is slightly less than one; the cathode follower therefore, has no value as a voltage amplifier. The value of this circuit lies in its excellent frequency response. In fact, for certain tubes, the frequency response is excellent up to 200 megacycles. It is often used in video and oscilloscope circuits.

Moreover, the cathode follower circuit has a high input impedance and a low output impedance. It is, therefore, useful as an impedance transformer. The power gain of the cathode follower is equal to the ratio of the output resistance to the input resistance.

3 HUM AND SELF-OSCILLATION. A high gain audio amplifier using several stages will amplify a weak signal. But, this high gain can also be a source of problems. In addition to amplifying a weak audio signal, it will also pick up and amplify stray voltages that we do not want to amplify. It can amplify 60 Hz hum from AC power lines through stray electromagnetic and electrostatic pick up. This 60 Hz hum is amplified along with the desired audio signal and is annoying to the listener.

A properly designed audio amplifier uses the following methods to reduce hum pickup: Shield all leads carrying AC power, shield the tubes and grid leads in the early stages of a high gain audio amplifier; use adequate filtering on the power supply; twist filament leads that carry AC; keep AC leads away from grid and plate leads.

If a small part of the output of an amplifier is picked up by its input, it will be amplified and reamplified until it goes into self-oscillation, and a howl or motorboating is heard in the speaker. Some of the causes of this condition are: Feedback from output to input via a common power supply; pickup of output to input via stray lead capacity; insufficient decoupling between the power supply and the individual stages, and poor layout of stages that makes it easy for output to input coupling.

The remedies for self-oscillation are as follows: Use sufficient capacity in filter capacitors in the power supply; decouple (with filters) all B+ leads from the power supply; shield leads of early stages and re-orient leads so they do not provide a feedback path from the output to the input.

THE HEADPHONE AND SPEAKER. Audio reproducers are used to convert audio power signals into sound energy. Of the many types of reproducers in use today, we will study the headphone and the permanent-magnet loudspeaker.

THE RADIO HEADPHONE. The radio headphone, or "telephone receiver," is the simplest type of audio reproducer. It consists basically of a coil of wire wound over one end of a permanent magnet. The earphone housing separates a thin metal diaphragm from the electo-magnets by a few thousandths of an inch. See Fig. 9-30. The impedance of the headphone coils ranges from 3 to 2000 ohms.

The input terminals of a high impedance (2000 ohm) headset can be connected directly to the plate circuit of an audio amplifier (see Fig. 9-10).

The plate current, which has an AC component varying at an audio rate, flows through the windings of the electro-magnets, causing a varying magnetic field to be produced. This field causes the diaphragm to move at an audio rate. The moving diaphragm sets the air surrounding it into motion in the form of sound waves which are converted by the listener's ear into audible sound.

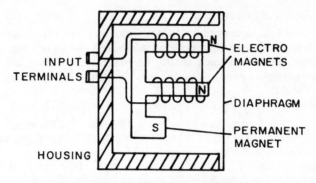

FIG. 9-30. THE RADIO HEADPHONE.

Whenever a headphone is connected directly to the plate circuit of an audio amplifier, its polarity must be observed. If connected backwards, the field of the electromagnet will tend to demagnetize the permanent magnet. The permanent magnet is important because it pulls on the diaphragm at a steady rate, which causes "magnetic damping" or tension on the diaphragm. Magnetic damping of the diaphragm tends to keep the frequency response of the headphones more even.

If we wish to hook up a pair of low impedance headsets to an amplifier, an impedance matching transformer is necessary in order to couple the maximum power from the tube to the headsets. See Fig. 9-31. In order to

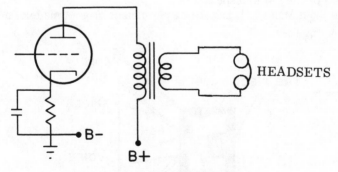

FIG. 9-31. PROBLEM.

calculate the turns ratio of the transformer, we would have to use a variation of formula (9-2). Formula (9-2) tells us what the impedance ratio is in terms of the turns ratio. By taking the square root of both sides of the equation, we arrive at formula (9-5), which tells us what the turns ratio is in terms of the impedance.

EXAMPLE: Calculate the turns ratio of a transformer that couples a tube with a plate impedance of 3600 ohms to a 73 ohm pair of headsets.
SOLUTION:

$$(9\text{-}5) \quad \frac{T_p}{T_s} = \sqrt{\frac{Z_p}{Z_s}} = \sqrt{\frac{3600}{73}} = \sqrt{49} = 7$$

The turns ratio should be 7 to 1.

Another problem occasionally comes up in design work. Suppose we have the 7 to 1 transformer of the above problem, but the tube's plate impedance is 7200 ohms. What resistance should be placed across the plate to effect an impedance match? Formula (9-3) tells us what the primary impedance should be.

$$Z_p = Z_s \left(\frac{N_p}{N_s}\right)^2 = 73 \left(\frac{7}{1}\right)^2 = 73 \times 49 = 3600 \text{ ohms} \quad \text{(approx.)}$$

We therefore require a primary impedance of 3600 ohms. We have 7200 ohms. A variation of formula (2-7) gives us formula (9-6) which gives us the value of the resistor that must be placed in parallel with a known resistance to give us a certain total resistance.

$$(9\text{-}6) \quad R1 = \cfrac{1}{\cfrac{1}{R_T} - \cfrac{1}{R1}} = \cfrac{1}{\cfrac{1}{3600} - \cfrac{1}{7200}} = \cfrac{1}{\cfrac{2}{7200} - \cfrac{1}{7200}} = \cfrac{1}{\cfrac{1}{7200}} = 7200 \text{ ohms.}$$

A 7200 ohm resistor should be placed across the 7200 ohm plate impedance to effect the proper match.

THE PM SPEAKER. The operation of a loudspeaker is very similar to the operation of headphones. Fig. 9-32 illustrates a modern loudspeaker. The major parts of the PM loudspeaker are:

(1) The Field Magnet: It is a strong permanent magnet made of a magnetic alloy, such as alnico steel.

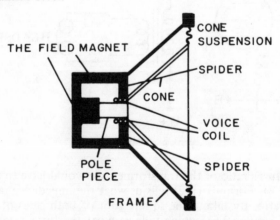

FIG. 9-32. THE P.M. LOUDSPEAKER.

(2) The Voice Coil: This coil consists of a few turns of wire wound over a cardboard or plastic cylinder. The cylinder fits loosely over the end of the pole piece and is free to move in and out of a narrow air gap formed between the pole piece and the outer poles of the magnet. The impedance of the voice coil is very low, usually from 2 to 20 ohms.

(3) The Cone. The cone of the speaker is made of heavy paper or cloth and is firmly attached to the voice coil.

(4) The Spider: The voice coil is suspended around the end of the magnetic pole piece by a flexible support called a "spider". The spider keeps the voice coil centered around the pole piece and allows the coil to move forward and backward over the pole piece.

The entire voice coil and cone assembly is thus able to move freely, in and out, but not sideways.

The speaker operates as follows: Audio currents flow through the voice coil and set up a varying magnetic field around it. The reaction between the magnetic field of the voice coil and the field of the permanent magnet causes the voice coil, together with the cone, to vibrate at an audio rate. The vibrating cone transmits its energy to the surrounding air, producing air pressure variations or sound waves.

Since the voice coil impedance is low, it must be connected to the audio output stage through a suitable impedance matching transformer. The turns ratio of a speaker matching transformer is calculated in the same manner as the turns ratio of the transformer that couples a pair of headsets to a tube. Fig. 9-33 illustrates the hookup of a speaker matching transformer. Note the step-down ratio to match the high impedance of the tube to the low impedance of the voice coil.

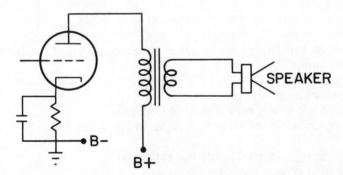

FIG. 9-33. A TRIODE INDUCTIVELY COUPLED TO A LOUDSPEAKER.

The quality of the transformer is important. In order to have a high fidelity amplifier, the audio output transformer should have excellent frequency response. It should be able to handle the primary and secondary currents with minor losses. In designing an output transformer, the class of operation of the final stage, as well as the power, must be taken into consideration.

Fig. 9-34 illustrates impedance coupling between a tube and a speaker. The capacitor C prevents DC from flowing through the speaker. However, it

179

allows the AC audio to get to the speaker. Impedance coupling is rarely ever used since the addition of a secondary winding to the choke adds little cost over the cost of a choke, and gives us the normal transformer coupling.

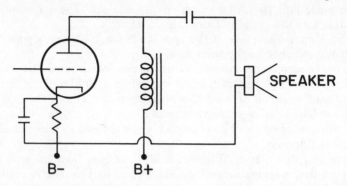

FIG. 9-34. A METHOD OF COUPLING A TUBE TO A LOUDSPEAKER.

PRACTICE QUESTIONS - LESSON 9

1. Which of the following is not a method of obtaining bias?
a. power supply bias   c. cathode bias
b. battery bias   d. capacitor bias

2. What is the cut-off bias in a stage where the tube has a μ of 20, a plate impedance of 4,000 ohms and a plate supply voltage of 180 V?
a. 2.25 V   b. 4.5 V   c. 9 V   d. 36 V

3. Which of the following is not a characteristic of a Class A amplifier stage?
a. high efficiency
b. no grid current drawn
c. average plate current remains constant
d. tube operates over linear portion of Eg-Ip curve

4. An advantage of push-pull operation is:
a. increased power output
b. complete DC core saturation
c. creation of even-harmonic distortion
d. production of regenerative feedback

5. In a Class A amplifier, the grid bias is adjusted for operation over:
a. the non-linear portion of the Eg-Ip curve
b. the bottom of the Eg-Ip curve
c. all over the Eg-Ip curve
d. the linear portion of the Eg-Ip curve

180

6. Harmonic distortion is caused by:
a. operating on the non-linear section of the tube characteristic curve
b. using pentode tubes
c. Class A operation
d. push-pull operation

7. Two tubes, whose plates are connected together and whose grids are connected together, are said to be in:
a. push-pull   c. parallel
b. push-push   d. pull-pull

8. Resistance coupling consists of:
a. two capacitors and a resistor
b. a choke, a capacitor and a resistor
c. two resistors and a capacitor
d. three resistors

9. Removing one of the tubes in a push-pull amplifier stage will:
a. increase the drive requirements
b. increase distortion
c. reduce output power
d. b and c are correct

10. A circuit that applies two equal and opposite signals to a push-pull amplifier is: (3)
a. an auto-transformer   c. an R-C network
b. a phase inverter   d. a low-pass filter

11. One of the advantages of Class B amplification over Class A amplification is:
a. higher power output can be realized
b. high transconductance
c. low interelectrode capacity
d. low plate resistance

12. The fifth harmonic is a frequency which is:
a. one-fifth of the fundamental   c. 20 times the fundamental
b. 10 times the fundamental   d. 5 times the fundamental

13. In a negative feedback audio circuit, the signal fed back is:
a. equal and 180º out of phase with the input signal
b. equal and 90º out of phase with the input signal
c. unequal and 180º out of phase with the input signal
d. unequal and 90º out of phase with the input signal

14. A remedy for motorboating is not:
a. decoupling circuits in B+ leads   c. use low gain tubes
b. adequate filter capacity   d. shielding of input leads

15. An advantage of resistance coupling over transformer coupling is:
a. high gain in coupling components   c. high plate voltage
b. better fidelity   d. more output power

16. Calculate the turns ratio of a transformer that couples a tube with a plate impedance of 5,000 ohms to a load impedance of 100 ohms.
a. 1:50   b. 5:1   c. 50:1   d. 7:1

17. A base boost tone control: (3)
a. increases high audio frequencies
b. increases mid-range audio frequencies
c. decreases high audio frequencies
d. decreases low audio frequencies

18. In a cathode follower, the: (3)
a. output is in phase with the input
b. output impedance is high
c. voltage gain is medium
d. input impedance is low

19. Removing the cathode by-pass capacitor in an audio stage will:
a. increase distortion   c. increase gain
b. decrease distortion   d. none of the above

20. Impedance matching is primarily necessary for:
a. miniaturization of equipment
b. economy of design
c. reduction of harmonic transfer
d. maximum transfer of power

21. Push-pull operation:
a. introduces harmonics into the grid circuit
b. improves the signal strength
c. cancels the third harmonic
d. eliminates the second harmonic in the plate circuit

22. Which of the following is not part of a PM speaker?
a. voice coil   c. spider
b. cone   d. electro-magnetic field

23. One of the advantages of a Class B amplifier over a Class A amplifier is:
a. a higher transconductance
b. lower interelectrode capacity
c. a higher power output can be realized
d. low plate resistance

24. Impedance coupling from a tube to a speaker utilizes:
a. a choke and a capacitor
b. a capacitor, a choke and a resistor
c. two chokes and a capacitor
d. two resistors and a choke

25. An upward fluctuation of Class A amplifier current when signal voltage is applied to the grid indicates:
a. insufficient negative grid bias
b. excessive negative grid bias
c. positive grid bias
d. proper operation

26. Frequency distortion is:
a. delay of harmonic frequencies during amplification
b. harmonic distortion
c. non-linear distortion
d. unequal amplification of the signal frequencies present at the input

27. Improper Class A bias results in:
a. phase distortion   c. distortion of the output waveform
b. improved operation   d. decrease in amplification

28. A downward fluctuation of the Class A amplifier plate current when signal voltage is applied to the grid, indicates:
a. insufficient negative grid bias
b. excessive negative grid bias
c. positive grid bias
d. proper operation

29. One of the advantages of a Class B amplifier over a Class A amplifier is:
a. low efficiency   c. higher operating efficiency
b. high gain   d. low plate voltage

LESSON 10*
TRANSISTORS

It would be advisable at this point to re-read the section on semiconductor diodes in Lesson 6. Note especially the meanings of forward and reverse biasing. Once these concepts are understood, the reader can go on.

3*THE TRANSISTOR. From what we have learned about tubes in a previous lesson, we know that we can make a diode into a triode by adding a new element called the control grid. This single, added electrode makes a tremendous difference, for the triode tube can amplify, whereas the diode cannot.

In a similar manner, semiconductor triodes that amplify can be made from the semiconductor diodes previously described. Fig. 10-1 illustrates a pair of P-N diodes placed back to back. Combining the two diodes gives us the unit shown in Fig. 10-2. Fig. 10-2 is known as a transistor, and is called a P-N-P type. If the two diodes of Fig. 10-1 are turned around, we will have the two N-sections on the outside and the two P-sections joining each other. In this case, the transistor would be an N-P-N type (see Fig. 10-3).

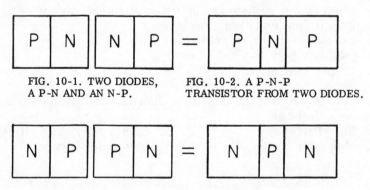

FIG. 10-1. TWO DIODES, A P-N AND AN N-P.

FIG. 10-2. A P-N-P TRANSISTOR FROM TWO DIODES.

FIG. 10-3. AN N-P-N TRANSISTOR FROM TWO DIODES.

The area where the P-type material joins the N-type is called a junction and transistors of this type are called Junction Transistors.

BIASING THE TRANSISTOR. The DC voltages applied to the transistor are called BIAS VOLTAGES. Fig. 10-4 shows the bias voltages on a P-N-P transistor. Note that we have named the three parts of the transistor -- Emitter, Base and Collector. Their vacuum tube equivalents are Cathode, Control Grid and Plate, respectively.

---

*This entire lesson is exclusive to Element 3.

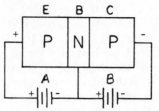

FIG. 10-4. METHOD
OF BIASING A P-N-P
TRANSISTOR.

E stands for Emitter
B stands for Base
C stands for Collector

Forward bias   Reverse bias

Let us consider the voltage on the left hand side P-N section. Battery A makes the emitter positive with respect to the base. We have learned in Lesson 6 that this is forward biased and a current will flow through this section. From our previous discussion, we learned that the right hand side N-P section is reverse biased and very little current flows.

SETTING UP A TRANSISTOR AMPLIFIER. If we examine the battery polarities of Fig. 10-5, we note that section EB is biased in the forward direction. A current will therefore flow from the negative side of the battery, through the E section to the B section, through the meter Ie and back to the positive side of the battery. The B-C diode section, however, has REVERSE BIAS applied to it and therefore, exhibits a high resistance. This causes the current Ic to be very small.

The P-type material forming the center section of the N-P-N transistor is made extremely thin. When we discussed the semi-conductor diode in Lesson 6, the assumption was made that both halves of the diode were equal in size. It was also assumed that the number of available electrons in the N section and the number of holes in the P section were approximately the same. Under these conditions, there were an equal number of majority carriers in each of the two halves to support the explanation of the diode's operation.

Here the case is quite different: the P-section is extremely thin and does not contain as many holes as each of the N-sections have electrons. As electrons move into the B region across the E-B junction, they encounter very few holes with which they can combine. Since few holes are neutral-

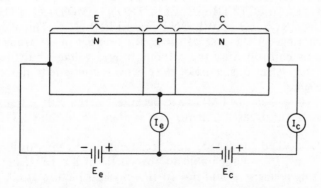

FIG. 10-5. BIAS VOLTAGES IN AN N-P-N TRANSISTOR.

ized, the negative charge produced in the P-type material is quite small. Therefore, the number of free electrons available to return to battery Ee is also correspondingly small. Electrons that enter B from E are now subject to the forces produced by two electric fields: (1) the field produced by battery Ee and (2) the field produced by batteries Ee and Ec connected in series aiding. Since battery Ec is generally of a larger voltage than Ee and, furthermore, since the two batteries in series give rise to a much stronger electric field than Ee alone, most of the electrons follow the electric lines produced by the stronger field, with relatively few taking the path offered by the weaker field. Hence, most of the electrons that enter B from E diffuse across the B-C junction, travel through section C and return through E_c to the positive end of the battery E_e. In Fig. 10-6, this comparative motion of electrons has been illustrated pictorially.

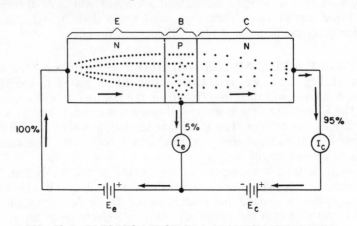

FIG. 10-6. ELECTRON FLOW IN A JUNCTION TRANSISTOR.

About 5% of the electrons that leave battery Ee and enter section E, return to Ee through the meter Ie. The other 95% proceed on through B, into C and return to the batteries through meter Ic. On the other hand, the voltage which governs the electron flow into E from Ee is that of battery Ee.

All of the foregoing leads to this conclusion: THE VOLTAGE BETWEEN E AND B CONTROLS THE TOTAL ELECTRON FLOW, BUT ELEMENT B DOES NOT COLLECT THESE ELECTRONS; MOST OF THE ELECTRONS CONTINUE TO MOVE ON INTO ELEMENT C. This should have a very familiar ring. In the case of tubes, the number of electrons that leave the cathode is controlled by the cathode to grid voltage, but the grid does not collect these electrons; most of the electrons continue to move on to the plate of the tube.

Section E is called the EMITTER because (in the N-P-N transistor) the electrons enter the transistor here, just as they do in the CATHODE of a tube.

Section B is called the BASE, and because it acts as a controlling element of the electrons, it is comparable to the GRID of a tube. Using the name "grid" for this element would not fit the physical picture at all, hence the name "base" was chosen.

186

Section C is called the COLLECTOR because, like the PLATE of a vacuum tube, it receives the "emitted" electrons.

Our discussion thus far has been based on an N-P-N transistor, only because the average reader is more accustomed to reasoning in terms of excess electrons and electron flow, rather than the movement of holes. The explanation of the behavior of a P-N-P transistor is entirely parallel, except that the majority carriers in the body of the semiconductor are holes rather than electrons. Because the carrier charge is reversed, the battery polarities must be reversed. Otherwise, the over-all performance for each is nearly

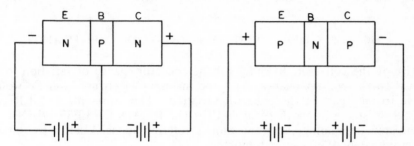

FIG. 10-7. BIAS POLARITIES FOR N-P-N AND P-N-P TRANSISTORS.

identical. The bias polarities for correct operation for both types are shown in Fig. 10-7.

Although transistors are rugged devices from the point of view of vibration and shock, they are affected by high temperatures. It is because of temperature effects that a REVERSAL OF BIAS POLARITIES CAN DESTROY A TRANSISTOR. The heat generated by the excessive collector current at the B-C junction, due to the application of forward rather than reverse bias in this circuit, is responsible for this danger.

HOW A TRANSISTOR AMPLIFIES. The voltage gain of a vacuum tube is defined as the ratio of the signal voltage developed across the load to the signal voltage applied to the input of the tube. The same definition is used for the voltage amplification of a transistor. It is somewhat easier, however, to make an analysis of transistor amplification by considering what takes place across the load resistor or other load impedance when a small change of DC voltage is applied across the input circuit. We might, therefore, set up the equipment shown in Fig. 10-8. Resistor Ri, in the emitter base circuit, permits us to vary the potential applied between these two elements. The output voltage Eo is equal to the collector current, multiplied by the resistance Ro.

Since the emitter is biased in a forward direction, its resistance is low; a typical value for an N-P-N transistor is 350 ohms. The collector-to-base resistance is high due to the reverse bias applied by E_c. This may be in the order of 350,000 ohms.

Due to the combinations and recombinations of electrons and holes in the base region, the variations in the collector current Io are always less than the corresponding variations in the emitter current Ie. This results from the fact that 5% of the electrons that form part of the emitter-base current never

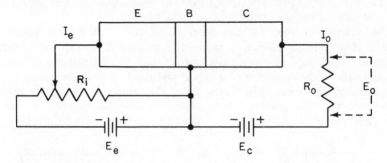

FIG. 10-8. CIRCUIT FOR STUDYING TRANSISTOR AMPLIFICATION.

arrive at the collector. In order for the collector change or variation to be equal to the emitter change, ALL the incoming electrons from Ee would have to take part in the collector variations. This represents a CURRENT LOSS or, stated in another way, a CURRENT GAIN OF LESS THAN 1. In transistor terminology, current gain is referred to as ALPHA (a) and is approximately .95 for most transistors.

To offset this loss however, we have the very substantial difference in input and output resistances – 350 ohms to 350,000 ohms. Since a voltage drop is always proportional to resistance, the higher output resistance indicates a higher voltage across the load. If there were no current loss, the voltage gain due to the higher resistance would be 350,000/350 or about 1,000 times. Since there is a current loss of about 5%, the voltage gain is reduced by this percentage.

Voltage gain = 1000 – (0.05 x 1000) = 950.

We must emphasize that this voltage gain is entirely theoretical. It could be obtained only if Ro were of infinite value, an impossible condition. With typical values of Ro, however, the voltage gain still compares favorably with that of a standard triode tube. It is not uncommon to find transistor circuits which yield actual voltage gains that exceed 20 or 30.

TRANSISTOR PROGRESS. A further extension of the frequency range of transistors has been realized by adding a fourth terminal to an N-P-N junction transistor, as shown in Fig. 10-9. Because of the four connections, this unit is called a JUNCTION TETRODE TRANSISTOR. The assembly resembles a conventional N-P-N junction transistor; the essential difference is the presence of bias battery Eb connected to the second of the base terminals, T2.

Although a rigorous explanation of the tetrode action is complex, no serious error is committed by imagining that the strong electrostatic field within the base section, from top to bottom, forces the flow lines of electrons to confine themselves to the lowermost section of the transistor. In other words, electrons traveling from emitter to collector can no longer pass through all parts of the junction; the electrostatic field drives them downward so that the electron stream is much narrower and more confined. (See Fig. 10-9C).

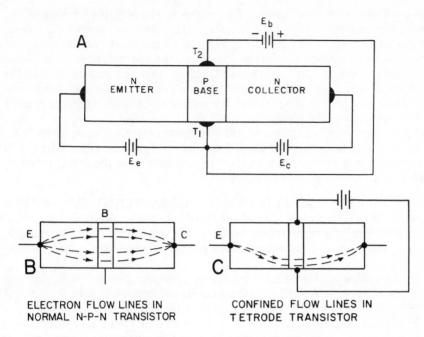

ELECTRON FLOW LINES IN
NORMAL N-P-N TRANSISTOR

CONFINED FLOW LINES IN
TETRODE TRANSISTOR

FIG. 10-9. A TETRODE TRANSISTOR.

This flow-line modification has two important effects, both of which operate to widen the useful frequency range of the transistor. The first is that the collector-to-base capacitance is decreased, reducing the shunting effect of the transistor on the load resistance. As in a vacuum tube, capacitive shunting by the amplifying device works to the detriment of high frequency response, by by-passing these frequencies around the output load. The second effect is that the BASE RESISTANCE of the transistor is reduced. As we shall show later when this transistor characteristic is discussed, a reduction of base resistance encourages improved high-frequency voltage gain.

One additional difference in structure is that the central P region of these units is made much thinner than it is in a standard N-P-N transistor. This permits the current carriers to move across the junctions in less time (the equivalent of shorter transit time in vacuum tubes). With a reduction in transit time, there is an improvement in high-frequency operation.

THE N-P-N AND P-N-P TRANSISTOR. Our discussion has emphasized N-P-N units since such transistor types more closely resemble vacuum-tube triodes than do P-N-P transistors.

If you will examine the P-N-P transistor shown in Fig. 10-7B you will see that the collector is connected to the negative terminal of the reverse bias battery, while the emitter is connected to the positive terminal of the forward bias battery. If you will compare this diagram with that of the N-P-N unit shown in Fig. 10-7A, you will see that the battery connections are exactly opposite. Since we have transposed the battery connections, the current will flow in the opposite direction.

189

In the P-N-P transistor, current flow starts at the negative terminal of the reverse bias battery. From here it goes to the collector, through the base, through the emitter and into the positive terminal of the forward bias battery. A small amount of current, known as base current, flows down from the base and back to the reverse battery. Thus, the main current flow in the P-N-P transistor, is from the collector to the emitter. Since the collector is the current source, it corresponds to the cathode of a tube, while the emitter can be compared to the plate.

In a vacuum tube, electron current can move only from cathode to plate. We have greater flexibility with transistors for we have two types - the N-P-N in which current moves from emitter to collector, and the P-N-P in which current flows from collector to emitter.

INTRODUCTION TO ELECTRICAL CHARACTERISTICS. Tabulation of transistor characteristics is usually divided into three parts:

(1) Absolute maximum characteristics. These generally refer to voltages, currents and temperatures which must not be exceeded under any circumstances.

(2) Average characteristics. This listing generally includes voltages, currents, impedances, temperatures, frequencies, capacitances, gain factors and noise factors which may be anticipated in properly designed equipment.

(3) Typical operation. Many of the quantities tabulated under this heading are repetitions of those found under Average Characteristics; others indicate changes or modifications that must be made in previously listed characteristics for special circuit conditions.

In addition to tabulations, most manufacturers also provide performance curves similar to those that appear in tube manuals.

To properly define and clarify the important terms, each characteristic will be discussed separately, relating it, where necessary, to other important transistor specifications. Unless otherwise stated, we shall be referring at all times to JUNCTION TRANSISTORS.

Before proceeding with a discussion of characteristics, however, it is advisable to mention two other important matters. First, there is the question of transistor symbols. Fig. 10-10 shows the symbols that are used

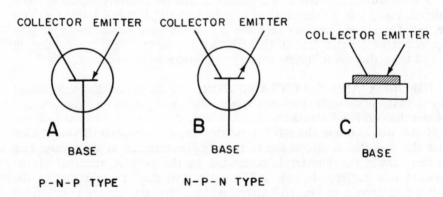

FIG. 10-10. TRANSISTOR SYMBOLS.

to represent transistors. Symbols A and B are more frequently used than C.

Second, there is the matter of transistor circuitry. In the explanatory diagrams previously shown, the base of the transistor was shown as the COMMON element. That is, THE BASE FORMED A PART OF BOTH THE COLLECTOR AND EMITTER CIRCUITS. This is quite similar to the situation encountered in vacuum tube circuits, in which the cathode is common to both the grid and plate circuits. See Fig. 10-11.

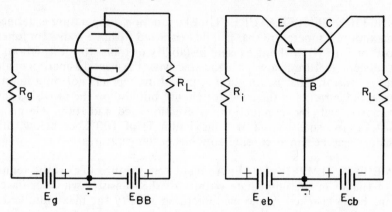

FIG. 10-11. COMMON CATHODE AND COMMON BASE CONNECTIONS.

As you will see, however, it is perfectly possible to make either the emitter or the collector the common element. When either of these is done, the behavior of the transistor alters radically. Hence, it is the usual practice to present figures concerning the performance of the transistor in all three basic connections, unless the unit is designed for specific application in only one of these circuits.

COLLECTOR VOLTAGE Ec. The collector voltage is defined as the DC potential applied between the collector and the base. If no load resistor is present, then Ec is equal to the voltage of the collector battery (Ecb in Fig. 10-11). With a load resistor in the circuit and collector current flowing, then Ec is equal to the battery potential, minus the voltage drop across R_L. Typical maximum collector voltage ratings range from a few volts to 80 volts or more. For P-N-P transistors, the collector voltage is given as a negative value (e.g. Ecb = -20 volts) to indicate that the battery polarity is such as to make the collector negative with respect to the base.

COLLECTOR CURRENT (Ic). The collector current, most often stated in milliamperes, is the current flowing into or out of the collector terminal. Collector current may be measured by inserting a milliammeter between the battery terminal and the load resistor. A typical maximum collector current value might be 20 ma for a transistor using 15 volts of collector potential. As the permissible collector voltage rises, there is an accompanying rise in the current rating. A junction transistor rated at Ecb = 45 volts can pass a current of approximately 40 to 50 ma without overheating.

COLLECTOR DISSIPATION (Pc). Collector dissipation, stated in milliwatts (or watts for power transistors), represents the maximum power that the collector junction can withstand without overheating. This rating is generally given for some specific ambient temperature such as 25°C. Very small transistors can dissipate small magnitudes of power, in the order of only 40 to 50 milliwatts; power transistors are larger in size, with consequent improvements in collector dissipation ratings.

JUNCTION TEMPERATURE (Tj). The junction temperature is defined as the maximum temperature that can be permitted within a transistor junction (N to P or P to N) without causing instability or transistor destruction. The junction temperature is always associated with the heat dissipation qualities of the transistor. That is, junction temperature depends not only upon the voltages and currents in the collector circuit, but also on the provisions made to remove heat by conduction, convection and radiation. Germanium transistors are usually rated at a maximum Tj of 100°C or below; silicon transistors may be run at considerably higher temperatures.

AMBIENT TEMPERATURE. Ambient temperature (Ta) is the temperature of the air in the immediate vicinity of the transistor whose characteristics are being checked. Some manufacturers specify the maximum ambient temperature, as well as the maximum junction temperature. A common maximum ambient temperature is in the order of 50°C.

AVERAGE CHARACTERISTICS. The average characteristics of a transistor specify the anticipated behavior of the unit in a circuit of conventional design, as well as the element voltages and frequencies to be used. The following table lists a few of the average characteristics of a typical junction transistor. The significance of each of these terms will be described in detail.

P-N-P JUNCTION TRANSISTOR
(common base, Tj = 30°C, f = 270 Hz)

Collector voltage	Ecb	-5.0 volts
Emitter current	Ie	1.0 ma
Output impedance	Zo	1.0 megohm
Input impedance	Zi	40.0 ohms
Current amplification	α	0.92
Frequency cutoff	fco	1 MHz

COLLECTOR VOLTAGE (Ecb). This particular transistor is rated at a MAXIMUM collector voltage of −45 volts, but in typical low power applications such as a voltage amplifier, the manufacturer suggests only −5.0 volts for continuous operation.

EMITTER CURRENT (Ie). Here again, although the maximum emitter current for this unit is given as 50 ma, a current of only 1.0 ma is characteristic in low power operation.

OUTPUT IMPEDANCE (Zo). A transistor, like a tube, may be considered

192

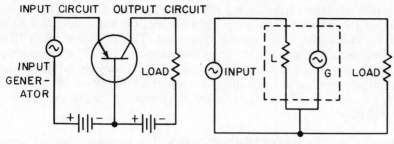

FIG. 10-12. A TRANSISTOR'S IMPEDANCES.

as consisting of two distinct parts: an input section and an output section. See Fig. 10-12. To the input generator, the transistor's input circuit behaves as a LOAD. Relative to the load into which the transistor works, the transistor's output circuit appears as a generator. The LOAD, looking back into the output circuit of the transistor, "sees" a certain "generator" resistance (or impedance, when dealing with AC). It is this apparent "generator" resistance (or impedance) that is referred to as Z_O. As is evident from the average characteristics, the output impedance is quite high -- 1,000,000 ohms. As we have seen, an output impedance of this magnitude results in a large voltage gain.

INPUT IMPEDANCE (Zi). The input impedance is the opposition presented by the input circuit of the transistor to the signal source. Unlike a vacuum tube, the transistor in the common base connection has a very low input impedance. This low impedance, however, considered in conjunction with the high output impedance, is the factor that gives the transistor its large resistance (or impedance) gain. That is, the resistance gain is Zo/Zi - 1,000,000/40 = 25,000. This, in turn, gives us a large voltage gain.

CURRENT AMPLIFICATION (α). Like all junction transistors, this transistor has a current amplification of less than unity. The formula for current amplification is:

$$\text{Current amplification } (\alpha) = \frac{\Delta I_c}{\Delta I_e}$$

where: ΔI_c is the change in collector current due to some small change in emitter current (ΔI_e).

FREQUENCY CUTOFF (fco). The current amplification (α) for the transistor under discussion is given as 0.92. As the heading of the listing indicates, alpha was obtained at a frequency of 270 Hz. for the input signal. Alpha begins to drop as the frequency is raised, an effect due partly to the output capacitance and partly to the transit time required for the movement of the carriers in the transistor. These factors are, in turn, due primarily to the thickness of the base. The thinner the base, the higher is the frequency at which the amplification drops off, and vice versa. We cannot make the base too thin since the collector-to-base voltage must be reduced as the base is made thinner.

193

Transistor engineers have agreed that the frequency at which alpha drops to .707 of its low-frequency value (in this case, the value 0.92 at 270 Hz) should be called the alpha cutoff frequency. This does not mean that a transistor will not operate at frequencies above its cutoff value; it simply indicates the frequency at which the transistor's performance is "down" by a significant amount. In our example, the current amplification of 0.92 at 270 Hz drops to 0.92 x .707, or 0.65, when the operating frequency is raised to 1,000,000 Hz.

AMPLIFICATION WITH TRANSISTORS. The strongest point of similarity between transistors and vacuum tubes is that they can perform identical functions in such circuits as amplifiers and oscillators. Here the similarity ends. Not only are their structures totally different, but their mode of operation and the functioning of their component parts diverge widely from each other. A transistor cannot be substituted directly for a tube in any circuit.

It is a mistake to try to fit vacuum tube ideas into transistor theory to any great extent. Although some of the amplifier and oscillator CIRCUITS are analogous in configuration, the role that the transistor plays should be approached as a brand new concept, rather than as a modification of an old one. In this way, there will be less to be unlearned.

There are three basic CONFIGURATIONS for connecting the elements of a transistor amplifier into its associated circuit: COMMON BASE, COMMON EMITTER and COMMON COLLECTOR. "Common" is sometimes replaced by the word "grounded" in describing these fundamental configurations. In many arrangements having an element common to two or more individual circuits, the common element is also at the system reference potential or "ground" potential. In this usage, "ground" does not imply an actual earthen contact, but rather connection to a terminal whose voltage is used as a reference for all the other voltages in the system.

COMMON-BASE CONNECTION. The common-base arrangement has been discussed in detail earlier in this chapter. From the table of Average Characteristics for a P-N-P junction transistor, the behavior of a common or grounded-base transistor can be summarized as follows: (The same characteristics would apply to an N-P-N transistor of corresponding structure).

(a) High output impedance.

(b) Very low input impedance.

(c) Current amplification (alpha) always less than one.

(d) Output capacitance rather high.

(e) Reasonably high power and voltage gains.

PHASE RELATIONSHIP. The common-base connection does not cause a phase inversion of input to output signal as a vacuum tube amplifier does. Let us see why this is so.

In the common-base transistor circuit of Fig. 10-13, the P-N-P unit is biased in the forward direction (low resistance) by battery E_{eb} and in the reverse direction (high resistance) by E_{cb}. Applying a negative-going half-cycle across R_i is similar to inserting a small cancelling voltage at this instant

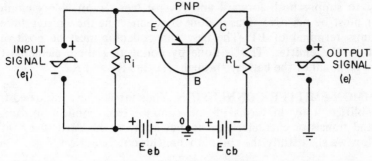

FIG. 10-13. PHASE RELATIONSHIPS IN COMMON BASE TRANSISTOR.

in series with E_{eb}, causing the emitter-base current to decrease. A reduction of emitter-base current leads to a corresponding decrease of collector-base current; hence, the voltage drop across R_L becomes smaller and the collector terminal becomes more NEGATIVE (with respect to the base). Since the input signal goes negative at the same time, the two signals are in phase.

VOLTAGE POLARITY. In tube circuits, the DC voltage applied to the plate is invariably positive. The control grid is made negative with respect to the cathode, or stated differently, the cathode is made positive with respect to the control grid.

However, we have two basic types of transistors, N-P-N and P-N-P, and so a direct comparison between the DC voltages applied to a transistor and those put on tube elements isn't suitable. For a P-N-P transistor, the DC voltage polarities are:

Emitter	positive
Base	negative
Collector	negative

For an N-P-N unit, the polarities are exactly opposite.

Emitter	negative
Base	positive
Collector	positive

If we take the emitter as the reference point, then for a P-N-P transistor, the base and the collector are negative with respect to the emitter. For a N-P-N unit, the base and collector are positive with respect to the emitter.

In Fig. 10-14 we have an N-P-N transistor circuit making use of one

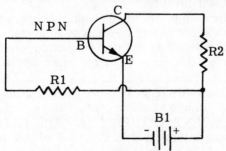

FIG. 10-14. A METHOD OF OBTAINING BIASES FROM A SINGLE BATTERY.

195

battery to supply both forward and reverse bias. In an N-P-N circuit, the emitter must be negative. This is done by connecting the emitter directly to the minus terminal of B1. The base and collector must be positive with respect to the emitter. This is done by connecting these elements to the positive terminal of the battery through resistors R1 and R2.

COMMON-EMITTER CONNECTION. Thus far we have discussed transistor amplifiers only in terms of the common-base connection, and have presented transistor characteristics as they apply to this particular configuration. Now we shall study the common- emitter configuration.

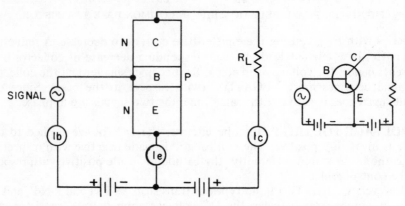

FIG. 10-15. COMMON-BASE AND COMMON-EMITTER CIRCUITS.

This circuit is shown in Fig. 10-15 in both pictorial and schematic form. An N-P-N type is illustrated and it should be noted that THE SAME BATTERY POLARITY IS USED FOR THE COMMON-EMITTER CONNECTION AS FOR THE COMMON-BASE ARRANGEMENT: the base is still positive with respect to the emitter, and the emitter is negative with respect to the collector. (For a P-N-P transistor, these polarities would be reversed). The fact that the emitter has been made common to the other two circuits, does not alter the following fundamental facts:

(1) For a given transistor type, changing the common element does not affect the battery polarity. The emitter-base circuit is still biased in the forward (low resistance) direction and the collector circuit is biased in the reverse (high resistance) direction.

(2) The base current Ib is still the difference between the emitter current Ie and the collector current Ic, and hence, is small in magnitude.

(3) The ratio of collector to emitter current does not depend upon the configuration; that is, this ratio stays the same whether the base or the emitter is common.

The really significant difference between the two arrangements is that the applied signal in the common-emitter configuration of Fig. 10-15 is used to vary the BASE CURRENT RATHER THAN THE EMITTER CURRENT. This means that we are interested in the ratio of ΔIc to ΔIb in this case, rather than ΔIc to ΔIe as we were when considering the current gain of the common-base connection. We can therefore see that the gain of any device is

196

actually a comparison between the size of a certain output variation and the size of the input variation that caused it. For the common-emitter circuit, we can vary the base current Ib by means of the signal and observe how Ic varies. We can then substitute these values in the following formula to arrive at the current gain.

$$\text{Beta (B)} = \frac{\Delta I_c}{\Delta I_b}$$

where: Beta (B) is the common emitter current gain,

ΔI_c is a small change in collector current,

ΔI_b is the small change in beta current that caused ΔI_c.

Beta for junction transistors is MORE THAN 1, ranging as high as 60 or better for many commercial types. We might have anticipated a current gain of this magnitude from the consideration given in (2) of the previous paragraph. Since the base current is VERY SMALL, it would be reasonable to expect a much larger change in collector current as a result of a small variation in I_b caused by a signal input.

COMMON-EMITTER CHARACTERISTICS. One of the best ways to arrive at a clear picture of the performance of any amplifier is to study its characteristic curves. In the common emitter circuit, the collector current Ic depends upon (a) the collector voltage and (b) the controlling base current. When the collector current that flows for various base currents is plotted against collector voltage, we obtain a graphic representation of transistor behavior in the common-emitter configuration. A set of curves for the typical transistor on page 192 is given in Fig. 10-16. The following information can be obtained from these curves:

(1) As the collector voltage is increased, base current being held constant,

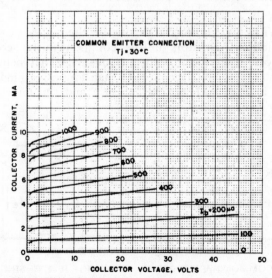

FIG. 10-16. CHARACTERISTIC CURVE FOR A TYPICAL TRANSISTOR.

197

the collector current increases. The increase is much more noticeable for the higher values of base current, as evidenced by their increasing slopes.

(2) Small increases of base current have a much greater effect upon the collector current than do small increments in collector voltage. Consider, for example, the rise of collector current when the base current goes from 400 microamperes to 500 microamperes at a collector voltage of 20 volts. Following the 20 volt line up, we note that it intersects the 400 microampere curve at a collector current of 5.0 ma, and the 500 microampere curve at 6.2 ma. Thus, a change of 100 microamperes (only 0.1 ma) of base current results in a change of 1.2 ma of collector current.

(3) From (2), we can immediately obtain the common-emitter current gain, beta, of this transistor:

$$B = \frac{\Delta I_c}{\Delta I_b} = \frac{1.2}{0.1} = 12$$

This, of course, corroborates what we have previously stated: the current gain (beta) for the common-emitter circuit is greater than 1. For our hypothetical transistor, beta is 12 while alpha is only 0.92. Another way of saying this is: THIS TRANSISTOR HAS A CURRENT GAIN OF 12 IN THE COMMON-EMITTER CONFIGURATION AND A CURRENT GAIN OF 0.92 IN THE COMMON-BASE ARRANGEMENT.

Other consequences of making the emitter the common element are the changes of input impedance, output impedance and power gain. For this transistor, these variations may be seen from the table below:

	Input Impedance	POWER GAIN	Output Impedance
Common-base	40 ohms	28	1,000,000 ohms
Common-emitter	450 ohms	36	60,000 ohms

SINGLE-BATTERY OPERATION. Beside the higher power gains available from junction transistors in the common-emitter connection, this configuration offers another significant advantage that helps explain why one sees more common-emitter circuits than any other kind. In the P-N-P circuit shown in Fig. 10-17A, the collector and emitter currents flow in

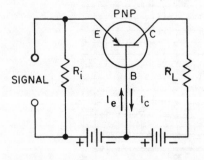

FIG. 10-17A. COMMON BASE CIRCUIT.

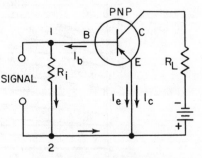

FIG. 10-17B. SINGLE BATTERY OPERATION WITH COMMON EMITTER CIRCUIT.

opposite directions in the base. Although an amplifier using a single battery can be built in common-base configuration, an auxiliary resistor is required whose value is quite dependent upon the particular transistor being used. This makes the selection of the resistor critical. In the common emitter arrangement, on the other hand, the currents in the emitter due to the collector and base, are in the same direction, making a single-battery source practical without biasing resistors (Fig. 10-17B). The battery is connected to provide the correct polarity between the emitter and collector; in this case, negative for the collector and positive for the emitter. Base current flowing through Ri makes point 1 negative with respect to point 2, so that the base is negative with respect to the emitter. This polarity is necessary for correct forward and reverse bias.

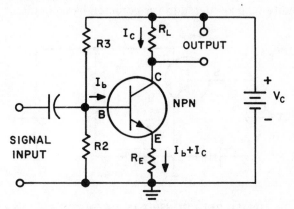

FIG. 10-18. A COMMON EMITTER AMPLIFIER WITH EMITTER BIAS.

Fig. 10-18 illustrates a common emitter amplifier with emitter bias. The bias between the emitter and the base is the difference between the voltage across R2 and the voltage across Re. This is because the polarity of the voltages are opposed to one another. The signal is applied between the base and the emitter. The output is taken from the load resistor R_L.

Resistor R_e is a stabilizing resistor. It contributes to the stability of the circuit by cancelling the temperature effects that tend to make the collector current (I_{co}) build up without limit until the transistor is destroyed. The collector current is temperature sensitive. As the temperature of a junction rises, I_c tends to increase slightly. This increases the dissipation and I_c again rises. The temperature goes up again and the run-away cycle continues until the rating of the junction is exceeded. R_e prevents this action by developing a voltage drop that opposes the increasing collector current. It does so in the following manner: When the collector current rises slightly, the top of R_e becomes more negative (due to the increased voltage drop), making the forward bias of the base-emitter circuit SMALLER. The emitter current and base current both diminish, reducing the tendency of the collector current to "run away".

PHASE RELATIONSHIP IN A COMMON-EMITTER CIRCUIT. The common-emitter configuration differs from the common-base type in

199

another significant way. You will recall that the output signal from a common-base amplifier is in phase with the input signal; that is, there is no phase shift from input to output. Let us see what phase relationships exist in the common-emitter circuit.

Referring to Fig. 10-19 in which a basic P-N-P common-emitter circuit is illustrated, assume that the input signal is POSITIVE-GOING at the instant of examination. The signal, therefore, ADDS to the forward bias, causing an increase in the base current. This causes the collector current to increase, and the voltage drop across RL takes on increased magnitude with the polarity shown. This means that the first half-cycle of output voltage is NEGATIVE-GOING, while the first half-cycle of input voltage is POSITIVE-GOING. Input and output waveforms are out-of-phase by 180°, in contrast with the in-phase condition encountered in the common-base circuit.

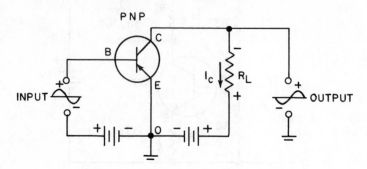

FIG. 10-19. PHASE RELATIONSHIP IN A COMMON EMITTER CIRCUIT.

DIRECT COUPLING. Transistor amplifier stages may be cascaded in the same manner as tube stages. One system of cascading two transistor amplifier stages is to use direct coupling between the stages. Direct coupling means that the output of one stage is directly connected to the input of the next stage. There is no capacitor or transformer to couple the two stages.

Several advantages are gained with direct coupling. All coupling capacitors and their respective input return resistors are eliminated. There is also a gain in the temperature stability due to the fact that a thermally initiated DC change in the second stage can be passed back to the first stage in a direction that tends to cancel the first variation. Direct coupling gives good frequency response because specific attenuating components, such as coupling capacitors, transformers and their distributed capacitors, shunting effect of bias resistor wiring, etc., are not present.

Fig. 10-20 shows an amplifier in which a P-N-P transistor is directly coupled to an N-P-N transistor. The incoming signal is fed to the base of T1 and the amplified output is taken from the collector of T1. It is then fed directly to the base of T2. The output is taken from the collector of T2. The gain of the two stages is greater than that of one transistor with two tuned circuits. It is also very stable. T1 sets the base bias for T2. This is so because the collector current of T1 flows through R1, which is part of the base bias of T2.

200

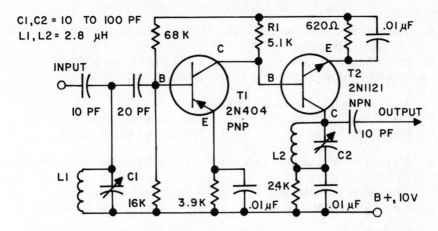

FIG. 10-20. A P-N-P TRANSISTOR DIRECTLY COUPLED TO AN N-P-N TYPE.

THERMISTORS. Another technique that is used to stabilize transistors includes a "THERMISTOR". A thermistor is a component whose resistance varies inversely with temperature. This means that as the temperature goes up, the resistance of the thermistor goes down, and vice versa. Thermistors come in a large variety of shapes, such as washers, rods or disks. They are made of manganèse, nickel oxide and cobalt oxide. Fig. 10-21 shows a transistor circuit using a thermistor. The thermistor symbol is shown as a

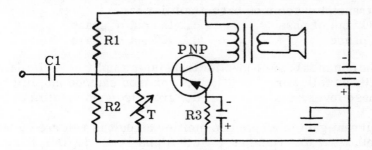

FIG. 10-21. A TRANSISTOR CIRCUIT USING A THERMISTOR.

variable resistor (which it really is). The thermistor is shunted across R2. Since R2 is connected between the base and emitter (the emitter resistor R3 has a very low value), the voltage across R2 determines the forward bias. The thermistor, shunted across R2, is mounted close to the transistor. If the temperature of the transistor should rise, the resistance of the thermistor will decrease. This, in turn, will decrease the resistance between the base and the emitter, thus decreasing the amount of forward bias. The decrease in forward bias will reduce the amount of current flowing between the collector and the emitter.

1. The vacuum tube equivalents of Base, Collector and Emitter, respectively, are:
   a. grid, cathode, plate
   b. cathode, plate, grid
   c. plate, grid, cathode
   d. grid, plate, cathode

2. A common base transistor has a:
   a. low output impedance
   b. high alpha value
   c. low input impedance
   d. low output capacitance

3. A transistor that has two leads connected to its base region is called:
   a. an N-P-N transistor
   b. a P-N-P transistor
   c. a dual base transistor
   d. a junction tetrode transistor

4. A "thermistor" is used to:
   a. keep the temperature around a crystal constant
   b. stabilize a transistor amplifier
   c. aid in voltage regulation
   d. reduce the reverse base-to-emitter current

5. Current gain in a common base circuit is referred to as:
   a. Beta   b. Gamma   c. Alpha   d. Delta

6. The phase relationship between the input and output circuits in a transistor common base amplifier is:
   a. 180⁰ out of phase
   b. in phase
   c. 45⁰ out of phase
   d. 90⁰ out of phase

7. The common base connection transistor amplifier is similar to a:
   a. cathode follower
   b. phase inverter
   c. common cathode amplifier
   d. grounded grid amplifier

8. Current gain in a common emitter circuit is referred to as:
   a. Beta   b. Gamma   c. Alpha   d. Delta

9. The purpose of a stabilizing resistor in a common emitter amplifier circuit is to:
   a. prevent the junction temperature from rising
   b. increase the dissipation capability of the collector
   c. prevent a build-up of collector current
   d. a and c are correct

10. An advantage of direct coupling of transistor stages is not:
    a. eliminate coupling capacitor
    b. improve temperature stability
    c. improve frequency response
    d. improves the gain of each stage

LESSON 11
AUDIO BROADCAST SYSTEMS

BROADCAST AUDIO AMPLIFICATION. The amplification of audio signals can take many forms. A simple two-stage audio amplifier is more than adequate in a small table model broadcast receiver. However, it is not sufficient in a radio broadcast studio. In a small table model receiver, we are not looking for high fidelity; neither are we looking for high power. We have only one signal to amplify and that is the audio signal that is coming in on the carrier that the receiver is tuned to.

The situation is quite different in a broadcast studio. The audio system in a broadcast studio is quite elaborate. The fidelity must be excellent. The amplifier must handle several inputs at one time. A studio generally has several microphones, a tape recorder and a record player, and must receive network programs, as well as other audio signals coming in on telephone lines. The studio must prepare its output audio signal so that it can travel on telephone lines to the transmitter which is generally located some distance from the studio. All these factors call for a rather complicated sound system at the broadcast studio.

In this chapter, we will first study the DECIBEL, which is a common unit used in audio work. Then, a few popular types of microphones will be discussed. The rest of the chapter will be devoted to the audio system used in broadcast studios.

DECIBELS. The decibel (db) is a unit used to express a ratio between two power, current or voltage levels in sound and electrical work. The decibel, as shown by the formula, is a logarithmic unit. This is used because our impression of loudness is proportional to the logarithm of the sound energy and not to the energy itself. For example, if a sound were increased in energy to 1000 times its original value, it would only appear to the ear to be 30 times as loud. In other words, the decibel is a comparison of power levels with respect to our hearing. One decibel is the minimum change in loudness just detectable by the human ear. The formulas for determining power, voltage or current gains or losses are as follows:

$$db = 10 \log \frac{P2}{P1}, \qquad db = 20 \log \frac{E2}{E1}, \qquad db = 20 \log \frac{I2}{I_1}$$

where:

P2, E2 and I2 represent the larger power, voltage and current values respectively.

P1, E1 and I1 represent the smaller power, voltage and current values, respectively.

When the ratio that is expressed in decibels is for an increase in level or gain, it is considered positive. When it is for a decrease in level, or when it is

203

a loss, it is considered negative and is written with a minus sign before the number, such as -24.3 db.

A few examples should clarify the use of the decibel formulas.

EXAMPLE #1. If the power output of the amplifier is decreased from 500 watts to 5 watts, what is the power reduction expressed in decibels?

ANSWER: We use the decibel formula with power in it, and substitute:

$$db = 10 \log \frac{P2}{P1} = 10 \log \frac{500}{5} = 10 \log 100.$$

The logarithm table tells us that the log of 100 is 2. Therefore:

$db = 10 \log 100 = 10 \times 2 = 20.$ The power loss is -20 db.

EXAMPLE #2. An amplifier has a power gain of 30 db. The output power is 12 watts. What is the input power?

ANSWER: We use the power formula and substitute:

$$db = 10 \log \frac{P2}{P1}, \quad 30 = 10 \log \frac{12}{P1}, \text{ dividing both sides by 10}$$

we have $3 = \log \frac{12}{P1}$. Looking at the log table we find that 3 is equal to the log of 1,000. Therefore, if $3 = \log \frac{12}{P1}$ and $3 = \log 1,000$, then $\frac{12}{P1} = 1,000$, $P1 = .012$ watts or 12 milliwatts.

EXAMPLE #3: An amplifier system increases the output of a microphone from 4 millivolts to 4 volts. What is the gain of the amplifier.

ANSWER: We use the formula that includes voltages.

$$db = 20 \log \frac{E2}{E1} = 20 \log \frac{4}{.004} = 20 \log 1000.$$

The log of 1000 (from the log table) is 3.
$db = 20 \times 3 = 60$ db.

THE MICROPHONE. A microphone is a device which converts sound energy into a varying electrical voltage or current. The microphone output signal is impressed on the grid of a voltage amplifier tube, which increases the signal's amplitude. Since there are many types of microphones in use today, a few of the more common ones will be discussed.

THE SINGLE-BUTTON CARBON MICROPHONE. Construction: The single-button carbon microphone consists mainly of a diaphragm and a small compartment filled with carbon granules. The compartment is called a "button". One side of the button is movable and is attached directly to the diaphragm. See Fig. 11-1. A 6-volt battery and the primary of a transformer are in series with the button.

Operation: When sound strikes the diaphragm of the microphone, the diaphragm vibrates at the frequency of the sound. This vibration causes the movable side of the button to move in and out, thereby causing the packing of the carbon granules to vary. This, in turn, causes the resistance of the

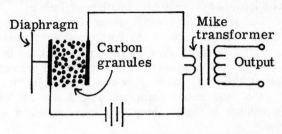

FIG. 11-1. SINGLE-BUTTON CARBON MICROPHONE.

button to vary. The varying resistance will cause the current in the circuit to vary. The result is that an audio current, with the same frequency as the original sound, flows through the primary of the microphone transformer.

Connection: The impedance of the button is about 100 ohms. A microphone transformer is used to match this low impedance to the high impedance of the grid of the first stage.

Frequency response: The single button carbon microphone responds well to audio frequencies between 250 and 2700 Hz. Since many of the tones of musical instruments lie above 2700 Hz, the carbon microphone is suitable only for speech. The general range of speech frequencies is below 2700 Hz.

OTHER CHARACTERISTICS.

(1) The carbon microphone is the most sensitive of all basic microphones in use at the present time. For a given level of sound input, this microphone will generate a higher signal voltage output than any other microphone. Output levels are in the order of −30 db.

(2) The carbon microphone is not directional; it picks up sound impulses equally well from all directions.

(3) The minute variations in the contact resistance of the carbon granules generate an annoying background hiss.

(4) Excessive current, flowing through the carbon granules, or jarring of the microphone while the current is on, will cause the microphone to lose its sensitivity.

THE CRYSTAL MICROPHONE. Construction: The active element in these microphones is a piezo-electric material, usually a Rochelle salt crystal or a ceramic element. Other crystals that may be used are quartz and tourmaline. There are two basic types of piezo-electric microphones:

(1) diaphragm type in which a thin diaphragm is rigidly fixed to one of the major faces of the element.

(2) sound cell type in which a series of elements are excited by sound pressure directly, without the use of a diaphragm.

205

We shall examine the sound cell type of microphone, since it is the most commonly used of the two types of microphones.

Operation: Certain crystals, such as Rochelle salts, develop a potential difference between two surfaces when a mechanical pressure is applied in the proper direction. Sound pressure, applied to a series string of crystals, develops an audio frequency signal across the output of the crystals. Output levels of crystal microphones are approximately −50 db.

Connection: The crystal or ceramic microphone is about the simplest microphone to connect. It requires no battery, since it generates its own potential. The crystal microphone requires no transformer because it has a high impedance (over one megohm) and is, therefore, a perfect match to the high impedance of the grid circuit. However, the cable that connects the microphone to the first audio amplifier should not be long. Since the microphone impedance is high, a long wire can become a source of hum pickup and noise.

Frequency Response: The frequency response of the crystal microphone is from 50 to 10,000 Hz. This is satisfactory for speech reproduction, but not quite satisfactory for high fidelity music.

Other Characteristics:

(1) A crystal microphone should be handled with care because any shock is likely to impair its operation.

(2) It should not be exposed to excessive temperature and humidity changes.

(3) It is used in portable, mobile and fixed station equipment.

(4) A single sound cell type of crystal microphone is not directional; multiple cell types can be designed for directional use.

THE DYNAMIC MICROPHONE. Construction: The dynamic microphone is actually a small electric generator. A small coil attached to a very delicate diaphragm moves in a very strong magnetic field.

Operation: Sound energy moves the diaphragm back and forth. The coil, being attached to the diaphragm, also moves back and forth in the field between the pole pieces of a strong magnet. The windings of the coil cut the magnetic lines of force and generate a very weak electrical signal. The impedance of the coil may be anywhere between 3 ohms and 100 ohms, although it is possible to have somewhat higher impedances.

The diaphragms of some microphones are deliberately stretched in order to make their natural resonant frequencies higher than the audio frequencies. In this way, they will not tend to vibrate on their own and introduce distortion when a particular audio frequency strikes them.

A matching transformer is required because of the dynamic microphone's low impedance. Some dynamic microphones often have matching transformers built right into the microphone case.

All dynamic microphones have low output levels, the average being approximately −50 db.

4 AUDIO BROADCAST SYSTEM. Fig. 11-2 illustrates a block diagram of the basic audio system that is used in broadcast stations. It is by no means complete or accurate in every detail. It is a simplified version of the system

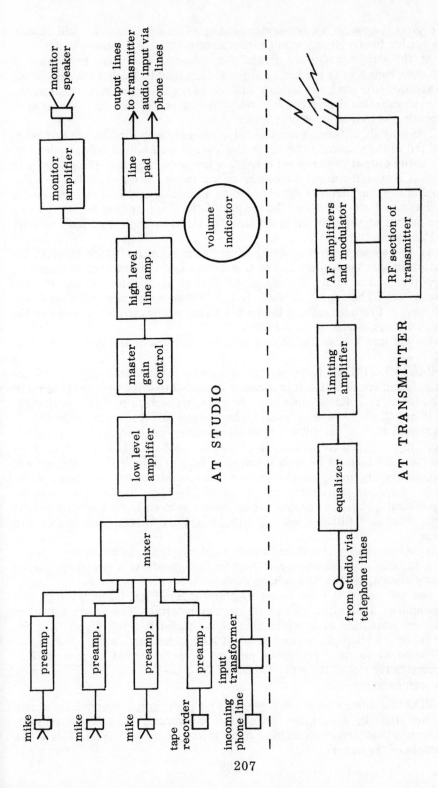

FIG. 11-2. A BASIC BROADCAST AUDIO SYSTEM.

AT STUDIO

mike — preamp.
mike — preamp.
mike — preamp.
tape recorder — preamp.
incoming phone line — input transformer

mixer → low level amplifier → master gain control → high level line amp.

monitor amplifier → monitor speaker

line pad → output lines to transmitter audio input via phone lines

volume indicator

AT TRANSMITTER

from studio via telephone lines → equalizer → limiting amplifier → AF amplifiers and modulator → RF section of transmitter and gives the reader a basic understanding of its operation. We will explain the system briefly; then we will cover the important components in detail.

At the studio, there are several microphones. They may be located in different rooms or in the same room and they may be used at the same time. In addition, the studio contains a tape recorder and a transcription turntable. The studio also has incoming telephone lines to pick up its network programs, as well as other programs.

The outputs of these various sound sources are amplified by pre-amplifiers and fed to the mixer. At the mixer, the level of each output is controlled and the entire output of the mixer is fed to a low level amplifier. The master gain control is able to control the volume of the entire signal and feeds it to a line amplifier. From here the signal is fed to a monitor amplifier and speaker, as well as a volume indicator. The output of the line amplifier is also fed to a line pad which prepares the audio signal to travel through the telephone lines to the transmitter.

At the transmitter, the signal goes to an equalizer which corrects for distortion that takes place in the telephone lines. It is then fed to a limiting amplifier which limits the signal so that it is not too strong for the transmitter. The signal is then fed to other audio amplifiers and the modulator. From here, it modulates the transmitter's carrier and is fed to the transmitting antenna, to be radiated.

We will now discuss the more important sections of the system in detail.

4 **PREAMPLIFIERS**. Most microphones and recorders have very low voltage outputs and considerable amplification is needed to bring their outputs up to the proper level. Rather than use one amplifier section to do the entire job, it is practical to use a preamplifier ahead of the main amplifier. A preamplifier is a carefully designed amplifier of moderate gain that is especially designed to have low hum and low noise levels in its output. Low noise and low hum are important since any hum or noise in the first stage will be considerably amplified to a point where it is intolerable. The preamplifier keeps the noise and hum level down by shielding, use of good quality components, choice of proper tubes, careful soldering and lead dress, short leads, adequate filtering, etc. A separate chassis for the preamplifier also helps.

Sometimes the preamplifier is built right into the head of the microphone so as to build up the audio signal in order to compete with any stray noise or hum picked up by the microphone cable.

You will notice that the incoming phone line in Fig. 11-2 does not go to a preamplifier. Instead, it goes to an input transformer. The reason for this is that the amplitude of the incoming phone signal is much higher than the output of the microphones and does not have to be amplified.

The input to the transformer primary is center-tapped to ground. This eliminates the noise, the stray fields and the cross-talk that are picked up by the telephone lines.

4 **MIXING**. Since several microphones and phonograph turntables are used at one time, it is necessary to control the volume of each one of them separately and then to combine them into one output signal. This is the purpose of the mixer.

There are two types of mixers used; high-level and low-level. In high-level mixing, the outputs of the microphones, etc. are first amplified, then passed on to the mixers to be controlled. This form of mixing is used in Fig. 11-2. In low-level mixing, the outputs of the microphones are first mixed, then amplified. The primary advantage of high-level mixing is that the audio signal is built up before getting to the mixer. The signal is therefore strong enough to overcome the noise that develops when the mixer controls are varied.

Fig. 11-3 illustrates a simple mixing system. It is known as a resistance mixer. Each of the three microphones are applied to separate volume controls and the three volume controls are in series. These volume controls are also known as variable attenuators since they can vary the amplitude of the signals fed to them. The signals are then mixed together. This circuit suffers from the fact that the three controls are not independent of one another. Changing one control will affect the other.

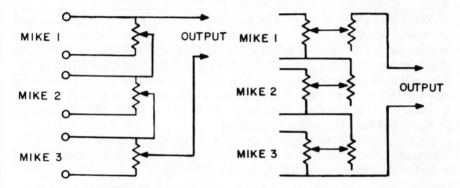

FIG. 11-3. A SIMPLE MIXING SYSTEM.   FIG. 11-4. A CONSTANT IMPEDANCE
MIXING SYSTEM.

Fig. 11-4 is a considerable improvement over Fig. 11-3. Each of the three circuits are more independent of each other than they are in Fig. 11-3. Also, the input and output impedances of the control units are kept constant. Sliding the potentiometer arms does not affect the input and output impedances. It is extremely important, in audio work, to keep the input and output impedances as constant as possible. This allows for the maximum transfer of energy and minimum distortion.

Some of the requirements for proper mixing are:
(1) Insertion loss of the mixer must be low.
(2) The impedances presented to each microphone and to the amplifier must not vary, regardless of the position of the mixer controls.
(3) The input impedances of the mixer must equal the output impedances of the microphones and the output impedance of the mixer must be equal to the input impedance of the amplifier.
(4) The action of the controls must not affect each other.
(5) There must be minimum noise from the mixer controls.

4 **AUDIO AMPLIFIERS**. The amplifiers must bring the output of the

program signal up to a level where it can be carried by telephone lines to the transmitter. This level is limited by the telephone company to 0 db (0.006 watts) because a strong signal can cause "cross-talk". Cross-talk is signal leakage from one line to another through the inductance or capacitance between the lines.

In order to operate the monitor speakers, a separate monitor amplifier increases the output of the line amplifier to at least 20 db. The purpose of the monitor speaker is to listen to the program that is being sent out.

Instead of having one large amplifier, the main studio amplifier of Fig. 11-2 is broken up into a low level amplifier and a line amplifier. One large amplifier would be very unstable. The slightest amount of feedback would result in oscillation.

The two amplifiers should have separate power supplies to prevent feedback via the power supply. If a common power supply must be used, adequate filtering and decoupling circuits should be used.

4 VOLUME INDICATOR. The broadcast and telephone industries have adapted a standard meter as a volume indicator and a standard unit as a volume unit. The meter is called a VU METER or VOLUME UNIT METER. The standard unit that has been decided upon is the VOLUME UNIT or VU. The meter is calibrated in VU's. The reference level of 0 VU is indicated when a .001 watt signal is delivered to a 600 ohm load. 600 ohms is chosen because it is the standard impedance value used in the studio for network lines, output lines and audio equipment.

Fig. 11-5 illustrates a VU meter. The meter is calibrated so that 0 VU represents 100% modulation. The top scale shows the percentage of modulation. The bottom scale shows the VU units.

For % modulation, scale is
made larger than VU scale.
Reading shown is 85% mod.

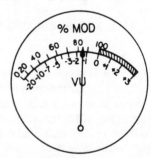

FIG. 11-5. A
VU METER.

The actual meter uses a DC movement and a copper oxide rectifier. It reads the RMS value of the signal. An isolation pad and special attenuators are placed ahead of the meter to prevent it from overloading the line and to give it flexibility in calibration.

4 LINE PADS AND ATTENUATORS. The line pad in the block diagram of Fig. 11-2 is used to reduce the output of the line amplifier to the proper level for transmission over the telephone line. The line pad also isolates the line from the line amplifier while maintaining the correct impedance between the amplifier and the line. Any changes taking place in the line will not be reflected back into the amplifier to affect its operation.

Three basic types of pads are the "L" pad, the "T" pad and the "H" pad.

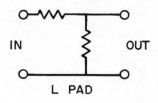

FIG. 11-6. BASIC FORMS
OF ATTENUATOR PADS.

These are shown in Fig. 11-6. These pads are actually attenuator networks. They reduce power or signal strength while maintaining the proper impedance match. This can be seen by examining Fig. 11-7. Fig. 11-7A represents a variable attenuator. It is a volume control. The three control arms are ganged together on a common shaft. As we turn the shaft in one direction, R1 and R2 decrease while R3 increases. This increases the output. As we turn the shaft or knob in the other direction, R1 and R2 increase while R3 decreases. This reduces the output. However, if the correct values of resistance are chosen, the impedance that the input and output circuits "see", will remain substantially the same.

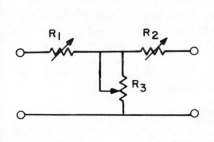

FIG. 11-7A. VARIABLE T PAD.   FIG. 11-7B. H PAD.

Fig. 11-7B shows an H pad with values that will maintain a 600 ohm impedance match, while at the same time attenuating a signal. Fig. 11-7B can be redrawn, as shown in Fig. 11-8. Fig. 11-8 shows what the input "sees". R2 and R5 are in series with the output Z. They equal 800 ohms. This 800 ohms is in parallel with R3 and the parallel circuit is equal to 400 ohms. The 400 ohms is in series with R1 and R4. The entire combination is equal to 600 ohms.

Thus, the 600 ohm input circuit "sees" 600 ohms. By the same reasoning, the 600 ohm output also sees 600 ohms. The impedances are therefore matched and attenuation will take place without introducing distortion, cross-talk, feedback, etc.

211

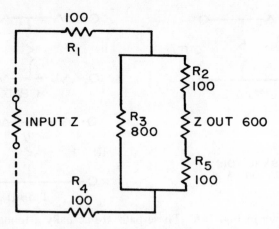

FIG. 11-8. H-PAD REDRAWN.

4 EQUALIZERS. A line equalizer is a high-pass filter that is used to compensate for the loss of high frequencies in an audio transmission line. A line equalizer is especially useful when a long telephone line is used to carry an audio program from the studio to the transmitter.

Since a line has distributed capacity, the higher audio frequencies will be shunted and therefore lost. The line equalizer deliberately reduces the low audio frequencies to the same extent that the higher frequencies are lost. This results in a "flat" over-all response.

The line equalizer can be placed at any point in the audio program line. However, it is good practice to insert it at the point where the line enters the transmitter's audio equipment. At this point, it is easy to adjust the equalizer, if necessary. (See Fig. 11-2.)

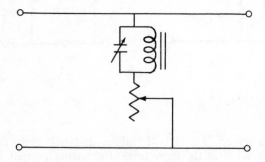

FIG. 11-9. A LINE EQUALIZER.

Fig. 11-9 shows a typical line equalizer. It consists of a parallel resonant circuit in series with a variable resistor. The parallel resonant circuit is resonant to approximately 5000 Hertz. High frequency audio signals (5000 Hz) will develop strong voltages across this circuit. At the lower frequencies, the circuit will not be resonant. The lower frequencies will be shunted or attenuated and will not be passed on. The variable resistor controls the amount of attenuation that takes place.

212

4 LIMITING AMPLIFIERS. A limiting amplifier is an amplifier whose output cannot be increased over a certain maximum value. A limiting amplifier is used in the audio section of a broadcast transmitter. (See Fig. 11-2). It limits the audio to a value that will not cause overmodulation with its subsequent distortion and interference. Since the limiter is an automatic device that prevents overmodulation, we can use a higher level of audio (just short of overmodulating) and thereby obtain a higher percentage of modulation than we could without a limiting amplifier. The subject of modulation will be fully discussed in Lesson 14.

There are many circuits that can be used for audio limiting purposes. In some of these circuits, a part of the output of an audio stage is rectified and fed back as additional bias to an earlier stage. If the audio signal should suddenly rise, an increased bias is fed back and the overall gain is reduced, thereby limiting or counter-acting the original rise.

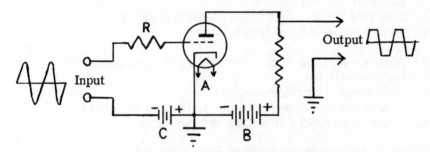

FIG. 11-10. A BASIC PEAK LIMITER.

Fig. 11-10 shows a simple basic method of limiting or clipping the peaks of a signal. The negative peaks are clipped because the grid is driven strongly negative and the plate current is cut off. During the positive peaks, grid current flows, creating a voltage drop across R which subtracts from the signal voltage applied to the grid. This effectively chops or limits the positive peaks.

Peak limiting amplifiers are similar in operation and usage to the limiting amplifiers described above. We reserve the term PEAK-limiting to those amplifiers that remove the strong audio peaks from the audio signal and prevent them from overmodulating the RF signal.

PRACTICE QUESTIONS - LESSON 11

1. What is the gain of an amplifier that delivers 10 volts at its output with 1 millivolt applied to its input?
a. 6 db   b. 8 db   c. 80 db   d. 60 db

2. Which of the following microphones has a coil of wire that moves in a magnetic field?
a. a ribbon microphone   c. a capacitor microphone
b. a velocity microphone   d. a dynamic microphone

213

3. In order to improve the fidelity of an amplifier, we sometimes introduce:
a. an H-pad attenuator   c. a neutralizing capacitor
b. a T-pad attenuator   d. degenerative feedback

4. Which of the following is used to express a ratio between two power levels in an audio system?
a. volume unit   b. H-pad   c. watt   d. decibel

5. Which of the following is not a form of attenuator pad? (4)
a. "H"   b. "T"   c. "L"   d. "P"

6. A microphone:
a. amplifies a sound
b. converts electricity
c. converts sound energy into electrical energy
d. amplifies electrical frequencies

7. A characteristic of the carbon button microphone is:
a. high sensitivity
b. wide frequency response
c. can be applied directly to the grid of an amplifier
d. non-sensitivity to vibration and handling

8. An audio preamplifier does not have: (4)
a. low hum   c. low noise
b. high gain   d. moderate gain

9. What is the power applied to the input of an amplifier having a power gain of 10 db if the output is 6 watts?
a. 60 mw   b. 600 mw   c. 100 mw   d. 20 mw

10. Which of the following is not correct in a mixer circuit? (4)
a. low insertion loss
b. values of controls must be equal
c. action of controls must not affect each other
d. impedances of input and output must be equal

11. A crystal microphone:
a. has a low impedance
b. requires a transformer
c. depends on the piezo-electric effect
d. requires a built-in amplifier

12. A line equalizer is used to: (4)
a. increase the frequency response of a transmission line
b. match the impedance of the microphone to the transmission line
c. flatten the frequency response of the transmission line
d. match the impedance of the transmission line to the transmitter

13. What is the formula for determining the db voltage gain in a circuit?

   a. $\log 20\dfrac{P2}{P1}$ b. $\log 10\dfrac{E2}{E1}$ c. $10\log\dfrac{P2}{P1}$ d. $20\log\dfrac{E2}{E1}$

14. Signal leakage from one line to another is called: (4)
   a. capacitive coupling   c. insertion loss
   b. inductive coupling   d. cross-talk

15. What unit has been adapted as a volume unit, equal to 1 milli-watt at 600 ohms? (4)
   a. volume unit   c. power factor
   b. decibel   d. dynamic unit

16. Preamplifiers are used ahead of mixers in order to: (4)
   a. reduce noise
   b. improve signal-to-noise ratio
   c. amplify telephone line signals
   d. equalize audio frequencies

17. The purpose of a line pad is not to: (4)
   a. maintain correct impedance
   b. prevent line losses
   c. isolate the amplifier from the line
   d. prevent line changes from getting into amplifier

18. A limiting amplifier will not: (4)
   a. prevent overmodulation   c. prevent interference
   b. prevent motorboating   d. improve modulation percentage

19. What value has been chosen as the standard reference imped-ance for network lines and audio equipment? (4)
   a. 72 ohms   b. 300 ohms   c. 400 ohms   d. 600 ohms

LESSON 12
OSCILLATORS

INTRODUCTION TO TRANSMISSION AND RECEPTION. The first eleven lessons of this course were devoted to the study of vacuum tubes, fundamental radio theory and basic circuits. These lessons contain the background material for our discussion of transmitters and receivers. However, before we go into a detailed study of actual transmitter circuits, we will take a bird's eye view of a complete communications system.

Fig. 12-1A illustrates a block diagram of a radio-telephone transmitter. The heart of the transmitter is the oscillator. Its sole purpose is to generate a high frequency AC or RF, as it is commonly called. The RF is fed to an amplifier where it is amplified. The output of the RF amplifier is then fed to an RF power amplifier which amplifies the RF in terms of power.

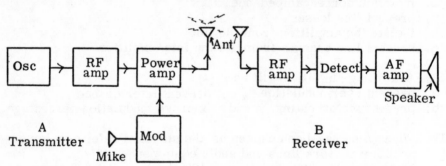

FIG. 12-1. RADIO TRANSMITTER AND RECEIVER.

The microphone's function is to convert sound energy into electrical energy. The output of the microphone is applied to the modulator, which is simply an audio amplifier. The modulator serves two functions: (1) it amplifies the weak audio output of the microphone and (2) it superimposes the audio on to the radio frequency energy that is present at the power amplifier. The audio is combined with the RF wave because an audio wave by itself is not capable of traveling through space. High frequency, such as RF, however, is capable of traveling through space. Therefore, the RF acts as the "carrier" for the audio. The combined audio RF output of the power amplifier is fed to the antenna where it is radiated out into space in the form of electromagnetic waves.

At the receiving end of the communications system, the electromagnetic waves induce small voltages into the receiving antenna. These signal voltages are quite weak because the electromagnetic waves have traveled some distance before striking the receiving antenna. Therefore, the signal voltages must be amplified; this is the function of the RF amplifier. The output of this stage is applied to the detector. Just as the oscillator is the heart of the transmitter, the detector is the heart of the receiver. The detector stage separates the audio from the RF carrier. The carrier has served its purpose in bringing the audio to the receiver. Now, all we are interested in, is the audio. The audio output of the detector is then fed to an audio amplifier stage to be amplified. The amplified audio is applied to a speaker which converts the audio back into the original sound that energized the microphone at the transmitter.

Thus, we have briefly described the overall picture of a communications system. The remaining lessons will go into the details of each stage of this system. We will first consider the oscillator of the transmitter.

OSCILLATORS. An oscillator is an electronic alternating current generator, a device used to generate AC of any desired frequency. All transmitters, and practically all receivers, use oscillators. Oscillators are also employed in various types of test equipment.

Several types of oscillator circuits have been developed because of the different demands of the electronic devices employing them. However, most of the oscillators operate on the same fundamental principles.

THE OSCILLATING TUNED CIRCUIT. The heart of an oscillator is a TUNED CIRCUIT consisting of a coil and capacitor in parallel. In order to understand how an oscillator works, it is necessary to understand how a simple tuned circuit, such as the one shown in Fig. 12-2, can produce AC

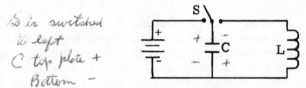

S is switched
to left
C top plate +
Bottom −

FIG. 12-2. AN ELEMENTARY OSCILLATOR.

oscillations. When switch S is thrown to the left, the capacitor, C, is placed across the battery and becomes charged. The upper plate of C becomes positively charged and the lower plate negatively charged. Electrical energy is stored up on the plates of the capacitor. When the switch is thrown to the right, the capacitor discharges through coil L. The electrons flow from the lower plate of C, through the coil and back to the upper plate of C. The flow of electrons through the coil builds up a magnetic field around the coil. The energy which was stored in the capacitor has now been transferred to the magnetic field surrounding the coil. When the capacitor has completely discharged, the electron flow through L ceases, causing the magnetic field to collapse. The collapsing magnetic field, however, induces a voltage of opposite polarity across L so that it maintains a flow of electrons to the upper plate of the capacitor. This occurs because an induced e.m.f. acts to prevent a change in the flow of current (Lenz's Law). The flow of electrons to the upper plate of C continues until the magnetic field has completely collapsed. The capacitor has now become charged again, with its top plate

217

negative and its bottom plate positive. The energy of the magnetic field has been transferred to the capacitor and is retained as a stored charge. The capacitor is now charged with a polarity opposite to its original charge. The capacitor again discharges through L and the entire action, as outlined above, repeats itself.

Thus we see that the current OSCILLATES back and forth between the coil and the capacitor. The alternating current in the tuned circuit produces an alternating voltage across the tuned circuit. The frequency of this AC voltage is determined by the values of L and C.

THE DAMPED AND UNDAMPED WAVE. If there were no resistance in either the coil or the capacitor, there would be no energy loss. The oscillations would continue forever at a constant amplitude. A graph, illustrating this condition, is shown in Fig. 12-3A. The wave is called an

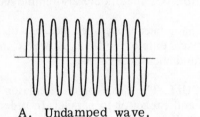

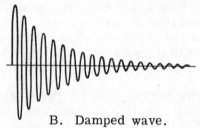

A. Undamped wave.   B. Damped wave.

FIG. 12-3. OSCILLATIONS.

UNDAMPED WAVE. However, such a situation is impossible in actual practice. Some resistance is always present in radio components, especially in a coil. This resistance causes some of the energy (which oscillates back and forth in the tuned circuit) to be transformed into heat. The heat, of course, is a loss of energy. Therefore, with each succeeding cycle, the amplitude of the oscillating voltage decreases until all of the energy has been dissipated in the form of heat. Fig. 12-3B illustrates the diminishing oscillations. We call this a DAMPED WAVE.

CONDITION FOR OSCILLATION. The function of an oscillator is to produce AC at a constant amplitude, just like the undamped wave of Fig. 12-3A. If the oscillations are to continue at a constant amplitude, we must make up for the energy losses that occur in the L-C circuit, due to resistance. Electrical energy must be injected back into the L-C circuit. In an oscillator circuit, an amplifier is used in conjuction with the L-C circuit to generate an undamped signal.

When a vacuum tube is hooked up as an amplifier, the AC energy developed in the plate circuit is much greater than that applied to the grid circuit. If the oscillating circuit of Fig. 12-2 is connected to the grid circuit of a vacuum tube, an amplified version of the oscillating voltage would appear in the plate circuit. If we could, somehow, continuously feed back some of the energy from the plate circuit to the grid circuit to compensate for the resistance losses in the L-C grid circuit, undamped oscillations would continue. A simple method of doing this is shown in Fig. 12-4. L1 and C1 represent the tuned circuit, sometimes called the TANK CIRCUIT. Fig. 12-4A is a triode tube circuit. The same circuit using a transistor is shown in Fig. 12-4B. Lp is a coil of wire wound on the same form and placed next to L1. Since Lp is in the output circuit, it is easy to see that some of the amplified energy from the plate or collector circuit is fed back to the grid or base circuit through the magnetic coupling between the two coils. If this energy can overcome the losses in the tank circuit, oscillations will be maintained.

The circuit of Fig. 12-4 is known as the TUNED GRID OSCILLATOR, TICKLER COIL OSCILLATOR, or the ARMSTRONG OSCILLATOR. We shall now discuss, in more detail, the operation of this oscillator.

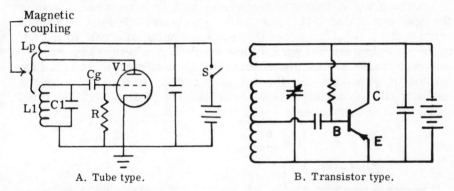

A. Tube type. B. Transistor type.

FIG. 12-4. TICKLER-COIL OSCILLATOR OR ARMSTRONG OSCILLATOR.

OPERATION OF AN OSCILLATOR. As soon as switch S is closed, a surge of current flows through Lp. This surging current builds up an expanding magnetic field around Lp which cuts L1 and induces a voltage in L1. The induced e.m.f. charges the capacitor of the tuned circuit. The capacitor then discharges through L1 and the oscillatory action, previously described, begins. The losses in the tank circuit are overcome by feedback of energy from the plate and collector circuits to the grid and base circuits by magnetic coupling between Lp and L1. In this manner, the oscillations of the tuned circuit are maintained at a constant amplitude.

Lp, called the TICKLER COIL, must be wound in such a direction so that an expanding field about it induces a voltage in L1, which causes the grid to go positive. A positive grid will cause the plate current, and the field around Lp, to further increase and induce energy back into L1. The process of transferring energy from Lp of the plate circuit, to L1 of the grid circuit, is called INDUCTIVE FEEDBACK or MAGNETIC FEEDBACK. Since the energy fed back to the tuned circuit is sufficient to make up for the energy lost in the resistance of the tank circuit, the oscillations will continue and will not die out. If the tickler coil is wound in such a direction so as to make the grid negative, the oscillator will NOT start oscillating at all.

From the above explanation, we realize that the transistor or the vacuum tube does not oscillate. The oscillations actually take place in the tuned circuit. The triode simply functions as an electrical valve which automatic-

219

ally controls the release of energy back into the tuned circuit. The feedback energy overcomes the circuit losses and maintains oscillation.

The frequency of the oscillator's output is equal to the resonant frequency of the tuned circuit, and can be found by using the formula for a resonant circuit (see formula (4-36) in Lesson 4).

In order to vary the frequency of the oscillator, it is necessary to vary the value of the inductance or capacitance.

FEEDBACK. It is not necessary to feed back energy continuously during the entire cycle of oscillation. The tank circuit has electrical inertia and will oscillate properly if it receives energy during only a small portion of the AC cycle.

Since it is not necessary to feed energy back from the output circuit to the input circuit during the entire cycle, plate current need not flow for the entire cycle. It is sufficient to feed back small pulses of energy to the tank circuit. If output current were to flow for the entire cycle, there would be too much feedback. Also, the efficiency of the oscillator would be reduced because of an unnecessary flow of plate current. In a properly designed oscillator, the plate current flows for about 1/4 of a cycle (90°). This is similar to Class C operation.

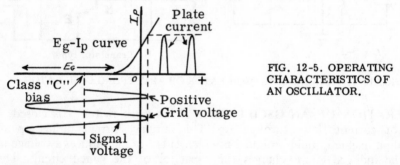

FIG. 12-5. OPERATING CHARACTERISTICS OF AN OSCILLATOR.

Fig. 12-5 shows the operating characteristics of a vacuum-tube oscillator. Waveforms for a transistor oscillator are similar to those shown. The bias is such that only the peaks of the oscillations bring the tube out of cut-off and cause current to flow.

GRID-LEAK BIAS. Efficient operation of an oscillator requires that it have a high cutoff bias. There are several ways of obtaining this large bias. One way is from a battery; another is by means of a negative voltage power supply. However, in the case of a vacuum tube oscillator, a practical way of obtaining this high cutoff bias is by using a resistor and capacitor connected in the grid circuit, as shown in Fig. 12-6. This is called GRID-LEAK BIAS, and is used in all oscillators. A simple explanation of grid-leak bias is as follows:

When the peaks of the oscillations in the tank circuit of Fig. 12-5 drive the grid positive with respect to the cathode, grid current flows in the circuit. The grid current flow charges up capacitor C_g, as shown in Fig. 12-6A. During the remainder of the cycle, the grid does not conduct and the capacitor discharges through R, as shown in Fig. 12-6B. Current flowing

220

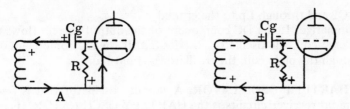

FIG. 12-6. GRID-LEAK BIAS.

through R produces a voltage drop that makes the grid side of R negative with respect to the cathode side. This voltage drop is the grid-leak bias voltage. The grid-leak bias is high and causes plate current to flow only during the positive peaks of the oscillations. Since the plate current flows for only a small part of a cycle, the average power wasted inside the tube is reduced, and the efficiency of the oscillator is increased.

One way of determining whether the circuit is oscillating is to measure the grid-leak bias voltage. If the circuit is not oscillating, there will not be any bias voltage present. If the circuit is oscillating, a voltage will be present. A high impedance voltmeter (preferably a vacuum tube voltmeter) should be used. A low impedance voltmeter might affect the circuit to the point where it ceases oscillating.

SERIES-FED AND PARALLEL-FED OCILLATORS. Fig. 12-4 is a schematic of a series-fed Armstrong oscillator. It is called a SERIES-FED OSCILLATOR because the DC plate current flows through the plate coil, Lp. In some cases, it is desirable to arrange the circuit so that the DC component of the plate current does not flow through the plate coil. This is shown in Fig. 12-7. In this circuit, capacitor C2 blocks DC from flowing through Lp. Only the AC component of the plate current flows through C2 and Lp. The oscillator of Fig. 12-7 is known as a PARALLEL-FED or

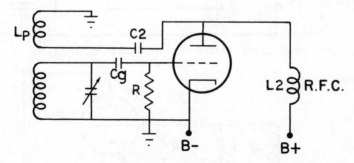

FIG. 12-7. A SHUNT-FED ARMSTRONG OSCILLATOR

SHUNT-FED OSCILLATOR. The coil labeled RFC (L2) is a radio frequency choke. It is designed to have a high impedance to RF. The purpose of the radio frequency choke is to prevent the RF currents from flowing to the power supply. Because the RF currents are blocked by L2, they flow

221

through C2 and through Lp to the ground.

To summarize: If the DC component of the output current flows through the feedback coil, the oscillator is series-fed. If the DC component does not flow through the plate coil, the oscillator is shunt-fed.

THE HARTLEY OSCILLATOR. A popular oscillator that is frequently used in radio receiver circuits is the HARTLEY OSCILLATOR. Its principle of operation is very similar to that of the Armstrong oscillator. Instead of having separate plate and grid coils, the Hartley oscillator has a single coil which is tapped. The Hartley oscillator (Fig. 12-8) can always be recognized by its tapped coil. One part of the coil, (Lp), is in the plate circuit and the other part, (Lg), is in the grid circuit. Capacitor, C, is across the entire coil. The resonant frequency of this oscillator is determined by C and Lg and Lp in series. You will recall that in the Armstrong oscillator, energy is fed back by the inductive coupling between the tickler coil and the grid coil. The feedback in the Hartley oscillator is also due to inductive coupling (between Lp and Lg). The amount of feedback can be controlled by varying the position of the tap on the coil.

Fig. 12-8A shows a series-fed Hartley oscillator, while Fig. 12-8B illustrates a shunt-fed Hartley oscillator. The purpose of the RF choke in Fig. 12-8B is to keep RF out of the power supply.

Note that grid leak resistor R in Fig. 12-8A is across Cg instead of between the grid and cathode as in Fig. 12-7. This does not change the operation of the grid leak bias. It operates in the same manner as was previously discussed and it is simply a designer's choice as to which method of grid leak bias should be used.

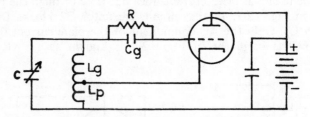

FIG. 12-8A. SERIES-FED HARTLEY OSCILLATOR.

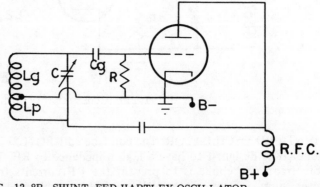

FIG. 12-8B. SHUNT-FED HARTLEY OSCILLATOR.

222

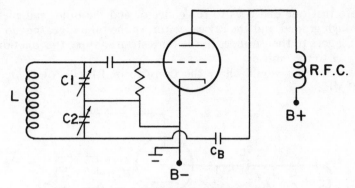

FIG. 12-9. COLPITTS OSCILLATOR.

THE COLPITTS OSCILLATOR. Fig. 12-9 illustrates a COLPITTS OS-CILLATOR. The only difference between the Colpitts oscillator and the Hartley oscillator is that the Colpitts oscillator has a split tank capacitor, whereas the Hartley oscillator has a split tank coil. Capacitor C2 is in the plate circuit and C1 is in the grid circuit. Energy is fed back from the plate circuit to the grid circuit by capacitive coupling between capacitors C2 and C1. This type of feedback is called CAPACITIVE FEEDBACK. The amount of feedback is controlled by varying the ratio of capacitance between the two capacitors. The frequency of this oscillator can be changed by varying the amount of inductance in coil L, or by changing the total capacitance of the series combination of C1 and C2. When both capacitors are made variable, they are usually ganged.

Fig. 12-10 illustrates a TRANSISTORIZED COLPITTS OSCILLATOR. It operates in a manner similar to that of the tube type of Colpitts oscillator. The output of the oscillator is taken from tank circuit C1L1. C2 and C3 form the split capacitor arrangement that accomplishes feedback. The 1K resistor is the emitter bias and the combination of the 47K and 4.7K resistors represents the base bias.

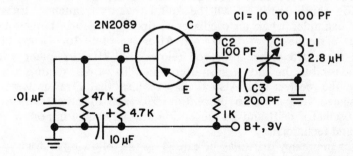

FIG. 12-10. A TRANSISTORIZED COLPITTS-TYPE OSCILLATOR.

Note the circuit similarity between the transistorized version and the tube version of the Colpitts oscillator. One end of the tuned circuit of the tube type goes to the plate. The other end goes to the grid. In the transistorized

223

type, note that one end goes to the collector and the other end goes to the base through ground and the .01 capacitor. In the tube type, the junction of C1 and C2 goes to the cathode. In the transistorized type, the junction of C2 and C3 goes to the emitter.

The values given would allow the transistorized oscillator to operate at about 10 MHz.

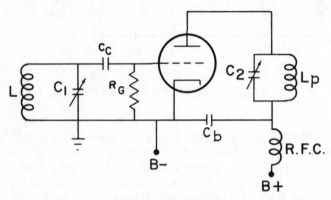

FIG. 12-11. A TUNED-PLATE TUNED-GRID SERIES FED OSCILLATOR.

TUNED PLATE - TUNED GRID OSCILLATOR. Fig. 12-11 is the circuit of a series-fed, TUNED PLATE - TUNED GRID OSCILLATOR, with the plate and grid circuits tuned separately. The plate coil, Lp, and the grid coil, L, are not magnetically coupled to each other. Energy is transferred from the plate circuit to the grid circuit through the internal grid-to-plate capacitance of the triode. Since the plate and grid, in effect, are two conductors separated by an insulator (dielectric), we have a "capacitor" existing between the grid and plate. This capacitance is known as the grid-to-plate interelectrode capacitance (Cg-p). Both the plate and grid circuits are tuned to approximately the same frequency.

FREQUENCY STABILITY OF OSCILLATORS. If an oscillator remains in operation continuously, it will be found that its frequency drifts with time. For example, when an oscillator is first turned on, it may start to oscillate at a frequency of 1000 kHz. After the oscillator warms up, the frequency may drift either above or below 1000 kHz. Frequency drift is highly undesirable in any transmitter since it would require constant retuning at the receiver end. Also, the law requires that a transmitter remain on its assigned frequency to prevent interference to other stations. The causes of oscillator drift and its prevention are subjects of importance to all engineers and technicians.

Oscillator frequency drift may be caused by the following factors:

(1) Improper design of the oscillator current. Choosing the wrong combination of L and C for the tank circuit.

(2) Poor voltage regulation of the oscillator power supply. Changes in B+ voltage will cause voltage variations at the screen and plate. This will vary the oscillator frequency.

224

(3) Changes in plate resistance and interelectrode capacitance of a tube will cause the frequency to vary.

(4) Changes in temperature will cause the inductance and capacitance of the tank circuit to vary. A physical change in either L or C will change the oscillating frequency.

(5) Changes in loading of the oscillator. If the output of the oscillator is fed directly into a varying load, the frequency of the oscillator will be affected. The oscillator must be isolated from the varying load in order to maintain good frequency stability.

Good examples of frequency-stable oscillators are: the electron-coupled oscillator and the crystal controlled oscillator. These two types of oscillators will now be discussed.

THE ELECTRON-COUPLED OSCILLATOR. Fig. 12-12 is a diagram of a series-fed ELECTRON-COUPLED OSCILLATOR (E.C.O.). Both tank circuits are tuned to the same frequency. Examination of the diagram shows that the cathode, control grid and screen grid circuits form a Hartley oscillator; the screen grid acts as the plate of the oscillator. The real plate circuit serves only to couple energy from the oscillator to the load.

The electrons flowing from the cathode to the plate are acted upon by the AC voltage which appears at the grid of the oscillator. Thus, the electron stream, in flowing to the real plate, is caused to vary at the frequency of the Hartley ocscillator. The plate current, in flowing through the tuned circuit (Lp, Cp), injects energy into it and causes it to oscillate at the same frequency as the grid tuned circuit (L1, C1). The oscillations in the plate tank circuit are sustained by pulses of energy which are coupled to the plate from the oscillator section via the electron stream of the tube. This is how this type of oscillator came to be called an "electron-coupled oscillator".

The frequency of the E. C. O. is determined by the tuned circuit in the control grid section. Variations in the load of the oscillator will not reflect back to the oscillator's grid circuit to vary the oscillator frequency because the only means of coupling between the two parts of the E.C.O. is through the electron stream. There is no capacitive interelectrode coupling between the plate and control grid because of the electrostatic shielding of the screen grid. Thus we see that the tuned circuit in the grid section is well isolated from load variations and therefore, can maintain a constant frequency.

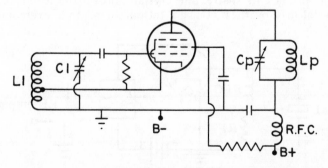

FIG. 12-12. AN ELECTRON-COUPLED OSCILLATOR.

225

The frequency stability of the electron-coupled oscillator is not affected by voltage variations occuring in the power supply. An increase in the screen voltage causes the oscillator's frequency to shift in one direction while, at the same time, an increase in the plate voltage causes the frequency to shift in the opposite direction. Since the screen grid and plate circuits receive their voltage from the same power supply, any frequency drift due to a varying plate voltage will be cancelled out by an opposite frequency shift due to a varying screen voltage. Thus, the frequency stability of the E.C.O. will remain constant regardless of slight B+ voltage fluctuations.

Because of its excellent stability characteristics, the electron-coupled oscillator is used extensively in instruments and equipment which require a stable oscillator whose frequency can be tuned over a wide frequency range.

CRYSTAL-CONTROLLED OSCILLATORS. The most stable of all oscillators is the CRYSTAL-CONTROLLED OSCILLATOR. The most important difference between the oscillators studied so far and the crystal oscillator is that the tuned circuit is replaced by a crystal. This crystal is usually made out of quartz, a mineral found in the earth. The quartz crystal has a property of generating an AC voltage if a mechanical vibration is applied to its surface. On the other hand, if we apply an AC voltage to the surfaces of the quartz crystal, it will vibrate mechanically. This property is known as the PIEZO-ELECTRIC EFFECT.

If we momentarily apply a voltage to two parallel surfaces of the crystal, it will start to vibrate mechanically; this mechanical vibration will, in turn, generate an AC voltage. This AC voltage will again cause the crystal to vibrate, etc., etc. This process will continue until all of the electrical energy which was injected into the crystal is used up. The crystal, from an electrical viewpoint, acts in the same manner as a tuned circuit. Since the vibrating crystal is similar to a tuned circuit, it can be placed in the grid circuit of an oscillator in place of the actual tuned grid circuit. This is shown in Fig. 12-13. Here, energy from the plate tuned circuit is fed back to the grid circuit through the grid-plate capacitance of the tube. This energy keeps the crystal oscillating. The oscillations occur at the resonant frequency of the crystal, and the plate circuit is tuned approximately to this frequency.

The strength of the crystal's vibration depends upon the voltage being fed back to the crystal. If the feedback is too great, the vibration may become strong enough to crack or shatter the crystal. Also, if the feedback is too great, the crystal may overheat. Using a tetrode or pentode overcomes this

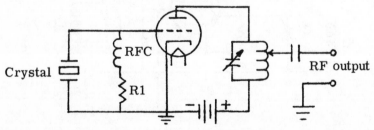

FIG. 12-13. A CRYSTAL-CONTROLLED OSCILLATOR USING A TRIODE TUBE.

difficulty because the screen grid reduces the feedback. However, the little energy that does get back is sufficient to sustain the crystal's oscillations.

If the plate-to-grid feedback is not sufficient to sustain the crystal's oscillations, a small capacitor may be placed between the grid and plate to increase the amount of feedback. The purpose of the R-F choke in Fig. 12-13 is to make sure that the feedback energy gets to the crystal, and is not by-passed to ground through the grid-leak resistor, R1.

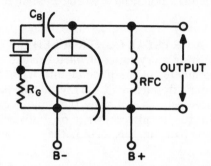

FIG. 12-14. A BASIC PIERCE OSCILLATOR CIRCUIT.

3 Fig. 12-14 shows a crystal controlled oscillator that is in widespread use. It is known as a PIERCE oscillator. The Pierce oscillator operates in a manner similar to the Colpitts oscillator of Fig. 12-9. The crystal takes the place of the coil and the interelectrode capacitances take the place of C1 and C2.

The crystal can take the place of the coil because it is inductive at a frequency slightly higher than its series resonant mode. The grid-to-cathode interelectrode capacitance takes the place of C1 and the plate-to-cathode interelectrode capacitance takes the place of C2.

The basic Pierce oscillator is novel in that it does not have an L-C tank circuit. It can always be recognized by the crystal between the plate and grid.

THE RESONANT FREQUENCY OF A CRYSTAL. The frequency at which a crystal vibrates and generates an AC voltage, is known as the crystal's RESONANT FREQUENCY. This resonant frequency is determined primarily by the THICKNESS of the crystal. The thinner the crystal, the higher is its resonant frequency; the thicker the crystal, the lower is its resonant frequency. Electrical contact to the surfaces of the crystal is obtained by a special crystal holder which has two metal plates that "sandwich" the crystal in the holder. Metal pins, similar to those found on vacuum tubes, are connected to the plates so that the unit can be plugged into a socket.

CARE OF CRYSTALS. The care and treatment of quartz crystals is very important for their efficient operation in oscillator circuits. It should be pointed out at this time that a crystal is thin and fragile and should normally never be removed from the crystal holder. If the crystal is dirty and fails to operate, it is necessary to remove it from its holder and clean it. Excellent cleaning agents are: soap and water, alcohol or carbon tetrachloride. After

227

cleaning, the crystal should be rinsed with water and then dried with a clean lint-free cloth. The fingers should not come in contact with the faces of the crystal, since oil or dirt getting on to the crystal surface may prevent it from oscillating. The crystal should be handled by grasping the edges, NEVER THE FACES.

Care must be taken not to allow a high DC voltage to be placed across a crystal. If a DC potential is applied to a crystal, the crystal will be physically strained. If the applied DC potential is strong enough, it might actually crack the crystal.

ADJUSTMENT OF A CRYSTAL CONTROLLED OSCILLATOR. The most accurate way of adjusting a crystal-controlled oscillator for stable operation is to use a DC milliammeter in the plate circuit. When the plate tank circuit is tuned to the resonant frequency of the crystal, the plate current will drop to a low value. However, as we vary the tuning to either side of the resonance point, the rise in plate current on both sides of the resonance point is not uniform. Note in Fig. 12-15, that, as the tuning capacitance

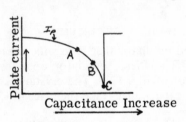

FIG. 12-15. CRYSTAL-OSCILLATOR, PLATE CURRENT TUNING CURVE.

(high frequency to a low frequency) increases, the plate current slowly decreases to point C, then suddenly jumps up to some high value; at which time, oscillations cease. Between points A and C, the circuit is oscillating. Before point A and beyond point C, the circuit stops oscillating. At point C, the plate circuit is tuned to the resonant frequency of the crystal, and the efficiency and output of the plate tank circuit are at a maximum. However, the oscillator is unstable at this point because any slight change in the loading conditions or any slight increase in the tuning capacitance might move the operating point beyond point C and cause the oscillator to drop out of oscillations. The oscillator should be operated in the region between A and B. In this region, the oscillator will continue to function properly, even with slight changes in load conditions.

In addition to the above, the following precautions should be taken to insure the stability of a crystal oscillator:

(1) Keep the voltages on the tube's elements constant. If possible, use a well-regulated power supply.

(2) Keep the feedback to the crystal at the minimum necessary for stable oscillations.

(3) Keep all parts of the oscillator circuit mechanically rigid.

CRYSTAL CUTS. The frequency of a crystal is affected by the temperature of the air surrounding it. Different types of crystals show different reactions to temperature changes. Crystals are classified according to the manner in which they are cut from the original raw quartz crystal. The

228

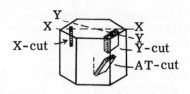

FIG. 12-16. CRYSTAL CUTS.

different crystal cuts from the raw crystal rock are shown in Fig. 12-16. Note that an X-cut crystal is one that is cut perpendicular to the X axis; a Y-cut crystal is one that is cut perpendicular to the Y axis; and an AT-cut crystal is one that is cut at a 35° angle to the Y-cut crystal.

The X-cut crystal has a NEGATIVE TEMPERATURE COEFFICIENT. This means that the natural resonant frequency of the crystal goes down as the temperature goes up, and its natural resonant frequency goes up as the temperature goes down. In actual practice, the temperature coefficient of an X-cut crystal varies from 10 to 25 Hz per MHz for each degree centigrade change.

Y-cut crystals have a POSITIVE TEMPERATURE COEFFICIENT. Their frequency goes up as the temperature goes up, and the frequency goes down as the temperature goes down. The Y-cut crystal has some undesirable operating characteristics, however. It tends to vibrate simultaneously at two different frequencies. Also, its frequency does not vary smoothly with changes in temperature. A slight change in temperature may cause a sudden large frequency shift.

Both the X-cut and the Y-cut crystals have been superseded by AT-cut crystals. AT-cut crystals have a LOW TEMPERATURE COEFFICIENT. A low temperature coefficient means that the frequency of the crystal varies very little with temperature changes. An AT-cut crystal oscillator is also capable of a comparatively high output.

4 **PROBLEMS RELATING TO CRYSTAL FREQUENCIES.** In order to operate a transmitter properly, it is important to know the exact frequency of its crystal oscillator. Since temperature changes affect the frequency of the crystal, we must be able to figure out the new crystal frequency resulting from a given temperature change. The following problems will illustrate how this is done:

PROBLEM ONE: A Y-cut crystal that is marked 1000 kHz has a positive temperature coefficient of 75 Hz per degree C, and is started in operation at 50°C. If the temperature-frequency characteristic is linear, what will the new crystal frequency be at 30°C?

SOLUTION: A linear temperature-frequency characteristic means that the 75 Hz change in crystal frequency will remain constant for each degree change in temperature. The temperature change is 20° (50° − 30° = 20°). Since the temperature coefficient is 75 Hz per degree C, the crystal frequency shift is 1500 Hz (20 x 75) or 1.5 kHz. THE NEW CRYSTAL FREQUENCY WILL THEREFORE BE THE ORIGINAL FREQUENCY, MINUS THE FREQUENCY DRIFT. (1000 kHz−1.5 kHz or 998.5 kHz).

PROBLEM TWO: A 3000 kHz low-drift crystal has a negative temperature coefficient of 4 Hz per MHz per degree C. The crystal is started in operation at 40°C. If the temperature-frequency characteristic is linear, what will be the frequency at 50°C?

SOLUTION: 3000 kHz is the same as 3 MHz because 1 MHz equals 1000 kHz. To convert the temperature coefficient (4 Hz per MHz per degree C) into the Hz change per degree C, we multiply the temperature coefficient by the crystal frequency in MHz. The product is a 12 Hz change per degree C (4 x 3 = 12). The change in temperature is 10°. (50° − 40° = 10°). The frequency change is, therefore, 10 x 12 = 120 Hz or 0.12 kHz. Since the temperature went up, the frequency of this negative temperature coefficient crystal will go down. The new frequency will therefore be 2999.88 kHz (3000 kHz − 0.12 kHz).

CRYSTAL STABILITY. When an X- or Y-cut crystal is used in the oscillator of a standard broadcast station, the maximum temperature variation around the crystal is usually maintained within 0.1°C by enclosing the crystal holder in a temperature-controlled oven. This insures that the crystal controlled frequency does not drift.

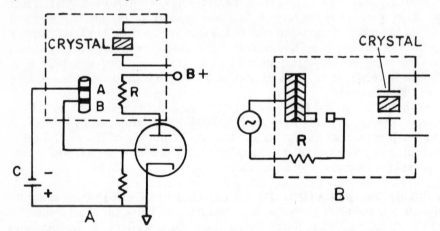

FIG. 12-17. TEMPERATURE CONTROLLED OVENS FOR CRYSTAL OSCILLATORS.

4 A temperature controlled oven using a mercury-thermometer type of crystal heater control is illustrated in Fig.12-17A. R represents a heater resistance that warms the air of the unit. As long as plate current flows, R will act as a heater. As soon as the temperature reaches a certain point, the mercury in the thermometer will rise and cause a short between contacts A and B. This will connect the negative terminal of C to the grid of the tube. The C battery voltage is high enough to stop the flow of plate current. R will cease heating up the unit. If the temperature drops below a certain point, the contact between A and B will be broken and plate current will again flow through R. The result of this action will be to keep the temperature of the crystal within a narrow range.

There are also temperature controlled ovens that use bimetallic thermostats instead of mercury thermostats. They consist of a strip of two metals with different coefficients of expansion. See Fig. 12-17B. The strip bends when heated and contact is either made or broken. This type of thermostat is cheaper than the mercury type, but it is not as reliable. It is subject to pitting and corrosion.

3 **OVERTONE CRYSTALS.** It was pointed out that the resonant frequency of a crystal is inversely proportional to its thickness. At frequencies above 20 MHz, the crystal becomes extremely thin and fragile. The use of extremely thin crystals can be avoided by using "overtone" crystals. An overtone crystal is one that produces a frequency which is a multiple of its fundamental frequency. In other words, if an oscillator is to generate a 40 MHz signal, an 8 MHz crystal can be used. The nature of the cut is such that it resonates strongly at its fifth harmonic or overtone. It therefore operates at 40 MHz. We refer to this crystal as a fifth overtone or fifth mode crystal. A third mode crystal is one which operates well at its third harmonic.

An overtone crystal does not operate at the exact harmonic frequency. It operates at close to the harmonic frequency. The frequency marking will show the overtone frequency that is actually being produced.

Overtone crystals are characterized by decreasing activity as the overtone is increased. To improve the operation of an overtone crystal, it will be necessary to add some regeneration so that it can start easier under loaded conditions.

MULTIVIBRATORS. A multivibrator is a resistance-capacitance (R-C) oscillator consisting of two amplifiers with feedback from the output of one to the input of the other. Fig. 12-18 shows a multivibrator circuit. The LC tuned circuits of the conventional oscillators have been replaced by resistor-capacitor combinations. The operation of the multivibrator is as follows:

Assume for the moment that V1 and V2 are identical in every respect, and that the plate current in each one is the same. Let us further assume that a slight change in V1 causes it to draw a bit more plate current. As this occurs, the voltage drop across R1 increases slightly, the plate end of it becoming more negative than it was before. This negative-going voltage is transferred to

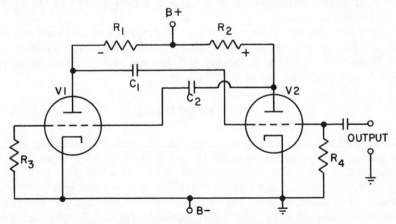

FIG. 12-18. BASIC VACUUM-TUBE MULTIVIBRATOR.

231

the grid of V2 through C1, causing the plate current of V2 to decrease. The voltage drop across R2 decreases so that the plate end of it becomes somewhat more positive than it was. The positive-going voltage is now passed on to the grid of V1 through coupling capacitor C2, to produce a further increase of plate current in V1. This action continues until the plate current in V1 reaches its maximum and the plate current in V2 drops to zero. This condition remains until the discharging of capacitor C1 causes a slight plate current flow in V2. In a manner similar to the action described above, the plate current in V2 quickly reaches maximum and the plate current in V1 drops to zero. This back and forth action continues and produces the square wave output shown in Fig. 12-19A. This may be changed to a sawtooth waveform by means of a special R-C circuit, known as a DIFFERENTIATION CIRCUIT. See Fig. 12-19B.

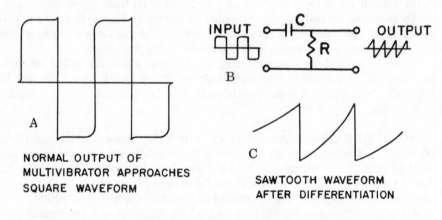

A

NORMAL OUTPUT OF
MULTIVIBRATOR APPROACHES
SQUARE WAVEFORM

C

SAWTOOTH WAVEFORM
AFTER DIFFERENTIATION

FIG. 12-19. OUTPUTS OF A MULTIVIBRATOR.

The frequency of the multivibrator depends upon the grid resistors and coupling capacitors (R3, R4, C1, C2). In the practical multivibrator, it is found that the frequency may be changed over a wide range by merely changing the value of C2.

Multivibrators may be synchronized by applying an external synchronizing voltage at the proper point (across R3 in Fig. 12-18). For reliable synchronization in this particular arrangement, the synchronizing voltage must have a peak value of at least 7.0 volts.

TROUBLESHOOTING

3 The Element 3 examination contains a number of questions on troubleshooting. The prospective radio operator must be able to analyze circuit troubles and know the symptoms that will result when these troubles occur. The questions and answers given below, as well as those given at the end of Lesson 14, should give the student an understanding of the basic troubleshooting that he will be responsible for on the examination. The following questions and answers are based on Fig. 12-11.

QUESTION: What will happen to the plate current if Cc is short-circuited?

ANSWER: If Cc shorts, there will no longer be a grid-leak bias. The grid will be at the same potential as the cathode and the plate current will rise.

QUESTION: What will happen to the plate current if C1 opens up?

ANSWER: If C1 opens up, there is no longer a tuned circuit and oscillations will cease. There will no longer be any bias and the plate current will rise.

QUESTION: What will happen to the plate current and grid current if Rg burns out?

ANSWER: If Rg burns out, the grid circuit is open and therefore, the grid current will fall to zero. Because the grid circuit is open, electrons will accumulate on the grid and cause a blocked grid condition. The grid will be strongly negative and the plate current will drop to a low value or to zero.

QUESTION: What will happen to the plate current if C2 shorts?

ANSWER: If C2 shorts, oscillations will cease. The normal negative grid bias will disappear and the plate current will rise.

QUESTION: What will happen to the grid current and plate current if Cb shorts?

ANSWER: If Cb shorts, the B supply will be short-circuited and no plate voltage will appear on the tube. The oscillations will therefore cease. This will cause the grid current to fall to zero. Since there is no plate voltage, the plate current will fall to zero. The R.F.C. will have the full supply voltage across it. A heavy current will flow through the R.F.C. and probably burn it out.

QUESTION: What will happen to the grid current and plate current if Lp opens up?

ANSWER: An open plate coil means that no plate voltage will appear at the plate. Oscillations will cease. The grid current will fall to zero and the plate current will fall to zero.

QUESTION: What would happen to the oscillations if Cb opened up?

ANSWER: Cb provides a path for the plate RF around the power supply. If Cb opened up, the RF path would open up and oscillations would cease.

PRACTICE QUESTIONS - LESSON 12

1. Which of the following should not be done to insure good frequency stability of a crystal controlled oscillator?
a. use a well-regulated power supply
b. use a constant temperature compensated oven
c. use a buffer stage between the oscillator and the final stage
d. maintain a large amount of feedback to the crystal

2. What type of feedback is employed by a Pierce oscillator? (3)
a. inductive   c. magnetic
b. capacitive   d. none of the above

3. The frequency at which a quartz crystal will oscillate is determined mainly by:
a. the surrounding heat   c. its thickness
b. the angle at which it is cut   d. the voltage across it

4. An electron-coupled oscillator:
a. has very good frequency stability
b. has very good efficiency
c. has low output power
d. is more stable than a crystal-controlled oscillator

5. In order to develop grid bias in an oscillator:
a. plate current flows through the grid-leak resistor
b. grid capacitor discharges current into the grid-leak resistor
c. the signal forces current to flow through the grid-leak resistor
d. the plate current and signal current cause an IR drop across the grid-leak resistor

6. In a shunt-fed oscillator, the DC component of the output current:
a. flows through the tube
b. is fed back to the grid circuit
c. does not flow through the plate coil
d. is in parallel with the input signal

7. Excessive feedback in a crystal oscillator may result in:
a. a cracked crystal   c. reduced output
b. loss of neutralization   d. tube cut-off

8. A Hartley oscillator is recognized by its:
a. split capacitor   c. tickler coil
b. tuned grid circuit   d. tapped coil

9. The temperature of a quartz crystal should:
a. vary according to the power input
b. be kept constant
c. not be kept constant for considerable lengths of time
d. be kept as low as possible

10. A Colpitts oscillator is recognized by its:
a. split capacitor   c. tickler coil
b. tuned grid circuit   d. tapped coil

11. An X-cut crystal, compared to a Y-cut of similar frequency is:
a. thinner   b. wider   c. rounder   d. thicker

12. A 28 MHz crystal has a positive temperature coefficient of 200 Hz per degree centigrade, and is started in operation at 45⁰ centigrade. What will the oscillating frequency be at 75⁰ centigrade? (4)
a. 28.500 MHz
c. 28.006 MHz
b. 34 MHz
d. 27.004 MHz

13. A high resistance meter is used to measure the grid voltage of an RF oscillator because:
a. it has a high resistance in the probe tip
b. it reduces the capacitance of the grid circuit
c. it loads the circuit very lightly
d. a high resistance voltmeter should not be used to measure the grid voltage of an RF oscillator

14. In order to improve the frequency stability of an oscillator:
a. temperature changes are introduced by means of blowers
b. a buffer stage should not be used
c. a high capacity to inductance ratio is employed
d. a high inductance to capacity ratio is employed

15. With reference to Fig. 12-11, what happens if C_c shorts?
a. the plate current and grid current decrease
b. the grid current falls and the plate current rises
c. the grid bias and the plate current rise
d. the grid current rises and the plate current falls

16. Which of the following is not a requirement for oscillation?
a. a tuned circuit
c. amplification
b. damping
d. feedback

17. An Armstrong oscillator uses:
a. inductive feedback
c. interelectrode feedback
b. capacitive feedback
d. negative feedback

18. A quartz crystal in the oscillator of a transmitter does not:
a. stabilize the output frequency
b. provide a high Q tank circuit
c. determine the frequency
d. amplify the signal

19. A desirable operating characteristic of an AT-cut crystal is:
a. high frequency drift
b. high output capability
c. positive temperature coefficient
d. negative temperature coefficient

LESSON 13
C. W. TRANSMITTERS

INTRODUCTION. The function of a radio transmitter is to transmit intelligence by means of a radio frequency wave. The RF wave is radiated into space by an antenna system. An antenna is a device which converts RF energy into electromagnetic radiation, known as radio waves. The RF wave traveling through space is then picked up by a receiver which converts the RF signal into an audio output.

Radio transmitters may be divided into two types. One is the CONTIN-UOUS-WAVE type of transmitter, which we shall now study; the other is the modulated type, which we shall study later on.

CONTINUOUS WAVES. Continuous waves, abbreviated CW, are radio waves of constant amplitude. In the CW transmitter, continuous waves are radiated into space by simply coupling the output of a vacuum tube power oscillator to a suitable antenna system. By interrupting the CW in accordance with the International Morse Code, intelligence can be conveyed.

The Morse Code consists of a series of dots and dashes which represent the letters of the alphabet. In order to transmit code, the CW transmission must be interrupted in a dot and dash sequence. An oscillator is made to stop and start oscillating by means of a telegraph key. By allowing the oscillator to operate for longer or shorter periods of time, we can produce dots and dashes. Figure 13-1 shows the output of an oscillator for the letter "D" (dash-dot-dot).

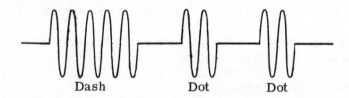

Dash   Dot   Dot

FIG. 13-1. KEYED OUTPUT OF AN OSCILLATOR
FOR THE LETTER "D" (DASH-DOT-DOT).

ONE-TUBE TRANSMITTER. In the original radio transmitters, the oscillator was directly coupled to the antenna system. In order to increase the output power, it was necessary to use a larger tube or to increase the operating voltages. There is a limit, however, to the amount of power that one can get from a one-tube transmitter. Another drawback of the simple oscillator type of transmitter is its poor frequency stability. Fig. 13-2 shows a one-tube transmitter. Ca represents the capacitance between the antenna and ground. This capacitance varies as the antenna swings in the wind. This varying antenna capacitance will be coupled back to the tank circuit and will cause the oscillator frequency to vary.

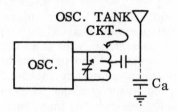

FIG. 13-2. ONE-TUBE TRANSMITTER.

MASTER-OSCILLATOR POWER-AMPLIFIER. A transmitter consisting of an oscillator and an amplifier (or a series of amplifiers) is called a MASTER-OSCILLATOR POWER-AMPLIFIER, MOPA for short. Such a transmitter is shown in Fig. 13-3. The output of the oscillator is amplified by V2. Capacitor C1 prevents the high DC voltage on the plate of V1 from being applied to the grid of V2. At the same time, it allows the RF energy to get through to the grid of V2. The RF choke L1 prevents the RF energy from flowing to ground through R1. This is because an RF choke opposes the flow of RF currents.

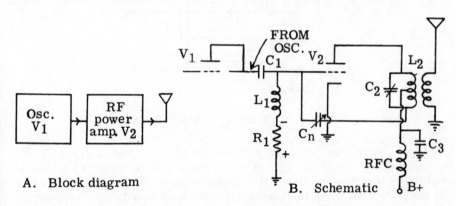

A. Block diagram   B. Schematic

FIG. 13-3. MASTER-OSCILLATOR, POWER-AMPLIFIER TRANSMITTER.

In addition to increased power output, the MOPA type of transmitter has much better frequency stability than the simple oscillator transmitter. High frequency stability is obtained because the oscillator is not coupled directly to the antenna. Changes in antenna-to-ground capacitance will not be coupled back to the oscillator.

The amplifier in Fig. 13-3 may feed the antenna directly, or it may be the first of a series of RF amplifiers, the last of which feeds into an antenna system.

237

HIGH EFFICIENCY CLASS C RF AMPLIFIER. In Lesson 7, we studied biasing methods for audio amplifiers. You will recall that most AF amplifiers use cathode bias. The audio amplifier tubes are operated as Class A or Class B because we are interested in obtaining good fidelity. The Class A amplifier sacrifices efficiency for fidelity.

In the case of an RF amplifier, we are not interested in fidelity since we are not amplifying an audio signal. We are interested in efficiency of operation. An RF amplifier operates most efficiently in a transmitter as a Class C amplifier. In order to operate the tube as a Class C amplifier, the bias must be between one and one-half to four times the bias value necessary for cut-off. This condition is shown graphically in 13-4. You will notice that with a pure sine wave applied to the grid, the plate current consists of small pulses which certainly do not resemble the input sine wave. Since the plate current wave does not resemble the grid signal, the fidelity of a Class C amplifier is poor. One important point to notice is that the plate current flows for only a fraction of the period of the input signal. Compare this to a Class A amplifier where the plate current flows continuously. Obviously, more power is wasted in plate dissipation in a Class A amplifier as compared

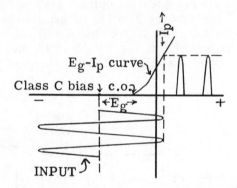

FIG. 13-4. CLASS "C" BIAS OPERATION.

to a Class C amplifier. Since the plate dissipation is decreased in the Class C amplifier, the useful power output is increased. The efficiency of a Class C amplifier is therefore excellent. It is approximately 70% efficient. The exact efficiency depends upon the bias voltage, the load impedance, the incoming signal amplitude, the plate voltage, etc.

Note in Fig. 13-4 that the input signal drive is quite large. This is so because the input signal must overcome the high negative bias and drive the grid positive.

The question that always arises at this point is: Of what good are the plate current pulses if we are interested in obtaining an amplified version of the sine wave input? The answer lies in the ability of the plate tank circuit to reproduce a pure sine wave from pulses of energy which are applied to it every cycle. From the discussion of the oscillatory circuit, it will be recalled that when the plate tank circuit is tuned to the resonant frequency of the grid circuit, the plate current pulses will reinforce the oscillations in the plate tuned circuit at just the right instant, and thereby sustain the oscillations. The surges of plate current give the tank circuit the shot of energy which results in the tuned circuit making up that portion of the sine wave missing in the plate current pulses. This is known as the FLYWHEEL EFFECT. Thus, we see that although the plate current is made up of pulses, the signal fed to the antenna or the next stage is a pure sine wave.

3 TRANSISTORIZED RF AMPLIFIER. Fig. 13-5 shows a transistorized RF amplifier with component values. The amplifier is designed to amplify a 10 MHz. signal. It is of the common emitter type. L1 and C1 represent the input tank circuit; L2 and C2 represent the output tank circuit. Resistor R3 is the emitter resistor that is used for stabilization. Bias is obtained from the base divider combination consisting of R1 and R2.

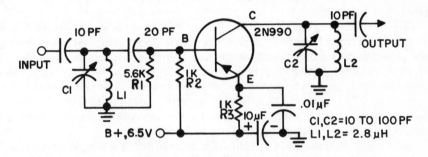

FIG. 13-5. A TRANSISTORIZED COMMON EMITTER AMPLIFIER.

MINIMIZING HARMONIC OUTPUT. It is very important that the output waveform of an RF amplifier contain a minimum of harmonic components. In other words, the output should be as close to a pure sine wave as possible. If the harmonic components are radiated by the antenna, unlawful interference with adjacent signals may result. It is especially important that the output stage of the transmitter produce a minimum amount of harmonic and spurious signals. This is because this output stage feeds the antenna and the harmonic and spurious signals are bound to be transmitted.

A Class C, RF amplifier should have the following characteristics if the generation of harmonics is to be kept to a minimum:

(1) The plate tank circuit should have a low inductance to capacitance ratio (low L-C ratio).

(2) Push-pull operation will eliminate second harmonic components.

(3) Use a Faraday shield. (The Faraday shield is discussed later on in this lesson.)

(4) Use high Q plate and grid tank circuits. By increasing the Q of the tank circuit, we increase the selectivity of the circuit. This means that we pass the desired frequency, but exclude the undesired signals (harmonics, etc.).

There is a limit as to how high the Q should be. Too high a Q will result in high internal tank currents and, therefore, less power transferred to the next stage or antenna. The ideal Q of an RF power amplifier tank circuit should be between 10 and 20.

239

(5) Use a low-pass filter between the transmitter and the antenna. The low-pass filter will pass the desired signal and stop the harmonic frequencies from passing.

(6) Use proper bias. The bias should be as low as possible for best harmonic attenuation.

(7) Use proper grid drive. The drive from the previous stages should be as low as possible. We will see in a later paragraph of this lesson how a large bias increases harmonic generation.

(8) Use link coupling. When a link is added to a tuned L-C circuit, a transformer is formed. A high degree of harmonic attenuation results because most of the energy transfer will be due to the magnetic coupling at the resonant frequency of the L-C circuit.

(9) Avoid capacitive coupling. Since a capacitor offers a decreasing impedance to the higher frequencies, there is little opposition to the high frequency harmonics.

(10) Use decoupling circuits. The use of decoupling circuits in the B+ leads will prevent harmonics and other signals from being fed back, through the power supply from stage to stage, and re-amplified and transmitted.

The coupling between tuned circuits should not be too tight. Tight coupling loads down the tuned circuits and reduces their Q and hence, their selectivity. This makes the tuned circuits more vulnerable to passing harmonics. Tight coupling also increases the capacitance between the coils which, in turn, allows for the coupling of harmonics.

Measuring the harmonic output of a transmitter is a simple procedure. A field strength meter, which is simply a receiver whose output is calibrated in decibels, is placed some distance away from the transmitter. First the receiver is tuned to the fundamental output frequency of the transmitter and the output is noted. The receiver is then tuned to the various harmonics of the transmitter's fundamental frequency and the outputs are noted. The arithmetic difference between the db readings gives the attenuation for the various harmonics.

GRID-LEAK BIAS. It was mentioned above that a Class C amplifier requires a bias of from one and one-half to four times the value of cut-off bias. There are several methods of obtaining Class C bias. The first method that we shall discuss is known as GRID-LEAK BIAS. You will recall that grid-leak bias is used in the self-biased oscillator. Figure 13-3 shows the RF amplifier, V2, employing grid-leak bias. R1 is the bias resistor and C1 is the bias capacitor. Before the signal from the previous stage is applied to the grid of the amplifier tube, the bias on the grid is zero. However, when a signal is applied, a grid bias voltage develops across R1. Let us see how this comes about: On the positive half of the incoming signal, the grid is driven positive with respect to the cathode. This causes a flow of grid current, which charges up capacitor C1. On the negative half of the signal, the capacitor discharges through R1. The discharge current that flows through R1 develops a DC voltage across R1. Capacitor C1, which is effectively in parallel with R1, tends to keep this voltage constant. Since the current enters R1 at the top, (the grid side), the top part of the resistor is negative with respect to the bottom part. The top of the resistor is connected to the grid. Therefore, the grid is negatively biased with respect to the cathode.

The amount of grid-leak bias that is developed depends upon the strength of the signal. This may sometimes be a serious disadvantage. If, for some reason, the signal or excitation is lost, the bias will disappear and the plate current may rise to excessively high values.

Since the grid in a Class C amplifier draws current, power is consumed. This power must be supplied from the previous stage.

Grid-leak bias could never be used in a Class A amplifier. In a Class A amplifier, the grid is never driven positive. Hence, there is no grid current flow to develop a bias voltage. Also, the amount of grid leak bias varies with the amplitude of the incoming signal. The operating point would be continuously changed. This would result in a heavy distortion of the signal. Thus we see that grid-leak bias is used primarily for Class C r-f amplifiers.

FIXED BIAS. Another method of obtaining bias for Class C amplifiers is through the use of a "C" battery, or a power supply. A "C" battery is just an ordinary battery used for biasing purposes. The negative terminal of the "C" battery is connected to the grid (through a coil or resistor) and the positive terminal is connected to the cathode. This makes the grid negative with respect to the cathode. An RF by-pass capacitor is usually shunted across the battery to complete the RF path around the battery. The amount of battery voltage to be used for a particular tube can be found by consulting a transmitting tube manual.

A well-regulated power supply could be used in place of the "C" battery to provide bias. This method is preferable to the use of a battery because batteries must be replaced.

If the excitation to the stage fails, the fixed bias is not affected and the plate current does not rise to dangerous values. This method is quite popular in the more expensive transmitters.

COMBINATION GRID-LEAK, CATHODE BIAS. This method is a combination of grid-leak and cathode bias. See Fig. 13-6. R1 provides most of the bias voltage. R2 is placed in the circuit to act as a protective bias in case the input signal to the stage should fail. Upon loss of grid-leak bias, the increased plate current will flow through R2 developing a heavy bias voltage which will, in turn, limit the plate current to a safe value. R2 will not cause any appreciable loss of plate voltage, since its value is small. It will simply serve to bias the tube, should the grid-leak bias disappear.

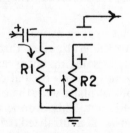

FIG. 13-6. GRID LEAK
AND CATHODE BIAS.

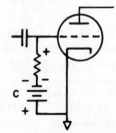

FIG. 13-7. GRID LEAK
AND BATTERY BIAS.

GRID-LEAK AND BATTERY BIAS. Another method of obtaining bias for an RF amplifier is shown in Fig. 13-7. This method is a combination of grid-leak and battery bias. Again, most of the bias voltage is obtained from the voltage drop across the grid leak resistor. The battery is connected in the circuit simply as a means of keeping some bias voltage on the tube in the event that the grid-leak bias drops to zero. The transmitting tube is thus protected against damage due to excessive plate current flow.

RF AMPLIFIER OSCILLATION. Examine the RF amplifier of Fig. 13-8. The tank circuit L2, C2 is not only the plate tank circuit of the oscillator, but can also be considered as the grid tank circuit of the RF amplifier. The portion of the schematic inside the dotted line is exactly the same as a TPTG oscillator and will oscillate just like a TPTG oscillator unless certain precautions are taken. An oscillating RF amplifier is very undesirable. An amplifier is only supposed to amplify and not to oscillate. An oscillating amplifier will generate spurious signals which will be radiated along with the desired transmission and cause interference with stations on nearby frequencies.

There are two general methods of preventing an RF amplifier from oscillating. One is to use a tetrode or pentode instead of a triode. The addition of a screen grid reduces the grid-plate capacitance and prevents oscillation, since there would be very little feedback from the plate circuit to the grid circuit. However, most high powered RF amplifier tubes are triodes, and this brings us to the second method of preventing an RF amplifier from oscillating.

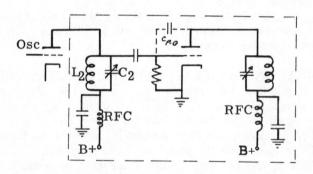

FIG. 13-8. OSCILLATORY CIRCUIT IN AN UNNEUTRALIZED RF AMPLIFIER.

PLATE NEUTRALIZATION. We realize that as long as we use a triode, we will have feedback from the plate circuit to the grid circuit through the interelectrode plate-grid capacitance. We must, in some manner, cancel out or neutralize this feedback if we are going to prevent oscillations. The remedy is to feed back a voltage that is 180° out of phase with the offending voltage and thereby NEUTRALIZE or cancel it out. This is done with the aid of an external capacitor. Fig. 13-9 shows a neutralized triode RF amplifier. Capacitor Cn is the neutralizing capacitor and Cp-g is the grid to plate interelectrode capacity. Notice that the B+ is fed to the plate through a

242

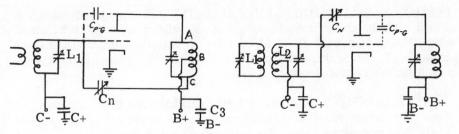

FIG. 13-9. PLATE NEUTRALIZATION.   FIG. 13-10. GRID NEUTRALIZATION.

center-tap on the plate coil. The center-tap is placed at RF ground (zero) potential through capacitor C3. The plate RF voltage with respect to ground is the voltage across the top half of the coil; it is the voltage between A and B. This voltage feeds energy back to the grid and tends to make the amplifier oscillate. The RF voltage between points B and C is the neutralizing voltage and is equal to the plate RF voltage. Because potentials at opposite ends of a coil are 180° out of phase with each other, the plate RF voltage is 180° out of phase with the neutralizing voltage. If Cn is made to equal Cp-g, the neutralizing voltage will cause a voltage to be fed back to the grid which will be equal and opposite to the voltage fed back by Cp-g. The two voltages will cancel each other out, and the amplifier will no longer oscillate. The above system of neutralization is called PLATE NEUTRALIZATION or HAZEL-TINE NEUTRALIZATION. We can recognize it by the fact that Cn is connected between the bottom of the plate coil and the control grid.

GRID NEUTRALIZATION. Fig. 13-10 shows a system of neutralization called GRID NEUTRALIZATION or RICE NEUTRALIZATION. The grid coil is split and Cn is connected between the bottom of the grid coil and the plate. The operation of the neutralization process in this system is similar to the plate neutralization system. The neutralizing voltage fed back from the plate to the bottom of the grid coil will cancel out the voltage fed back from the plate to the top of the grid coil by the grid to plate capacitance.

CRISS-CROSS NEUTRALIZATION. Fig. 13-11 shows a third system of neutralization. This is the system used to neutralize an RF amplifier stage consisting of two triodes in push-pull. It is called CRISS-CROSS NEUTRAL-

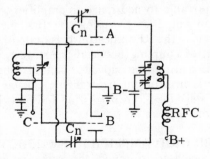

FIG. 13-11. CRISS-CROSS NEUTRALIZATION.

243

IZATION or BALANTINE NEUTRALIZATION. The plate of tube A is joined with the grid of tube B through a neutralizing capacitor; the plate of tube B is joined with the grid of tube A through another neutralizing capacitor. If you examine this circuit, you will see that criss-cross neutralization is really a double Hazeltine system.

STEPS IN NEUTRALIZING AN RF AMPLIFIER. It is important to know the actual steps in neutralizing an RF amplifier. There are two methods in general use today. The first method is as follows:

1. Remove the plate voltage from the stage to be neutralized. This is very important since it is impossible to neutralize an amplifier with the plate voltage applied.

2. The stage preceding the stage to be neutralized should have its power on and should be properly tuned to the correct frequency. The filament voltage of the stage being neutralized should be on.

3. The grid and plate tank circuits of the stage being neutralized should now be tuned to resonate with the signal coming from the preceding stage. This is done by tuning the grid and plate tank capacitors for a maximum indication of an RF indicator which is coupled to the plate tank circuit. The RF indicator may be a neon bulb, a flashlight bulb connected to a small loop of wire or a thermocouple ammeter. Any coupling between an indicating instrument and plate tank coil should be made as loose as possible.

4. The neutralizing capacitor or capacitors are then adjusted until the RF indicator shows that the RF energy in the plate tank circuit is at a minimum.

5. Repeat steps 3 and 4 to make sure that the stage is as completely neutralized as possible.

The second neutralization method is as follows:

1. Remove the plate voltage from the stage to be neutralized. Keep the filament voltage on.

2. Tune the preceding stages so that there is excitation (a signal input) to the stage to be neutralized.

3. Insert a DC milliammeter in the grid circuit, if one is not already present.

4. Rock the plate tuning capacitor of the stage to be neutralized back and forth, and observe the grid meter. If the grid meter varies, the stage is not neutralized. Then adjust the neutralizing capacitor until rocking of the plate tank capacitor no longer causes the grid meter to vary.

It is not always possible to neutralize an amplifier completely. Therefore, if you neutralize an amplifier by using the first method, do not always expect a zero reading of the RF indicator. It is quite likely that there is stray inductive or capacitive coupling between the stage being neutralized and a preceding stage. The neutralizing capacitor cannot cancel this out. It is also possible that there is insufficient neutralizing capacity or too much stray capacity within the stage itself. Proper wiring and parts layout would remedy this situation to a great extent.

THE GROUNDED GRID AMPLIFIER. Fig. 13-12 illustrates a grounded grid amplifier. It operates in much the same manner as the ordinary grounded cathode amplifier. The principle difference is that in the grounded

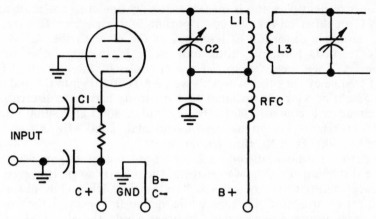

FIG. 13-12. A CLASS B GROUNDED GRID TRIODE AMPLIFIER.

grid amplifier, the control grid is grounded, while the cathode is "hot". The signal voltage is applied between the cathode and grid in both cases. The grid bias requirements are the same for both amplifiers. In both cases, the output is taken from the plate circuit.

Neutralization is not required in the grounded grid amplifier because the grid acts as a shield between the output (plate) and the input (cathode). The capacitance between the plate and cathode is about 1/25th of the grid to plate capacity of the same tube in a grounded cathode circuit. The circuit shown in Fig. 13-12 is biased for Class B operation. Class B operation requires that the grid be biased at cutoff. Hence, the plate current will flow only during one-half of the input cycle. However, the L1C2 tank circuit exhibits the "flywheel effect". This means that once the LC circuit is excited, it provides the complete cycle of voltage.

The input impedance of the grounded grid amplifier is low and therefore, requires more driver power than a similar circuit using a grounded cathode. The output capacity of the grounded grid system is about one-half that of the grounded cathode system. This allows the grounded grid system to be used at much higher frequencies. The grounded grid amplifier is satisfactory for use as a linear amplifier, for AM, SSB and TV. In the receiving RF amplifier services, the grounded grid amplifier is useful because it is capable of a better noise figure than the grounded cathode system and can therefore be used at much higher frequencies.

A grounded grid amplifier cannot be modulated 100% unless the driver is also modulated about 70%.

FREQUENCY MULTIPLIERS. It is not always desirable to have the oscillator of a transmitter generate the frequency which is to be radiated. In order for a crystal-controlled oscillator to produce a high frequency, the crystal must be ground very thin. Since a thin crystal can crack easily, it is a good idea to operate the oscillator at a low frequency and to step up the frequency by means of special RF amplifiers. These special RF amplifiers are called FREQUENCY MULTIPLIERS.

245

Frequency multiplication is made possible by operating a vacuum tube as a Class C amplifier on the non-linear portion of its characteristic curve. As a result, harmonic distortion is developed in the plate circuit. As you have already learned, harmonic distortion results in the generation of new frequencies. These new frequencies are multiples of the original or fundamental frequency. In other words, if we feed 1000 kHz into the grid circuit of an amplifier which is operated to give strong harmonic distortion, the plate circuit will contain 1000 kHz, 2000 kHz, 3000 kHz, 4000 kHz, etc. The 1000 kHz is known as the fundamental, 2000 kHz is the second harmonic, 3000 kHz is the third harmonic, etc.

Ordinarily, harmonic distortion is to be avoided in an amplifier circuit because distortion alters the waveshape of the original signal. However, when frequency multiplication is required, the signal is deliberately distorted to form strong harmonics. The desired harmonic frequency is then selected with a properly tuned plate circuit. In other words, the plate tank circuit is made resonant to the desired harmonic frequency.

In order to develop strong harmonic distortion, the frequency multiplier tube is heavily biased; even more so than an ordinary Class C amplifier. The bias voltage may be as high as ten times the value of cut-off bias. However, this large grid bias requires very strong grid excitation or drive. The signal must be large enough so that the positive peaks of the signal can overcome the large negative grid bias voltage. The plate current consists of positive pulses, but the inertia or flywheel effect of the plate tank circuit will make up the remaining portion of the sine wave of the harmonic frequency peaks.

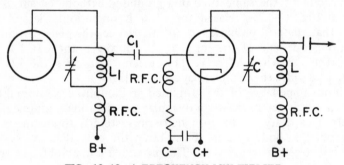

FIG. 13-13. A FREQUENCY MULTIPLIER.

Fig. 13-13 illustrates a basic frequency multiplier. Except for the fact that it is not neutralized, it resembles any other triode amplifier. The values of the voltages and components are what make it a frequency multiplier. The complete C. W. transmitter of Figure 13-15 contains a FREQUENCY DOUBLER (V2). We call it a frequency doubler because the plate tank circuit is tuned to the second harmonic of the fundamental. If the plate tank were tuned to three times the fundamental, we would call it a FREQUENCY TRIPLER. Note that there is no neutralizing capacitor in the frequency multiplier, even though a triode is being used. This is because the plate and grid circuits of a frequency multiplier are tuned to different frequencies and there is no danger of oscillation due to feedback. Other characteristics of a

246

frequency multiplier not mentioned in previous paragraphs are as follows:

1. The plate current flows for approximately 90° or one quarter of the time of an input cycle.

2. The plate efficiency of the frequency multiplier is lower than that of a straight Class C amplifier.

3. The plate tank circuit has a high impedance to the harmonic frequency to which it is tuned (high L to C ratio).

A PUSH-PUSH AMPLIFIER. Fig. 13-14 illustrates a push-push amplifier. The grids are connected in the normal push-pull fashion, while the plates are connected to each other in a parallel manner.

In a single tube doubler, the plate circuit receives a pulse of plate current on the positive grid alternation. On the other alternation, there is no pulse of plate current and the plate circuit is "on its own" in developing the cycle. In the case of a single tube tripler stage, there is one pulse of plate current for every three cycles of output. This tends to be inefficient and unstable.

When two tubes are used, there are two pulses of plate current for every input cycle. On one alternation, one grid goes positive and causes a plate current pulse. On the other half of the cycle, the other grid goes positive and causes a plate current pulse. Thus, the use of two tubes improves the stability and efficiency of a single tube frequency multiplier stage. The efficiency of a push-pull or push-push multiplier is almost the same as a normal Class C amplifier.

Since even harmonics cancel out in the plate circuit of a push-pull amplifier, the push-pull amplifier cannot be used for doubling. Instead, the push-push amplifier is used as a frequency doubler, while the push-pull amplifier is used as a frequency tripler.

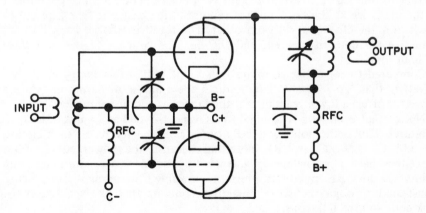

FIG. 13-14. A PUSH-PUSH FREQUENCY MULTIPLIER.

COUPLING BETWEEN STAGES. There are three types of stage-to-stage coupling used in transmitters. The first type is called CAPACITY COUPLING and is shown in Fig. 13-13. C_1 is the coupling capacitor. It is similar to the resistance-capacity coupling that is used in audio amplifiers. Capacitive coupling is the simplest and least expensive method of coupling. It consists merely of a coupling capacitor which transfers the RF voltage from the plate of one tube to the grid of the next. Sometimes, capacitor C_1 is tapped down on L_1 for impedance matching purposes. The disadvantage of capacity coupling, as compared to other coupling methods, is that undesired harmonics are easily transferred from stage to stage.

Fig. 13-12 shows a second method of coupling between stages. It is called INDUCTIVE COUPLING. The RF voltage is magnetically or inductively coupled from L1 to L3. Inductive coupling is more expensive than capacitive coupling since it requires two tuned circuits. It also requires additional tuning. The advantage of inductive coupling is that the addition of a tuned grid circuit results in increased gain and power output at the desired frequency. More tuned circuits will reject unwanted harmonics.

The third method of coupling RF from stage to stage is called LINK COUPLING. Link coupling is a very efficient form of coupling and it may be used between the oscillator and RF amplifier stage, between two RF amplifier stages, between an RF amplifier stage and the final RF amplifier stage, and between the final RF amplifier stage and the antenna coupling network. Fig. 13-15 shows the doubler (V2) link coupled to the power amplifier (V3, V4). The actual coupling consists of a pair of wires with a loop of two or three turns at each end. The chief advantage of this form of coupling is that two stages which are physically some distance from each other, can be coupled. Capacitive or inductive coupling methods could not be used in such a case since long wires cause heavy losses at high frequencies. Long leads have sufficient inductive reactance at high frequencies to build up a counter-EMF and cut down the signal strength to the next stage. In link coupling, however, no counter-EMF is induced in the long leads since the current in one leg at a certain instant is opposite in direction to the current in the other leg at the same instant. The resulting magnetic fields are out of phase and therefore, cancel each other. The result is that no back EMF or inductive reactance is created, and the signal is coupled to the next stage without loss.

Compared to capacitive coupling, link coupling transfers energy inductively rather than capacitively. This reduces the transfer of harmonics since a capacitor offers a lower reactance at the higher harmonic frequencies.

Notice that each loop is coupled to its respective coil at a point of low RF potential. This is the point where B+ or C− is connected to the tank circuit. B+ and C− are at zero RF potential because the power supply filter capacitors have a negligible impedance to ground at RF. Coupling from points of low RF potential prevents unwanted harmonics from being transferred through the stray capacitive coupling that exists between the tank coils and the link coils.

A TYPICAL CW TRANSMITTER. Fig. 13-15 is a schematic of a typical MEDIUM POWER CW TRANSMITTER. It consists of two power supplies, an oscillator, a frequency doubler and an RF push-pull amplifier. Let us first dicuss the power supplies.

You will note that there are TWO power supplies instead of one. The oscillator and first RF amplifier (doubler) connect to one power supply, and

248

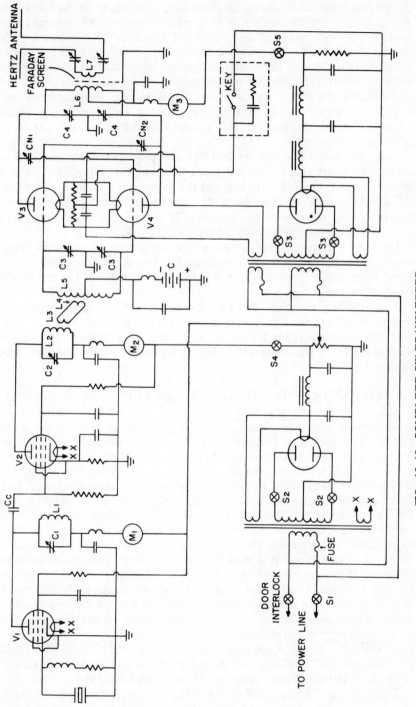

FIG. 13-15. COMPLETE CW TRANSMITTER.

the power amplifier connects to the other. The reason for having a separate power supply for the oscillator is to prevent the oscillator from becoming unstable. If the oscillator and the final amplifier have a common power supply, any load changes which occur in the amplifier would be fed back to the oscillator through the common supply. These load changes would cause the voltages on the elements of the oscillator tube to change. This, in turn, would cause the frequency of the oscillator and the transmitter to vary. A transmitter whose frequency drifts or varies is very undesirable because it causes fading at the receiver and spurious sidebands, which interfere with adjacent frequencies.

The fact that the oscillator and first RF amplifier use a common power supply, does not affect the oscillator's frequency stability. The power levels of the first RF amplifier are low and the antenna is not the load for the first RF amplifier. On the other hand, the power amplifier has high power in it and is directly coupled to the antenna. The variations in this stage are large and we don't want them coupled back to the oscillator.

One of the requirements for good frequency stability in a transmitter is a well-regulated power supply. A well-regulated power supply contains a choke input filter and a bleeder. The rectifier tube is usually of the mercury vapor type for two reasons:

1. A mercury vapor rectifier tube has a constant voltage drop regardless of load current changes. This improves the voltage regulation.

2. The mercury vapor tube is capable of supplying the large load current requirements of the transmitter. For a review of power supplies, refer to Lesson 7.

OSCILLATOR AND FREQUENCY DOUBLER. The oscillator in Fig. 13-15 is a conventional pentode crystal-controlled oscillator. M1 is a milliammeter which is placed in the plate circuit to measure plate current and to tune the plate tank circuit to resonate with the crystal frequency. Correct plate tank tuning is indicated by a dip reading (minimum reading) in M1. The oscillator is capacity-coupled to the frequency doubler. The frequency doubler is an RF amplifier whose plate circuit is tuned to twice the oscillator frequency. Since it is located between the oscillator and the final amplifier, it is called a BUFFER STAGE. It isolates the oscillator from the final amplifier and thereby prevents changes that occur in the final amplifier from affecting the oscillator. The final amplifier handles large amounts of power and it is important to keep these large power variations as far away as possible from the oscillator. The buffer serves this purpose and thereby improves the frequency stability of the oscillator. Notice that there is no neutralization of the frequency doubler. There are two reasons for this. As we mentioned previously, frequency multipliers do not require neutralization since the grid and plate circuits are tuned to different frequencies. Also, since the tube used is a pentode, the grid-plate capacitance is very small and the plate to grid feedback will therefore be negligible. Neutralization of a pentode or tetrode is only necessary at very high frequencies.

The bias for the frequency doubler stage is a combination of grid-leak bias and cathode bias. Most of the bias voltage comes from the grid-leak resistor; the cathode bias is simply a protective bias.

250

The buffer RF amplifier is series-fed. We recognize this by the fact that the DC component of the plate current flows through the plate coil. RF amplifiers are series fed or shunt fed in the same manner that oscillators are.

The buffer amplifier is coupled to the final RF amplifier by a link coupling system. The final amplifier (output) stage is coupled to the antenna by means of a tuned line.

The RF power amplifier is connected in push-pull. The advantages to be gathered from push-pull operation are as follows:

(1) Even harmonics are cancelled out in the plate circuit, reducing the possibility of serious second harmonic radiation.

(2) The power output is higher than the power output of a single-ended amplifier

(3) There is no need to re-neutralize when the transmitter is tuned from one frequency output to another.

The RF power amplifier employs criss-cross neutralization, as well as battery bias in the grid circuit.

THE FARADAY SHIELD. One way of attenuating the undesirable radiation of harmonics is to place a FARADAY SHIELD between the tank coil of the power amplifier and the antenna coupling circuit. The Faraday shield reduces the harmonic transfer of energy through the stray capacity that exists between the inductively coupled coils, L6 and L7. The Faraday shield is actually a mesh of metal strips which is grounded to the chassis of the transmitter.

TUNING THE TRANSMITTER. It is important to know how to tune up a transmitter. We will use the transmitter of Fig. 13-15 in describing the complete procedure in tuning up a basic CW transmitter. The tuning procedure is as follows:

(1) The main switch S1 is closed to allow the filaments of all the tubes in the transmitter to heat up. Since the rectifier tubes are of the mercury-vapor type, the filaments of these rectifiers must be heated for several minutes before voltage is applied to the rectifier plates.

(2) After the filaments have heated up for a few minutes, switch #2 is closed. Switch #2 is a double pole single throw switch which applies AC voltage to the plates of the rectifier tube of the oscillator- buffer power supply. The oscillator tube now has plate voltage and is ready to be tuned.

(3) The oscillator is tuned by varying capacitor C1 and observing meter M1 for the characteristic crystal oscillator dip. The oscillator plate tank circuit is now resonant to the crystal frequency.

(4) By closing switch #4, we apply B+ voltage to the plate of the buffer-doubler stage. This stage is now ready for tuning.

(5) The plate of the buffer-doubler stage is tuned by adjusting C2 until the plate milliammeter, M2, dips. The tuned circuit, C2, L2, is now resonant to the second harmonic of the oscillator frequency.

(6) The push-pull power amplifier stage is now ready to be neutralized. We use either of the two neutralization methods previously described. Neutralizing capacitors C_{N1} and C_{N2} are adjusted at the same time.

(7) Switch S3 is closed next. This applies AC voltage to the plates of the

251

high voltage rectifier. However, the high B+ voltage is still not applied to the power amplifier stage. With switch S5 still open, the plate tuning capacitor is turned to the approximate resonant point, as indicated by a marked line on the plate tuning dial. This mark had been previously recorded under operating conditions as being the point of resonance for the plate tank circuit. We can now close switch #5 and be assured that the plate tank is close enough to resonance to prevent excessive plate current flow at the instant the key is closed. Upon closing S5, depress the key and immediately adjust C4 for a minimum reading on M3. A minimum reading indicates that the tank circuit is at resonance. If the tank circuit is not at resonance, the plate current will rise to a high value.

(8) The dummy antenna (not shown) is next hooked up to L7 and the last stage is then retuned for a minimum reading of M3.

(9) The dummy antenna is removed and the actual antenna is hooked up to the transmitter. C1, C2, C3 and C4 are retuned slightly and the transmitter is now ready for operation.

3 **TRANSISTORIZED PUSH-PULL RF AMPLIFIER.** Fig. 13-16 illustrates a Class B push-pull RF amplifier. It operates in a manner similar to the push-pull amplifier used in the complete CW transmitter of Fig. 13-15. The input signal from the previous stage is fed to the input tuned circuit L1C1. From here it is applied to the bases of the transistors. The output is coupled from the output tuned circuit C2L2. The opposite ends of the output tuned circuit are connected to the collectors. R1 and R2 provide the base bias for the transistors so as to bias them at approximately cut-off for Class B operation. R3 is the emitter resistor that provides stabilization against thermal runaway.

Neutralizing capacitors are not shown in Fig. 13-16. This is because the transistors chosen have a low input impedance. This prevents feedback from the collector to the base. In the event that the circuit is used at a high frequency where it may oscillate, then push-pull neutralization of the type shown in Fig. 13-11 may be used.

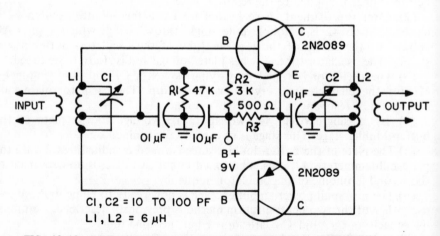

FIG. 13-16. A TRANSISTORIZED CLASS B PUSH-PULL AMPLIFIER.

THE PI-SECTION OUTPUT CIRCUIT. Fig. 13-17 illustrates a type of output circuit that is widely used. It is called a pi-section tuned circuit and consists of C1, L1 and C2.

In tuning a pi-section tank circuit, C1, the input capacitor, is adjusted for minimum plate current (resonance). C2, the loading capacitor, is then adjusted for proper loading. C1 is then readjusted for a plate current dip. This procedure is repeated until the correct plate current and loading are attained.

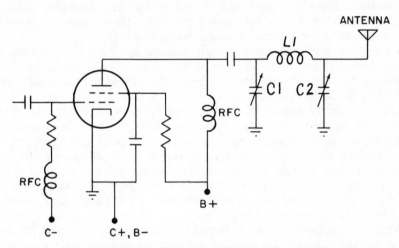

FIG. 13-17. AN AMPLIFIER USING PI-SECTION OUTPUT CIRCUIT.

PARASITIC OSCILLATIONS. "Parasitic oscillations" are spurious oscillations that occur at frequencies other than the desired output frequency. Parasitic oscillations cause the following:

(1) Reduction of overall transmitter efficiency. The energy that is used by parasitic oscillations is taken away from the energy of the desired signal.

(2) Distortion of the modulated carrier wave.

(3) Difficulty in tuning the transmitter properly.

(4) Excessive heating. Part of the energy of the parasitic oscillation is dissipated in the form of heat.

(5) Spurious emissions and their harmonics are radiated at the parasitic frequencies.

Parasitic oscillations are not easy to cure. One or more of the following must be tried in order to eliminate parasitic oscillations:

(a) Insert a small, non-inductive resistor in series with the plate and/or grid of the stage where the oscillations occur.

(b) Change the "dress" of the leads. Shielding some leads may be necessary.

(c) Insert low value RF chokes in series with the plate and/or screen leads.

(d) Insert low value RF chokes shunted by low value resistors in series with the plate lead and/or grid lead.

(e) Heavily bypass points in the circuit that should be "cold" to RF.

253

AN OSCILLATING RF AMPLIFIER. An oscillating RF amplifier is a source of parasitic oscillation. It has been previously pointed out that an oscillating RF amplifier is very undesirable. An amplifier is only supposed to amplify and not to oscillate.

In testing a transmitter for self-oscillation, the first step is to tune it up normally. The crystal is then removed and the transmitter is keyed. If self-oscillation is present, we will see grid current and/or RF output. This check should be made with the tuning controls in all positions. In many transmitters, there is a high risk of overloading and damaging tubes and components if the key is held down too long. The transmitter should be keyed for only a few seconds at a time during this test.

To localize the undesirable circuit that causes the self-oscillation, it is necessary to disable all but the suspected circuits. In a typical transmitter consisting of an oscillator, a multiplier, a driver and a final amplifier, the procedure would be as follows:

The most likely source of trouble is in the final amplifier. This stage is isolated by removing the driver tube and doing the tests described above. The grid, plate and loading controls should be rotated to all positions and combinations while turning the transmitter on for short periods of time. If there are no grid current or plate current jumps, or if there is an absence of RF output, the final amplifier stage is probably stable. The driver tube should be replaced and the tests should be repeated with each succeeding stage until the oscillation is found.

When the oscillating stage is found, it is necessary to localize the cause. Check the following: Is the shielding between the grid and plate satisfactory? Is neutralization necessary? If it is neutralized, is the adjustment of the neutralizing circuit correct? Is the tube good? Is there any path, such as a filament, B+ or a control line that a signal can follow, from output to input, for one or more stages? Additional by-passing and filtering of such lines may be necessary.

The frequency of the oscillation can be identified by the use of a general coverage receiver or a wavemeter. The frequency is often far above or below the operating frequency of the transmitter. For example, when a grid choke and a plate choke in the same stage, are of the same value, the circuit may behave as a tuned grid-tuned plate oscillator, at a frequency determined by the RF chokes and capacities in the circuit. This type of oscillation can usually be corrected by adding parasitic suppressors to the circuit.

TELEVISION INTERFERENCE. Transmitters frequently cause interference to television receivers. One of the main reasons for this is the fact that the frequencies of the television channels are harmonically related to the transmitter frequencies. An example will make this clear. Let us assume that a transmitter output is 29 MHz. Regardless of how well the transmitter is designed, a certain amount of energy at the second harmonic (58 MHz) will also be transmitted. Since television Channel 2 is from 54 to 60 MHz, the 58 MHz signal will cause interference to Channel 2.

One of the important methods of preventing harmonics from being radiated from the transmitter is to install a low-pass filter between the transmitter and its antenna. A low-pass filter will pass signals below a certain

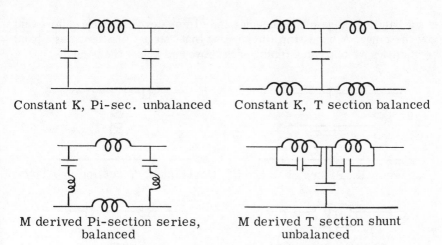

Constant K, Pi-sec. unbalanced   Constant K, T section balanced

M derived Pi-section series,   M derived T section shunt
            balanced   unbalanced

FIG. 13-18. VARIOUS TYPES OF LOW-PASS FILTERS.

cut-off frequency and block signals above that frequency. In this way, the harmonics will not get through to the antenna to be radiated. In the above example, we would install a low-pass filter with a cut-off frequency of 40 MHz. The 29 MHz signal would get through, but the 58 MHz harmonic would be suppressed.

Fig. 13-18 illustrates some simple forms of single section low-pass filters, together with the designations of the filters. The designations come about from the fact that the appearance of the various filter configurations resemble letters of the American or Greek alphabet.

A second important method of preventing interference to a television receiver is to install a high-pass filter at the television receiver's antenna terminals in series with the antenna. A high-pass filter will pass signals above a certain cut-off frequency and reject signals below this frequency. We choose the high–pass filter with a cut-off frequency below the television frequencies. The television signals will pass through without attenuation, but the signals below the cut-off frequency will not be allowed to pass. The reason we wish to reject the signals below the television channel is that they can overload the front end of the television receiver and cause harmonics and other spurious interference. Reference to the previous example will make this clear. Let us assume that the transmitter operating at 29 MHz has a low pass filter at the transmitter and transmits only at 29 MHz with no harmonics. A TV receiver located close by will be swamped with the 29 MHz signal. It will overload the receiver's front end and by means of rectification in the receiver, harmonics will be produced. The second harmonic of 29 MHz is 59 MHz which falls inside of Channel 2 and will cause interference similar to what would result if 58 MHz were radiated from the transmitter. Some typical single section high-pass filters are illustrated in Fig. 13-19.

If we replace the coils of the basic high and low-pass filters with resistors, we will have R-C circuits that also behave as high and low-pass filters.

In addition to the filters described above, there are also filters known as BAND-PASS and BAND-STOP FILTERS. A band-pass filter is a filter that passes a band or range of frequencies and attenuates frequencies above and below the range. A band-stop filter is one that "stops" or attenuates a band of frequencies while passing frequencies above and below the band.

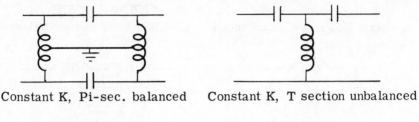

Constant K, Pi-sec. balanced   Constant K, T section unbalanced

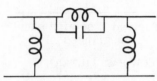
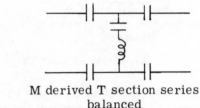

M derived, Pi-section shunt   M derived T section series
unbalanced   balanced

FIG. 13-19. VARIOUS TYPES OF HIGH-PASS FILTERS.

PRACTICE QUESTIONS - LESSON 13

1. The principal advantage of a tetrode over a triode is:
a. more power can be had
b. more voltage gain can be had
c. neutralization is not required
d. distortion is considerably reduced

2. Frequency shift is caused by:
a. poor voltage regulation
b. high plate and screen voltages
c. overmodulation
d. inadequate by-passing

3. In tuning a transmitter's pi-network circuit:
a. the plate tuning capacitor is tuned for a dip in antenna current
b. the loading capacitor is tuned for a dip in antenna current
c. the plate tuning capacitor is tuned for a dip in plate current
d. the loading capacitor is tuned for a dip in plate current

4. An advantage of a grounded grid amplifier is:
a. the full excitation voltage appears between cathode and ground
b. low driving power is required
c. a higher noise figure is possible
d. the input impedance is high

5. Excessive production of harmonics cannot be eliminated by:
a. a Faraday shield
b. capacitive coupling
c. a low-pass filter
d. a high Q plate tank circuit

6. As compared to a Class A amplifier, a Class C amplifier:
a. has less distortion   b. requires less driving power
c. operates over the linear portion of its characteristic curve
d. operates over a greater part of its characteristic curve

7. The first step in neutralizing an RF amplifier is to:
a. remove the plate voltage
b. tune the plate circuit to resonance
c. adjust the neutralizing capacitor for minimum output on the RF indicator
d. tune the grid circuit to resonance

8. A buffer amplifier is used to:
a. improve the efficiency of an RF thermocouple
b. decrease the amplifier output
c. raise the Q of the oscillator
d. improve the frequency stability of the oscillator stage

9. The circuit condition which will NOT minimize harmonic components in the output circuit of an RF amplifier is:
a. low L/C ratio   c. push-pull operation
b. improper neutralization   d. proper bias voltage

10. Fig. 10 is a circuit of an RF amplifier. What is wrong?
a. the grid RF choke is missing
b. there is no grid bias
c. C- should be connected to a tap on the ground coil
d. the bottom of C should go to the bottom of the plate coil

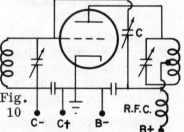

Fig. 10

11. What type of neutralization is used in Fig. 10?
a. grid   b. plate   c. criss-cross   d. Ballantine

12. What type of feed is used in the plate circuit of Fig. 10?
a. series   b. shunt   c. inductive   d. capacitive

13. How many RF doublers and triplers must we use to bring an oscillator's output of 5.0 MHz up to 90 MHz?
a. two doublers and a tripler
b. two doublers and a quadrupler
c. two triplers and a doubler
d. two triplers and a quadrupler

14. An advantage of a push-push RF amplifier over a push-pull RF amplifier is that:
a. it has greater efficiency
b. the push-push amplifier can be used as a frequency tripler
c. the push-push amplifier can be used as a frequency doubler
d. the push-push amplifier need not be neutralized when used as a tripler

15. What type of coupling should be used between two RF stages which are located some distance from each other?
a. capacitive   b. inductive   c. resistive   d. link

16. Tubes in parallel are recognized by the fact that:
a. their grids are connected together
b. their plates are connected to opposite ends of the load
c. their plates are connected together   d. a and b are correct

17. In a Class C vacuum tube amplifier, efficiency may run as high as:
a. 85%   b. 100%   c. 50%   d. 200%

18. In a Class C amplifier, plate current flows for:
a. the entire cycle   c. half the cycle
b. three-quarters of a cycle   d. one-third of a cycle

19. A Class C amplifier:
a. is biased at several times cutoff   c. requires low drive
b. has low efficiency   d. has excellent fidelity

20. Which of the following do not eliminate parasitics:
a. short grid and plate leads   c. resistance in series with grid
b. low Q tuned circuits   d. use of button mica capacitors

21. An advantage of a grounded grid amplifier is:
a. the full excitation voltage appears between cathode and ground
b. low driving power is required
c. a higher noise figure is possible
d. the input impedance is high

22. A separate power supply is used for the oscillator stage of a transmitter:
a. because the filaments require a separate heating source
b. because a lower B+ voltage is required
c. to prevent frequency instability due to load variations being fed back through a common power supply
d. to increase the frequency bandwidth radiated due to a common power supply

23. A triode radio frequency power amplifier must be neutralized:
a. to increase power output   b. to prevent self-oscillations
c. to eliminate second harmonic radiation
d. when used as a frequency doubler

24. What is a method for protecting a tube with grid-leak bias if the excitation should fail?
a. use chokes at the plate and grid leads
b. increase the grid-leak bias   c. use cathode bias
d. use small resistors in the plate and grid circuits

25. A power output RF amplifier SHOULD NOT:

a. be coupled to the antenna system
b. have minimum plate current at resonance
c. couple high harmonics to antenna
d. be matched to the output circuit impedance

26. A circuit that passes all frequencies above a certain frequency is called a:
a. high-pass filter
b. low-pass filter
c. high-level attenuator
d. low-level attenuator

27. Excessive plate current can result from:
a. a shorted grid bias supply
b. a loss of screen voltage
c. an open in the grid bias supply
d. excessive transfer of harmonics

28. Optimum power output from an RF amplifier can be obtained:
a. when the stage is a frequency doubler
b. when the output impedance matches the tube load impedance
c. when the plate impedance is equal to the grid load impedance
d. when the plate circuit is slightly off resonance

29. A tetrode RF amplifier will not oscillate because:
a. there are no space charges in a tetrode
b. the plate of a tetrode is larger than the plates of other tubes
c. it is impossible for any RF amplifier to oscillate
d. the screen grid reduces the plate-grid capacity

30. A frequency multiplier in a transmitter will:
a. increase the power of the fundamental frequency
b. increase the voltage of the fundamental frequency
c. increase the frequency in odd multiples
d. increase the frequency in multiples of 2, 3, 4, etc.

31. Tubes operated as Class C amplifiers are not suitable for use in audio-frequency amplification because of:
a. harmonic radiation
b. low voltage requirements
c. insufficient output
d. excessive distortion

32. TVI can be eliminated by a:
a. high-pass filter at the receiver
b. high-pass filter at the transmitter
c. high-pass filter at the receiver and a low-pass filter at the transmitter
d. low-pass filter at the receiver

33. Which of the following will not minimize harmonic generation?
a. link coupling between stages
b. use of a high-pass filter
c. use of low plate and screen voltages
d. use of high Q plate tank circuits

LESSON 14
MODULATED TRANSMITTERS

INTRODUCTION. In the previous lesson, we learned how a CW transmitter operates. Communication by means of CW transmission is known as RADIOTELEGRAPHY. The disadvantage of radiotelegraphy is that the radio operator must know the code. In order for an operator, who is not familiar with code, to be able to send and receive messages directly, the transmission of speech is necessary. The transmission of audio (speech) by means of radio communication is called RADIOTELEPHONY.

A radiotelephone transmitter consists of a CW transmitter (minus the telegraph key), plus an audio frequency amplifier system. The audio frequency system amplifies the audio signals and superimposes them on the RF signal. The process of superimposing the audio on the RF is known as MODULATION. The RF signal is called a CARRIER since it "carries" the audio through space to the receiving antenna. The "carrier frequency" is the frequency of the carrier or the output frequency of the transmitter when there is no modulation.

AMPLITUDE MODULATION (AM). In amplitude modulation, the modulating frequency is the audio intelligence (voice or music) which is to be transmitted. The audio, by itself, cannot be transmitted. A radio-frequency wave, however, is capable of being transmitted through space. If we combine or mix an audio-frequency wave with a radio-frequency wave in a special mixing circuit, we obtain an RF output which contains the audio and can be transmitted. Fig. 14-1 illustrates a voice modulated radio-frequency wave. Its amplitude varies according to the amplitude of the audio wave, thus the term "amplitude modulation". An AM wave is, therefore, a radio-frequency wave which contains in its amplitude variations, the audio or intelligence which we desire to transmit.

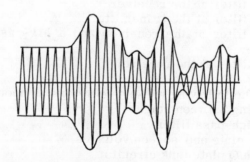

FIG. 14-1. RADIO WAVE MODULATED WITH VOICE.

260

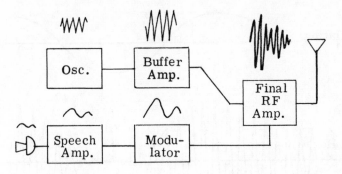

FIG. 14-2. BLOCK DIAGRAM OF AMPLITUDE-MODULATED TRANSMITTER.

THE AM TRANSMITTER. A block diagram of a typical amplitude modulated radiotelephone transmitter is shown in Fig. 14-2. Above each block is drawn the waveshape of the voltage output of that particular stage. With the aid of these waveshapes and the block diagram layout, we shall discuss the operation of the radiotelephone transmitter.

To begin with, the oscillator stage generates the RF carrier. The buffer-amplifier stage amplifies the output of the oscillator and isolates the oscillator from the power amplifier. The final RF power stage amplifies the output of the buffer stage and delivers the power to the antenna. The output waveshape of the final RF stage does not resemble the input waveshape. The RF waveshape has been altered by modulation. This brings us to the modulation or audio section. The microphone converts the sound that is to be transmitted into electrical variations. The weak output of the microphone is amplified by an audio amplifier (speech amplifier). The output of the speech amplifier drives an audio power amplifier called a MODULATOR. The modulator injects the audio signals into the RF power amplifier to produce the modulated RF output.

PERCENTAGE OF MODULATION. The method by which the audio signal is actually injected into the RF amplifier will be discussed later on. We will now explain the term "percentage of modulation".

It is possible to modulate with a large audio voltage or with a small audio voltage. A large modulating voltage causes a large variation in the peaks of the RF carrier, which results in a large percentage of modulation. A small audio voltage causes a small variation in the peaks of the RF carrier, which results in a low percentage of modulation. By examining the waveshape of a modulated carrier, it is possible to determine the numerical percentage of modulation.

For example, Fig. 14-3 illustrates a carrier that is 100% modulated. Notice that the highest peak of the modulated wave is exactly twice as high as the peak of the carrier before modulation. Also notice that the minimum point of the modulated signal is at zero amplitude. In other words, the peaks of the modulated signal vary 100% above and below the peaks of the unmodulated carrier. This is the condition for 100% modulation. Fig. 14-4 shows an example of 50% modulation. The carrier of Fig. 14-4 is the same in

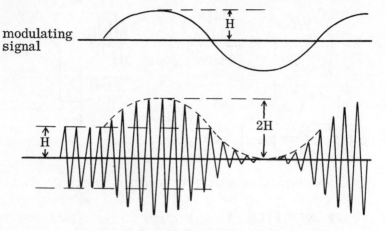

modulating
signal

FIG. 14-3. 100% AMPLITUDE MODULATION.

amplitude as the carrier of Fig. 14-3. The modulating signal of Fig. 14-4 is, however, half the amplitude of the modulating signal of Fig. 14-3. The maximum peak of the modulated signal is one and one-half times the peak of the unmodulated carrier, and the minimum is one half times the peak of the unmodulated carrier. In other words, the peaks of the modulated carrier vary 50% above and below the peaks of the unmodulated carrier.

If the carrier level is kept the same and the modulating signal is increased above that of Fig. 14-3, we get the wave shown in Fig. 14-5. This illustration is the waveshape of an OVERMODULATED carrier. During the interval labeled "C", there is actually no output from the transmitter.

The 100% modulated carrier of Fig. 14-3 is theoretically the most desirable in terms of reception. It produces the strongest possible undistorted signal at the receiver end. The 50% modulated signal is considered an UNDERMODULATED signal. It produces an undistorted but weak signal at the receiver end. The overmodulated signal is highly undesirable since it results in a distorted signal at the receiver end. Overmodulation also produces spurious radiation, which causes interference with nearby frequencies. The relationship between the percentage of modulation and the shape

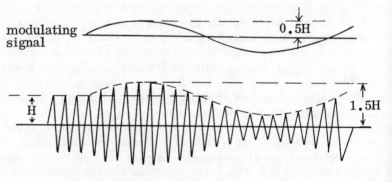

modulating
signal

FIG. 14-4. 50% AMPLITUDE MODULATION.

262

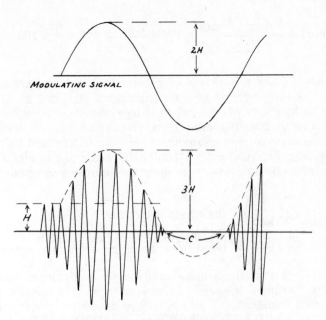

FIG. 14-5. OVERMODULATION.

of the modulated waveform is given by the formula:

$$\% \text{ modulation} = \frac{E_{max} - E_{min}}{2 E_O} \times 100$$

where: E_{max} is the peak amplitude of the modulated wave,
E_{min} is the minimum amplitude of the modulated wave,
E_O is the amplitude of the carrier with no modulation.

An example will illustrate the use of the formula. Find the percentage of modulation of the wave of Fig. 14-6.

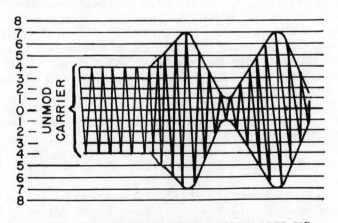

FIG. 14-6. A CARRIER THAT IS MODULATED 75%.

263

$$\% \text{ mod.} = \frac{E_{max} - E_{min}}{2 E_O} \times 100 = \frac{7 - 1}{2 \times 4} \times 100 = \frac{6}{8} \times 100 = 75\%$$

SIDEBANDS. The waveshapes of Figures 14-3 and 14-4 are actually the result of a combination of several frequencies. It is not possible to tell, merely by looking at a waveshape, what frequencies are combined to give it the shape that it has. However, these frequencies can be determined by mathematical analysis. For example, it has been determined that when a 1 kHz audio-frequency modulates a 1000 kHz carrier, the resultant signal will be a complex modulated wave containing the following component frequencies:

$$\left.\begin{array}{l}1 \text{ kHz} \\ 1000 \text{ kHz}\end{array}\right\} - \text{ the original frequencies}$$

1001 kHz - the sum of the original frequencies
999 kHz - the difference of the original frequencies

Whenever any two frequencies combine by modulation, the resultant waveshape will contain the *original frequencies plus the sum and difference of the original frequencies.* These new sum and difference frequencies are known as SIDEBAND FREQUENCIES or simply SIDEBANDS. In the above example, the 1001 kHz component is known as the UPPER SIDEBAND. The 999 kHz component is known as the LOWER SIDEBAND. If the audio frequency had been 2 kHz, the upper sideband would have been 1002 kHz, and the lower sideband would have been 998 kHz. The higher the audio modulating frequency, the farther both sidebands are removed from the carrier frequency.

When speech or music is used to modulate a carrier, many audio modulating frequencies are present. Each audio frequency will produce an upper sideband frequency and a lower sideband frequency. Therefore, speech or music modulation generates a wide band of frequencies. The difference in kHz between the uppermost side band and lowest sideband is called the BANDWIDTH of the modulated carrier. The bandwidth of a carrier is equal to twice the highest audio modulating frequency used. For example, if the carrier is 1000 kHz and the highest audio modulating frequency is 5 kHz, the band width is 10 kHz (1005 −995). If the highest audio modulating frequency is 3 kHz, the bandwidth is 6 kHz. In other words, this AM signal, consisting of a carrier and sidebands actually occupies 6 kHz of the radio frequency spectrum. Compare this to a CW signal which consists of only a carrier and therefore, has no bandwidth.

The FCC permits each station in the broadcast band (535-1605 kHz) to occupy a maximum channel width of 10 kHz. This means that the maximum audio modulating frequency must be limited to 5 kHz. If the broadcast station were to modulate with an audio signal greater than 5 kHz, the sidebands would interfere with the reception of stations occupying adjacent channels.

Overmodulation increases the bandwidth of the signal. It does so in the following manner: Overmodulation produces a distorted wave, including clipping of the negative part of the signal. This is shown in a previous paragraph. A distorted wave automatically produces new frequencies that modulate the carrier and generate additional sidebands. These additional sidebands are located some distance away from the carrier and thereby increase the bandwidth. The extent to which the additional sidebands interfere with other signals depends upon the amount of overmodulation.

POWER IN THE SIDEBANDS. If the modulator of a radiotelephone transmitter were turned off, the carrier would continue to be radiated. As soon as the modulator is turned on, the carrier is amplitude modulated and the sideband frequencies come into existence. Since the modulated wave contains frequencies in addition to the carrier, there must be more power in the modulated wave than in the unmodulated wave. The additional power is supplied by the modulator stage and is contained in the sidebands of the transmission.

The following formula tells us how to find the power in the sidebands when the modulation percentage and carrier power are known:

$$P_{sb} = \frac{m^2}{2} \times P_c$$

where: P_{sb} is the sideband power, m is the % of modulation $\div 100$ and P_c is the power in the unmodulated carrier.

From the formula, it can be seen that the sideband power varies with the square of the % of modulation. In other words, if we double the modulation, we double the sideband power; if we triple the modulation %, we multiply the sideband power by 9, etc.

EXAMPLE: How much power is in the sidebands of a 2,000 watt transmitter modulated 80%.

SOLUTION:

$$P_{sb} = \frac{.8^2}{2} \times 2000 = .32 \times 2000 = 640 \text{ watts}.$$

METHODS OF MODULATION. In the last few paragraphs, we have discussed the general principles of amplitude modulation. We are now ready to study exactly how the audio signal is superimposed on to the carrier.

There are many different methods of amplitude modulation. The most common method is to apply the audio-frequency modulating voltage to the plate of one of the RF amplifiers. This popular method is known as PLATE MODULATION. If the audio-frequency modulating voltage is applied to the control grid of the RF amplifier, we have GRID MODULATION. If a pentode power amplifier is modulated by applying the audio-frequency modulating voltage to the suppressor grid, we have SUPPRESSOR MODULATION. SCREEN GRID MODULATION and CATHODE MODULATION can be similarly accomplished by applying the audio-frequency modulating voltage to the screen and cathode electrodes respectively. In other words, the method of modulation is determined by the electrode of the RF amplifier tube to which the audio frequency modulating voltage is applied.

Modulating the final RF stage of a radiotelephone transmitter is known as HIGH-LEVEL MODULATION. The term is derived from the fact that the modulation takes place at the highest power level of the transmitter. If the modulation process takes place in a stage preceding the final stage, the system is known as LOW LEVEL MODULATION. In low level modulation, the RF amplifiers which follow the modulated stage are operated as linear or Class A amplifiers, rather than Class C. A Class C amplifier will distort the audio component of the modulated signal, whereas a Class A amplifier will amplify all signal frequencies without distortion. In high level modulation, the final RF amplifier is always operated as a Class C amplifier. High level modulation is the most efficient modulation system, and is also much more popular than low level modulation.

PLATE MODULATION. There are several methods of plate modulation. The simplest one is illustrated in Fig. 14-7. The audio-frequency output of the modulator stage is coupled through transformer, T, to the plate circuit of the power amplifier. Transformer T is called the modulation transformer. The audio voltage across the secondary, S, of the modulation transformer is in series with the plate voltage of the RF amplifier. Fig. 14-8A shows this audio voltage.

When the audio voltage causes the top of the transformer secondary, S, to go positive with respect to the bottom, the audio voltage and the power supply voltage aid each other. The plate voltage of the RF amplifier stage will, therefore, be the sum of the power supply voltage and the audio voltage. Fig. 14-8B shows this rise in the RF amplifier plate voltage above the B+ value. Since the plate power input to the stage is directly dependent

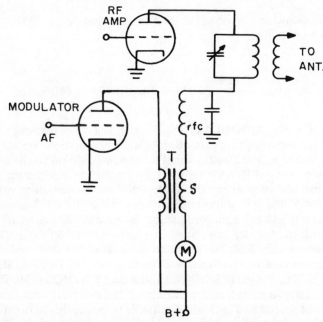

FIG. 14-7. TRANSFORMER-COUPLED MODULATOR CIRCUIT.
266

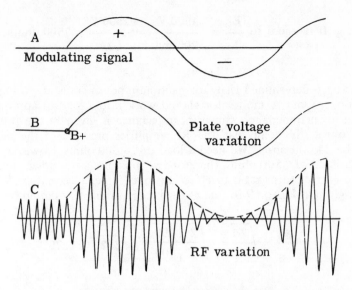

FIG. 14-8. AMPLITUDE MODULATION.

upon the plate voltage, the plate power input will increase during the positive audio alternation. An increase in plate power input will, in turn, cause the useful power output to increase. The RF output, therefore, rises during the positive half of the audio cycle.

During the negative half of the audio cycle, the top of the transformer secondary, S, is negative with respect to the bottom. Now, the audio voltage and the power supply voltage are in series opposing. Therefore, the two voltages buck each other and the plate voltage is the difference between the two voltages. Fig. 14-8B shows the drop in the RF amplifier plate voltage below the B+ value during the negative alternation of the audio. The drop in plate voltage causes the plate power input to decrease which, in turn, causes the useful power output to decrease. Fig. 14-8C shows the RF output over a complete sinewave cycle. Fig. 14-1 illustrates the RF output from a transmitter that has been modulated by speech or music.

The modulation transformer T is actually a coupling device that couples audio frequency energy from the modulator tube to the plate circuit of the RF amplifier. The plate impedance of the RF amplifier is actually the load of the modulator. The modulation transformer T is therefore not only a coupling device, but also a matching device. In order to couple the maximum audio frequency energy to the plate circuit of the RF amplifier, the impedance of the load (plate circuit of RF amplifier) and source (modulator tube) should be matched. An example will illustrate these relationships.

EXAMPLE: Let us assume that the RF amplifier has a plate voltage of 1500 volts and a plate current of 200 ma. The modulator tube has a plate voltage of 1000 volts, a plate current of 100 ma. and a plate impedance of 12,000 ohms. What is the proper turns ratio for the modulation transformer?

ANSWER: First, we determine what the load upon the modulator tube actually is. The load on the modulator tube is the DC plate impedance of the RF amplifier.

267

It is equal to $\dfrac{E_p}{I_p} = \dfrac{1500\ V}{200\ ma} = \dfrac{1500\ V}{.2A} = 7500$ ohms.

It has been determined that, for maximum power transfer with minimum distortion, a Class A modulator should work into a load of approximately twice its own impedance. Since its impedance is given in the problem as 12,000 ohms, the load that the RF amplifier presents to the modulator should be 24,000 ohms. We need a load of 24,000 ohms. However, we have an actual load of 7500 ohms, therefore we must use a stepdown transformer with the correct turns ratio to effect a proper impedance match. We use the formula given in Lesson 9 to find out what the turns ratio should be.

$$\frac{N_p}{N_s} = \sqrt{\frac{Z1}{Z2}} = \sqrt{\frac{24,000}{7,500}} = \sqrt{3.2} = 1.79$$

PLATE CURRENT IN PLATE MODULATION. In Fig. 14-7, "M" is a DC milliammeter which measures the DC plate current of the modulated RF stage. During normal modulation (100% or under), the DC plate current should REMAIN CONSTANT. If the percent modulation does not increase beyond 100%, there will be no distortion of the RF wave. The instantaneous increase in plate current will, therefore, be exactly the same as the instantaneous decrease in the plate current. Therefore, the average plate current change is zero. The DC plate current meter, therefore, reads the same plate current when the power RF amplifier stage is either modulated or unmodulated. This is also true of grid modulation.

In the event that the DC plate current does vary during modulation, one or more of the following conditions may be the cause:

(1) Improper neutralization of the first RF stage.
(2) Improper bias in the first RF stage.
(3) Insufficient RF excitation to the final RF amplifier.
(4) Overmodulation.
(5) Positive or negative carrier shift (discussed later in this lesson).
(6) A defective RF amplifier tube.
(7) Tank circuit improperly tuned.

THE PUSH-PULL MODULATOR. The single-ended (one tube) modulator stage of Fig. 14-7 is operated Class A so that there will be no distortion of the amplified modulating signal. The disadvantage of a one-tube Class A amplifier is that it operates at low efficiency. A low efficiency tube cannot always deliver the power that is required of a modulator stage. A push-pull amplifier is therefore preferred because it is capable of delivering more power than a single tube. Fig. 14-9 illustrates a push-pull modulator circuit being used in a high level modulation system.

The push-pull modulator may be operated either Class A or Class B, depending upon the power output requirements. A Class B push-pull

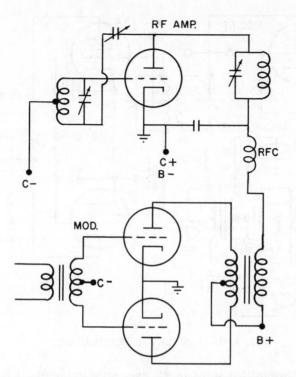

FIG. 14-9. A PUSH-PULL CLASS B MODULATOR WITH THE RF STAGE.

amplifier is more efficient, but it does require a large driving power applied to its grid circuit. The positive peaks of the grid signal usually drive the grid into grid current. The flow of grid current causes power to be dissipated in the grid circuit. The driver stage must be able to supply the power dissipated in the grid circuit. Also, the regulation of the power supply of a Class B modulator has to be very good.

If the bias power supply of the modulator of Fig. 14-9 becomes short-circuited, there would be no bias voltage on the grids. The plate current would rise and probably cause damage to the tubes.

A push-pull amplifier operated Class A, does not operate in the grid current region and therefore, requires very little grid driving power from the driver stage. The Class A push-pull amplifier amplifies the audio modulating voltage without distortion. The Class B modulator introduces a slight amount of distortion into the modulating signal.

LOW-LEVEL MODULATION. Fig. 14-10 illustrates low-level modulation. It has been pointed out that, in a system using low-level modulation, a stage prior to the final RF stage is modulated. In Fig. 14-10, V4 and V5 constitute a push-pull audio amplifier that modulates V1. T1 is the modulation transformer.

The principle advantage of low-level modulation is the fact that very little audio power is required. In order to plate modulate an RF stage properly, the modulator should supply approximately one-half of the input power to

269

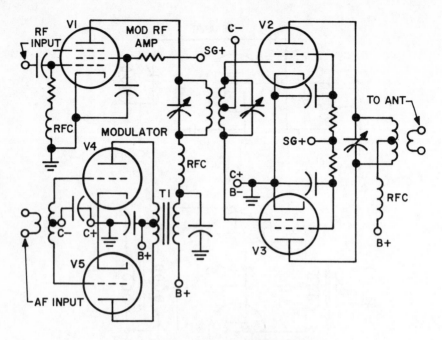

FIG. 14-10. LOW-LEVEL MODULATION.

the stage. It is obvious that since an RF stage prior to the final RF stage has a much lower input power than the final stage, the modulator must supply far less power for low-level modulation than high-level modulation. This reduces the size of the modulator transformer, the size and number of tubes used in the modulator section and the amount of power drawn from the power source.

The chief disadvantage of low-level modulation is the reduced overall efficiency of the transmitter. This is because the final stage or stages that follow the modulated stage must be linear with its inherent low efficiency characteristic. A stage that follows a modulated stage must not distort the signal because it contains the audio intelligence. A high efficiency Class C stage cannot be used because it distorts the signal. A Class A or Class B amplifier (in push-pull) must be used because they are linear. That is, they reproduce the signal without distortion. However, Class A and Class B amplifiers have low efficiencies.

Although a properly operated Class B amplifier distorts the individual RF cycle, it does not distort the modulation envelope. Linear amplifiers generally use Class AB or Class B operation because Class A is too inefficient. Class A has an efficiency of approximately 25%, whereas Class B is approximately 40%.

A linear amplifier looks like any other amplifier. A linear amplifier is designed by choosing the proper tube and using the correct grid bias, screen and plate voltages. The final RF amplifier stage of Fig. 14-10 is operated Class B.

One of the characteristics of a Class B linear amplifier is that the RF power

270

output varies with the square of the excitation voltage. If we double the excitation voltage, we quadruple the output power. If we triple the excitation voltage, we increase the output power nine times. The reason for this is as follows: Since the amplifier operates on the linear portion of its curve, doubling the input grid voltage will double the output voltage. If the output voltage doubles, the output power quadruples because of the power formula:

$$P = \frac{E^2}{R}$$

Note that the power increases as the square of the voltage. Another way of looking at this is to realize that in a linear amplifier, the plate current varies directly with the grid voltage. Examining the power formula that involves power and current, we see that the power varies as the square of the current. Thus, if we were to double the plate current, we would be quadrupling the output power.

4 THE DOHERTY AMPLIFIER. It has been stated above that the ordinary linear Class B modulated r-f amplifier has an efficiency of about 40%. This results in a tremendous waste of power when we are dealing with a high power station. The search for a more efficient linear power amplifier led to the development of the DOHERTY amplifier. The Doherty amplifier has an efficiency of approximately 65%. Fig. 14-11 illustrates the form that a

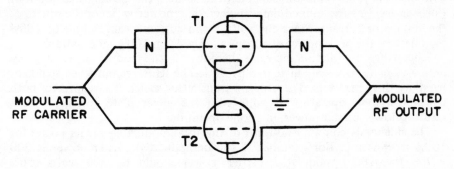

FIG. 14-11. A DOHERTY AMPLIFIER.

Doherty amplifier takes. Two tubes are used. Each tube amplifies a different part of the modulated signal. T1 alone amplifies that part of the signal from 0 to the level of the unmodulated carrier. It operates as a conventional Class B amplifier. T2 operates only on the positive peaks of the modulated signal. Its bias prevents it from operating until the positive modulation peaks reach it. T2 operates as an efficient Class C amplifier. The "N" blocks are coupling networks that effect the proper phase shifts and impedance matching.

POWER RELATIONS IN A PLATE MODULATED TRANSMITTER. We can summarize the power relations that exist in a Class C modulated power amplifier by stating that the power required to generate the carrier wave is supplied from the RF amplifier DC plate supply, while the power required to generate the sidebands is supplied by the modulator. The amount of modulating power required to modulate a transmitter depends upon three factors. First of all, it depends upon the type of modulation that is being used (plate modulation, grid modulation, etc.). Secondly, it depends upon the percentage of modulation. Thirdly, it depends upon the nature of the audio that is doing the modulating.

In order to modulate a carrier 100% with a pure audio sine wave, the audio output power of the modulator stage must be equal to one-half of the input power to the RF stage. For example, if the unmodulated plate power input to the final RF power amplifier stage is 200 watts, the modulator power output should be 100 watts. The power input to the RF power amplifier stage has been increased by 50% from 200 to 300 watts. If speech or music is used to modulate the carrier, the output modulator power that is required need be only one fourth of the RF input power. In the above example the average modulator power output for speech modulation would be 50 watts. This prevents the peaks of the speech modulation from overmodulating the RF power amplifier.

An examination of Fig. 14-3 will show that the peak modulated RF output voltage during 100% modulation is twice as high as the unmodulated output carrier voltage. This is also true for the plate current. The RF power amplifier when modulated must, therefore, be capable of handling peak voltages and currents that are twice as great as unmodulated voltages and currents. They must also be capable of handling peak powers that are four times as great as the unmodulated power. The power varies as the square of the voltage or current. Since the voltage and current peaks double on 100% modulation, the peak power quadruples ($2^2 = 4$) on 100% modulation.

Since 100% modulation increases the power to the modulated RF stage by 50%, the plate losses are increased by 50%. The RF stage must be capable of handling this extra loss. Therefore, a transmitter which is designed for both CW and phone operation is adjusted for a lower plate voltage, with a resulting lower carrier power, in phone operation.

The sidebands contain one-third of the total modulated carrier power for 100% modulation. For example, if the unmodulated carrier power is 200 watts, the 100% modulated carrier power would be 300 watts (50% increase). The increased 100 watts of power is contained in the sidebands. The sidebands, therefore, contain one third of the total modulated carrier power. Since the total sidebands contain one third of the power, the upper and lower sidebands each contain one sixth of the total power.

From the above, it can be seen that the higher the percentage of modulation, the greater is the audio power in the sidebands. Since the sidebands contain the audio intelligence, it is obvious that a signal with more "Intelligence Power" in the sidebands will produce a stronger audio signal at the receiver. We therefore try to modulate a carrier as close as possible to 100%.

A signal with more power in its sidebands will be understood by receivers at a greater distance from the transmitter than the signals with less sideband power. A signal with high power in the sidebands will override the noise that is present in the receiver. It will also be able to compete with interfering stations and other spurious signals.

GRID MODULATION. Plate modulation requires a large amount of audio modulating power. Grid modulation, in comparison, requires very little audio modulating power.

Grid modulation operates by varying the bias to the grid of the RF power amplifier in accordance with the audio modulating voltage. The varying bias, in turn, causes the power output of the RF power amplifier to vary.

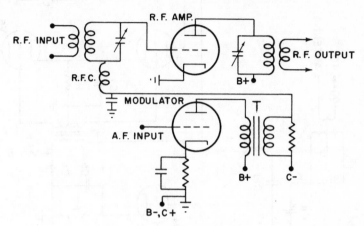

FIG. 14-12. GRID MODULATION.

Grid modulation is illustrated in Fig. 14-12. The primary of the modulation transformer T is connected to the plate of the modulator. The secondary of T is in series with the grid bias power supply of the RF amplifier. The audio modulation varies the voltage across the secondary of transformer T in polarity and amplitude. This varying voltage adds to or subtracts from the bias supply, resulting in a varying bias voltage on the grid of the RF power amplifier. This varying bias causes a varying RF output, which is the modulated carrier.

The last audio or modulator stage must be operated as a Class A amplifier if fidelity of reproduction is to be maintained. The comparatively low output of a Class A audio amplifier is sufficient for grid modulation because low power is required for grid modulation.

The efficiency of a grid modulated amplifier is much less than that of a plate modulated amplifier. It is approximately 30%. Also, it is very difficult to achieve 100% modulation with a minimum of distortion. The adjustments of a grid modulated system are critical. Because of the poor linearity and low power output, grid modulation is used less than plate modulation.

A TYPICAL RADIOTELEPHONE TRANSMITTER. Fig. 14-13 illustrates a simple, low power, plate modulated radiotelephone transmitter. The power supplies have been omitted from the diagram for the sake of simplicity.

V1 is a triode crystal-controlled oscillator that is capacity coupled to V2, the modulated RF amplifier. V2 is neutralized by Cn. V3, the speech amplifier, is a high gain pentode which amplifies the weak audio voltage output of a high impedance crystal microphone. The output of V3 is

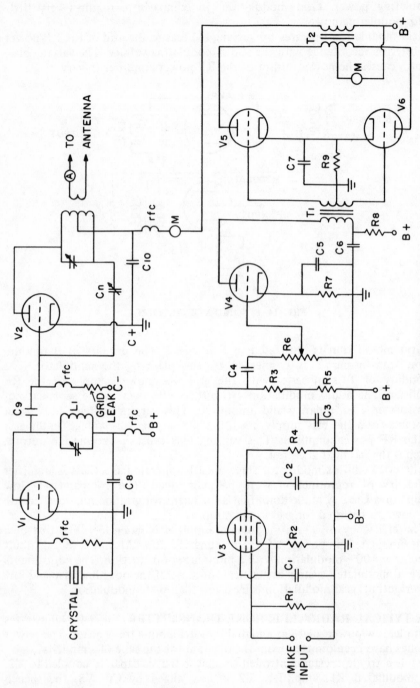

FIG. 14-13. A TYPICAL RADIOTELEPHONE TRANSMITTER.

274

coupled to a medium gain triode V4, through R3, C4 and R6 (the audio volume control). The setting of R6 will determine the average percentage modulation of the carrier. The output of V4 is transformer-coupled to V5 and V6 by T1, an interstage transformer. It serves to match the impedance of the plate of V4 to the grids of V5 and V6. V5 and V6 may be operated in Class AB push-pull. Class AB is commonly used since it exhibits efficiency and fidelity characteristics which are midway between Class A and Class B operation. T2 is the modulation transformer.

The power supplies are not shown in the figure. In actual practice, there would be several power supplies for this transmitter. One large power supply, even if it could deliver sufficient power, should not be used. One power supply would result in "frequency shift" and frequency modulation of the RF carrier.

"Frequency shift" or dynamic instability, as it is sometimes called, refers to small changes in the frequency of the emitted signal. These changes are due to variations in the plate voltage and in the loading of the oscillator. For instance, if a common power supply were used, the large variations in the modulator would cause the power supply voltage to vary. This means that the oscillator plate voltage would vary, which in turn could cause the oscillator's frequency to vary. A separate well-regulated power supply for the oscillator stage would remedy this situation. Other remedies for "dynamic instability" are: use an oscillator tuned circuit with a high effective Q, loose coupling between the oscillator and the following stage, use a high value grid-leak resistance and reduce the oscillator stage feedback to the lowest possible amount that still allows for stable oscillation.

If the audio that is present in the modulator is permitted to affect the oscillator's plate voltage, the frequency of the oscillator will vary in accordance with the audio. This, in effect, is frequency modulation with its resultant wide band and interference on nearby channels. The only modulation that we want in the transmitter is amplitude modulation. Separate, well regulated power supplies for both the modulator and the oscillator, in addition to the remedies given above, will prevent this.

R5, R8, C3 and C6 are called DE-COUPLING or ISOLATING resistors and capacitors. Their purpose is to isolate the plate circuit of one stage from the plate circuit in another stage where a common power supply is used. They are, in effect, filters. When they are not used, it is possible for a signal in a higher level audio stage to be fed back to a lower level audio stage, through the common power supply. When this happens, the signal that is fed back may reinforce the signal that is present at the lower level stage and audio oscillation will occur. The use of de-coupling networks prevents this from occurring.

CHECKING FOR PERCENT OF MODULATION. For maximum undistorted output, a properly adjusted transmitter should be operated at 100% modulation. It is, therefore, important to be able to determine the point of 100% modulation of a transmitter.

A very simple method of determining 100% modulation is to observe the DC plate current meter in the modulated RF stage. The modulator output is adjusted up to the point where the needle of the plate current meter just

275

begins to flicker. When this occurs, we are modulating at approximately 100%. It was previously pointed out that there should be no variation in the plate current reading of a modulated RF amplifier. A slight movement of the DC plate current meter indicates that the peaks of the speech modulation are driving the RF power amplifier stage slightly above 100% modulation.

Another check on the proper point of 100% modulation is to observe the RF ammeter in the antenna circuit. When the transmitter is modulated, power is added to the carrier. During 100% sine wave modulation, the total output power is increased by 50%. When this happens, the antenna current should rise approximately 22%. This can be proven with the aid of the power formula:

$$I = \sqrt{\frac{P}{R}}$$

If we modulate 100% by a sinusoidal tone, the power, P, increases by 50% to 1.5 times its original value. It can be seen from the formula that I is proportional to the square root of P. The square root of 1.5 is 1.225. Therefore, the current I increases by 0.225 or 22.5% of its original value.

If a pure sine wave audio note is not available to check for this 22% rise, the operator should whistle or hum a steady note into the microphone to simulate a pure sine wave note.

A third method of checking modulation is by means of the OSCILLO-SCOPE. This instrument shows the graph or waveshape of the signal being checked. By means of the oscilloscope, we can tell the approximate percentage of modulation.

There are two ways in which the oscilloscope can be connected to the modulated RF amplifier to check modulation. Fig. 14-14 shows one method.

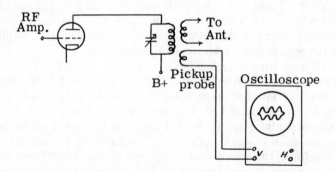

FIG: 14-14. CHECKING PERCENTAGE MODULATION.

The output of the transmitter is coupled directly to the vertical plates of the oscilloscope. The internal sweep of the oscilloscope is turned on. Fig. 14-15 illustrates three possible patterns that would be seen on the screen of the oscilloscope for three different conditions of modulation. It is assumed that the modulating voltage is a pure sine wave. Fig. 14-15A shows the waveshape for 50% modulation. Fig. 14-15B shows 100% modulation and Fig. 14-15C shows overmodulation..

276

A. 50% modulation.   **B.** 100% modulation.   **C.** Over-modulation.

FIG. 14-15. WAVE-ENVELOPE MODULATION PATTERNS ON THE OSCILLOSCOPE.

The second method of using an oscilloscope to check modulation is illustrated in Fig. 14-16.

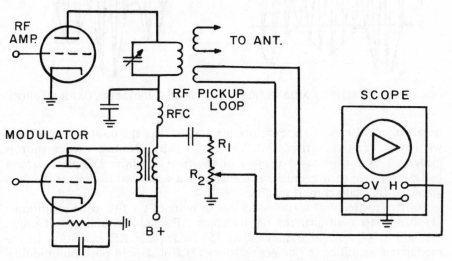

FIG. 14-16. USING THE OSCILLOSCOPE TO OBTAIN
MODULATION TRAPEZOID PATTERNS.

The transmitter output is coupled to the vertical plates of the oscilloscope. The audio output of the modulator is connected to the horizontal deflecting plates. The internal sweep of the oscilloscope is turned off. This produces a wedge-shaped pattern called a TRAPEZOID. Fig. 14-17 illustrates three trapezoidal patterns for three different conditions of modulation. Fig. 14-17A shows the pattern for 50% modulation; Fig. 14-17B shows the pattern for 100% modulation and Fig. 14-17C shows the pattern for overmodulation.

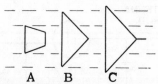

A. 50% modulation. **B.** 100% modulation. **C.** Over-modulation.

FIG. 14-17. TRAPEZOIDAL MODULATION PATTERNS ON OSCILLOSCOPE.

CARRIER SHIFT. Carrier shift refers to the condition when the positive and negative amplitudes of a modulated carrier are not equal. Carrier shift does not refer to a change in the carrier frequency.

When the positive portion of the modulation envelope is greater than the negative portion, we have "positive carrier shift". See Fig. 14-18A. When the

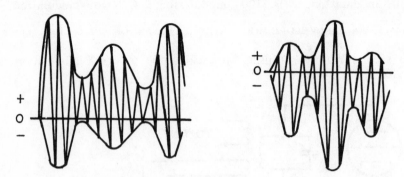

FIG. 14-18A. POSITIVE CARRIER SHIFT. FIG. 14-18B. NEGATIVE CARRIER SHIFT.

negative amplitudes of the envelope are greater than the positive amplitudes, we have "negative carrier shift" (Fig. 14-18B). Positive carrier shift is evidenced by an increased reading of the final amplifier DC plate current meter. Negative carrier shift is evidenced by a decreased reading of the final amplifier DC plate current reading.

Positive carrier shift is caused by one or more of the following conditions: (1) inadequate neutralization (2) improper RF amplifier tuning (3) parasitic oscillations (4) excessive audio drive (5) inadequate RF excitation to the modulated amplifier (6) defective tubes (7) Unbalanced push-pull modulation stage. Negative carrier shift is caused by one or more of the following conditions: (1) improper modulator bias (2) modulator is overdriven (3) poor regulation of modulator power supply (4) Unbalanced push-pull modulator stage (5) overmodulation (6) impedance mis-match between the modulator and the r-f amplifier.

Fig. 14-19 illustrates a carrier shift detector. With the carrier on and no modulation, we note the reading of the meter. When modulation is turned on, the meter reading should not vary. If there is no carrier shift, the average current will remain the same. If the current increases, we have positive carrier shift. If it decreases, we have negative carrier shift.

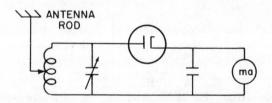

FIG. 14-19. A CARRIER SHIFT DETECTOR.

278

3 TRANSMITTER INTERMODULATION. Transmitter intermodulation is the generation of spurious, unwanted signals that result from the mixing of signals in a non-linear stage of a transmitter. The signals that are mixed may originate within the transmitter, or one of the signals may originate in another transmitter. Nevertheless, the signals do mix and generate new spurious signals. These signals are amplified and radiated, along with the desired signal, and cause distortion, splatter and interference with other transmissions. Transmitter intermodulation comes about in the following manner:

Non-linear stages in a transmitter will distort a signal. This distortion contains harmonic frequencies not present in the original signal. These new undesired frequencies will mix with other signals and will modulate the carrier to produce new sideband frequencies known as "INTERMODULA-TION PRODUCTS". These intermodulation products, also called "odd-order products" tend to distort the original modulating signal.

The signal of a nearby transmitter can get into the transmitter via the antenna and mix with the transmitter's signal in the RF power amplifier, which may be operated Class C (non-linear). This mixing will generate new unwanted sidebands. The obvious remedy for this is not to locate the transmitting antenna close to other transmitting antennas. If the antenna must be located in an area where there are other antennas, traps tuned to the undesired frequencies should be used.

Other remedies for preventing transmitter intermodulation are: Operate the various transmitter stages in as linear a manner as possible; use sharply tuned circuits; use sufficient de-coupling networks; use sufficient shielding and filters; use Faraday shields.

FACTORS CAUSING DECREASE IN ANTENNA CURRENT DURING MODULATION. Sometimes the operator may find that the antenna current drops during modulation, when it should be increasing. The operator should then immediately check the transmitter for one or more of the following troubles:

1. Insufficient RF excitation to the modulated amplifier.
2. Insufficient bias on the grid of the modulated amplifier.
3. Heavy overloading of the modulated Class C, RF amplifier.
4. Defective tube.
5. Poor voltage regulation of a power supply common to both the modulator and the RF amplifier.
6. Faulty or insufficient capacity of output filter capacitor in power supply of RF amplifier.

The decrease in antenna current during modulation is known as DOWN-WARD MODULATION.

3 SINGLE SIDEBAND TRANSMISSION. The system of amplitude modulation that we have been discussing all along, is widely used. However, it does have a number of major drawbacks. For one thing, it occupies more of the frequency spectrum than is necessary. Both the upper and lower sidebands are transmitted. This is a waste since the same information that is transmitted in the upper sidebands is duplicated in the lower sidebands.

Another disadvantage of AM is that a tremendous amount of power is used at the transmitter in order to transmit a certain amount of information.

It has been explained that two-thirds of the power is in the carrier and one-third in both sidebands. Thus, one-sixth of the power is in one half of the sidebands (upper or lower). Since all of the information is contained in the upper or lower sidebands, five-sixths of the power delivered to the transmitter's antenna is unnecessary for communication.

The principle of single-sideband suppressed carrier (SSSC) transmission is to develop and transmit only one of the sidebands (upper or lower). Thus, a single sideband signal will occupy one half the bandwidth that an AM signal occupies.

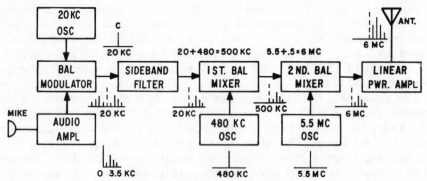

FIG. 14-20. BLOCK DIAGRAM OF A SINGLE-SIDEBAND, SUPPRESSED CARRIER TRANSMITTER.

Fig. 14-20 is a block diagram of a filter-type single-sideband suppressed carrier transmitter. The frequency components at the output of each block are indicated to the right of each block by the frequency and a sketch.

The 20 kHz oscillator generates the basic carrier and feeds it to a balanced modulator. Here, the carrier is modulated by the audio coming from the audio amplifier. The balanced modulator generates both the upper and lower sidebands, but it suppresses the basic carrier. The dotted line in the frequency sketch indicates the suppressed carrier. The double-sideband signal is passed on to a sideband filter which eliminates one of the sidebands. The signal leaving the sideband filter is now a single-sideband suppressed carrier signal.

In order to increase the frequency of the signal to the frequency to be transmitted, it is "heterodyned" or mixed up to the desired frequency. Two balanced mixers are used to do this. The first mixer beats the 20 kHz sideband with a signal from a 480 kHz oscillator to develop 500 kHz. The second mixer heterodynes the 500 kHz signal with 5.5 MHz to give a 6 MHz signal. The heterodyning process does not harm the audio. The reason for two mixers is to insure the suppression of the original 20 kHz.

The single sideband signal is now fed to a linear power amplifier which brings the signal up to the required power level. We use a linear amplifier because the signal contains audio and a linear amplifier does not distort the audio.

A complete discussion of single sideband transmission and reception is beyond the scope of this text. If the reader desires more information, there are many excellent books on the market that cover this subject thoroughly.

TROUBLESHOOTING

3 The following questions and answers are based on Fig. 14-13:

QUESTION: What would happen to the plate current of V1 and the plate current of V2 if L1 opened up?

ANSWER: If L1 opened up, the plate circuit of V1 would be open and there would be zero plate current flow in V1.

Since no RF would be delivered to the grid circuit of V2, the additional negative grid bias that would normally develop across the grid-leak resistor of R2 would drop and the plate current in V2 would rise.

QUESTION: What would happen to the plate current of V2 if C9 were to short?

ANSWER: A shorted C9 would place the B+ voltage of V1 on to the grid of V2. This would cause a dangerously high plate current to flow in V2.

QUESTION: What would happen to the antenna current if the r.f.c. in the V2 grid circuit opened up?

ANSWER: An open r.f.c. means an open grid circuit. The RF excitation would fall. An open grid circuit means a blocked grid, which would cause the plate current of V2 to fall to zero. There would be no RF excitation in the plate circuit of V2 and the antenna current would fall to zero.

QUESTION: What would happen to the antenna current if C10 shorted?

ANSWER: If C10 shorts, there will be no plate voltage on V2 and therefore, no RF at the output of V2. The antenna current would fall to zero. The secondary of T2 and the r.f.c. in the plate circuit of V2 might be damaged by a heavy plate current.

QUESTION: What would happen if C1 opened up?

ANSWER: If C1 opened up, we would have some degenerative feedback in V3. This would improve the fidelity of the audio, but would reduce its output.

QUESTION: What would happen if C2 developed a short-circuit?

ANSWER: The screen grid voltage of V3 would drop to zero. This would cause the tube to be inoperative and the audio output would be zero. A heavy current would flow through R4.

QUESTION: What would happen if C3 opened up?

ANSWER: C3 is part of a de-coupling filter network. It would cause audio instability and possible audio oscillations.

QUESTION: What would happen if C4 opened up?

ANSWER: The audio output of V3 would be prevented from getting to V4 and the audio output of the transmitter would be zero.

QUESTION: What would happen if C4 became leaky?

ANSWER: Some of the plate voltage of V3 would get on to the grid of

V4. This would change the bias of V4 radically and introduce considerable audio distortion. A high plate current would flow in V4.

QUESTION: What would happen to the antenna current if the primary of T1 opened up?
ANSWER: The audio would be stopped and the audio modulation would fall to zero. This would cause the antenna current to drop. Normally, the antenna current rises 22-1/2% if an RF signal is modulated 100% by a sinusoidal wave.

QUESTION: What would happen to the modulator plate current if R9 burns out?
ANSWER: The modulator plate current would fall to zero since R9 is in the cathode circuit.

PRACTICE QUESTIONS – LESSON 14

1. In high-level modulation, the audio is added to the carrier:
a. in the oscillator stage   c. in the final amplifier stage
b. in the buffer stage   d. through a phase shift network

2. A dip in the antenna current in a plate modulated RF amplifier is not caused by:
a. low-grid bias   c. incorrect load impedance
b. inadequate excitation   d. insufficient modulation

3. What is the bandwidth of an emission in an AM transmission if a 2 MHz carrier is modulated by audio whose highest frequency is 4,000 Hz?
a. 2.004 MHz   b. 4.008 MHz   c. 8 kHz   d. 4 kHz

4. Overmodulation does not result in:
a. distortion   b. spurious harmonic radiation
c. interference to adjacent frequencies
d. parasitic oscillation

5. Which of the following is not characteristic of a Doherty amplifier? (4)
a. high efficiency   b. a linear amplifier
c. each tube amplifies a different portion of the modulated carrier
d. operates in a push-pull manner

6. Feedback in an audio amplifier, having a single power supply, can be prevented by:
a. de-coupling resistors and capacitors
b. reducing the filter capacitor values
c. increasing the screen voltage
d. reducing the plate and screen voltages

7. Undesired frequencies resulting from the mixing of signals (in a transmitter) not present in the original signal, are called:
   a. single sidebands
   b. upper and lower sidebands
   c. intermodulation products
   d. even-order products

8. What type of a power amplifier is used in a single-sideband transmitter?
   a. linear
   b. non-linear
   c. sideband amplifier
   d. double sideband power amplifier

9. Referring to Fig. 14-13, what would happen if C8 opened up? (3)
   a. the plate current of V1 drops and the plate current of V2 rises
   b. the plate current of V2 drops and the antenna current rises
   c. the plate current of V1 rises and the antenna current drops
   d. the plate current of V2 and the antenna current decrease

10. Referring to Fig. 14-13, what would happen if C4 opened up? (3)
   a. V3 plate current would rise and V4 plate current would drop
   b. V4 AF current would drop and antenna current would cease
   c. V3 AF current would drop and antenna current would rise
   d. V4 AF current and antenna current would drop

11. The signal in a sideband transmitter is increased up to the desired frequency by means of: (3)
   a. frequency multipliers
   b. frequency dividers
   c. heterodyning
   d. filtering

12. What is the bandwidth of an 840 kHz AM signal that is modulated by audio from 20 Hz to 5 kHz?
   a. 845 kHz   b. 40 Hz   c. 10 kHz   d. 9.960 kHz

13. Positive carrier shift in a modulated Class C RF amplifier, is not caused by:
   a. excessive audio
   b. improper neutralization
   c. insufficient audio drive
   d. improper tuning

14. What is the error in the diagram shown?
   a. grid bias is missing from V1
   b. a cathode resistor is missing from V2
   c. a neutralizing capacitor is missing from V2
   d. transformer of V2 should not have an iron core

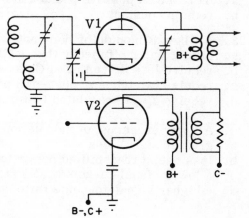

15. The diagram shown is a schematic illustrating:

a. reactance tube modulation   c. a balanced modulator
b. a two-tone test oscillator   d. grid modulation

16. A downward deflection of the antenna RF current meter during modulation might indicate:
a. sufficient RF excitation to the modulated stage
b. proper filament emission of the modulated stage
c. excellent voltage regulation of power supply common to both modulator and RF stage
d. insufficient bias on grid of modulated stage

17. Frequency modulation of an amplitude modulated wave:
a. causes no output signal   b. doubles the output power
c. causes spurious sidebands and interference
d. causes undesired harmonics

18. The ratio of the audio power to the input power of the final stage in 100% sinusoidal plate modulation is:
a. 25%   b. 30%   c. 50%   d. 100%

19. The percentage of power in the upper sideband in an AM system is:
a. 16.7   b. 33.33   c. 50   d. 66.67

20. If the grid bias supply of a Class B modulator was suddenly short-circuited:
a. plate current would increase to excessively high values
b. grid current would increase   c. overmodulation would result
d. the output power of the carrier would be in the sidebands

21. Class B modulation, compared to Class A modulation, requires:
a. larger excitation voltage   c. no power to drive the grid
b. lower excitation voltage   d. zero bias operation

22. The average plate current in an amplitude-modulated RF amplifier should:
a. increase on positive peaks and decrease on negative peaks
b. remain constant   c. decrease   d. increase

23. A Class B modulator does not:
a. have greater efficiency than a Class A modulator
b. require less drive than a Class A modulator
c. require two tubes in push-pull circuits
d. require a well-regulated power supply

24. A high percentage of modulation would result in:
a. greater signal loss
b. less useful transmitted power for a given carrier power
c. a lower signal-to-noise ratio at the receiver
d. a higher signal-to-noise ratio at the receiver

LESSON 15
RECEIVERS

FUNCTIONS OF A RADIO RECEIVER. Up to this point, we have covered the principles of radio transmission in detail. We will now consider the problems of the reception of radio signals.

The radio receiver must be able to perform the following functions:

(1) pick up the radio frequency signals radiated by transmitters.

(2) tune to one desired signal and reject the remaining signals.

(3) amplify the desired radio frequency signal.

(4) separate the audio intelligence from the radio frequency carrier.

(5) amplify the audio signal and drive a speaker with it.

DETECTION. It has been pointed out in a previous lesson, that the detector is the heart of the receiver. It is the detector that extracts the audio intelligence from the signal that enters the receiver. Actually, a detector, by itself, can be considered as a simple type of receiver.

We shall study two different types of detection: diode detection and grid-leak detection.

THE DIODE DETECTOR. Fig. 15-1 illustrates a diode detector. With its antenna, ground and headphones, it is a simple one-tube receiver. Let us see how this circuit operates.

The radio frequency waves radiated by the transmitter cut across the receiver antenna and induce a signal voltage into it. This RF signal is brought down into coil L1, by means of the transmission line that connects the antenna to the receiver. Because of the coupling between L1 and L2, the signal is induced into L2. L2 and C1 form a resonant circuit. By varying C1, we can make this circuit resonant to any one of a great many frequencies.

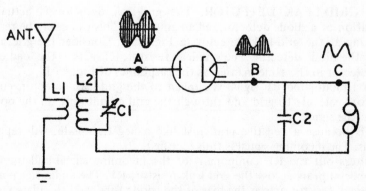

FIG. 15-1. DIODE DETECTOR.

285

Since each broadcast station transmits a signal on a different frequency, we can use C1 to tune in the station that we wish to listen to.

Once we choose the desired signal, we can then proceed to "detect" the information in this signal. In Fig. 15-1, we show the waveshape of the signal as it appears at different points of the circuit. Notice the wave at point A, the output of the tuned circuit. The upper half is exactly the same as the lower half. Since the audio is represented by a line joining the peaks of the wave, we actually have the audio duplicated in the upper and lower halves of the signal. Either the upper or the lower part of the signal must be removed because the upper audio signal which is positive, and the lower audio signal, which is negative, would cancel each other when the RF component of the signal is removed. Removing the upper or lower half of the signal will in no way harm the audio intelligence, since each half of the signal contains the complete audio information.

Cancelling one half of the signal is accomplished by means of the principle of rectification. The entire RF signal is simply a high frequency AC signal, and we use a diode vacuum tube or semiconductor to remove half of the signal. Rectification is accomplished in the following manner: When the positive half of the signal drives the plate of the diode positive with respect to the cathode, the tube conducts and current flows through the circuit. When the negative half of the signal drives the plate of the diode negative with respect to the cathode, the tube will not conduct and current will not flow through the circuit during this half of the cycle. The lower half of the RF signal will therefore be cut off and does not appear at the output of the detector tube. (See point B).

We still have not extracted the audio from the RF carrier. This is accomplished by C2, a low value capacitor in the order of .0001 mf. The signal across C2 consists of two components: the low frequency audio intelligence and the high frequency RF carrier. Because a low value capacitor has a low reactance to the high frequency RF, the RF component will be shorted by the capacitor and will not appear in the headphones. Because C2 has a high reactance to the low audio frequencies, the audio will not be shorted and will appear in the headphones. Thus we have succeeded in extracting the audio intelligence from the RF carrier by means of the diode detector.

3 THE GRID-LEAK DETECTOR. The grid-leak detector is actually a combination of a diode detector and an amplifier. This can easily be realized by looking at the grid-leak detector in Fig. 15-2. Consider the grid as the plate of the diode detector. The grid-leak resistor, R1, acts as the load of the diode detector in the same manner as the earphones of Fig. 15-1.

When a modulated RF signal is applied to the grid-leak detector, current flows from cathode to grid and through the grid circuit only on the positive halves of the signal.

This is because a negative grid, just like a negative plate, will repel the electrons. The incoming signal is thus rectified.

C1 filters out the RF component of the incoming signal and the audio intelligence appears across the grid-leak resistor, R1. The audio signal across the grid-leak resistor acts as the bias of the triode tube, and the plate current

286

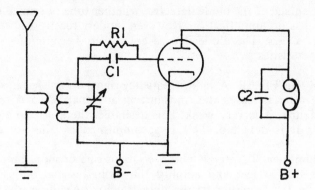

FIG. 15-2. GRID-LEAK DETECTOR.

will vary in accordance with the voltage across R1. Because of the amplification property of a triode, we find that the audio developed in the plate circuit, across the headsets, is much larger than that across the grid-leak resistor. Capacitor C2 filters out any RF that might appear in the plate circuit.

While the grid-leak detector has more gain than the plate detector, it has the disadvantage of being easily overloaded by strong RF signals and causing distortion of its output.

3 THE SOLID-STATE DETECTOR.

3 THE SOLID-STATE DETECTOR. Although Fig. 15-1 shows a tube used as a diode detector, solid-state detectors are more commonly employed for a number of reasons. Unlike a tube, a semiconductor does not require filament voltage. Semiconductor crystal diodes are also light in weight, do not require a socket, and can be wired into position as easily as any resistor. Also, since no heating time is needed, crystal diodes work immediately.

Fig. 15-3 illustrates a typical semiconductor detector circuit. The only difference between this circuit and Fig. 15-1 is that the diode tube has been replaced by a semiconductor diode. The operation of both circuits is the same.

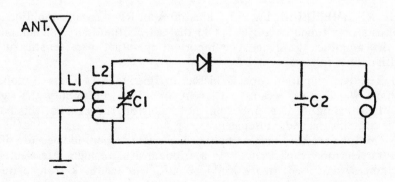

FIG. 15-3. A SOLID-STATE DETECTOR CIRCUIT.

The disadvantage of the diode detector, whether tube or semiconductor, is that a diode has no amplification. However, modern receivers have adequate gain in other stages. The diode is used extensively because of its excellent fidelity characteristics.

THE TRF RECEIVER. A radio frequency signal diminishes in strength at a rapid rate after it leaves the transmitting antenna. When it reaches the receiving antenna, it is very weak. It is desirable, therefore, to amplify the signal before it is detected. This is accomplished by the use of an RF amplifier.

The RF amplifier, like the detector, contains one or more tuned circuits. This enables it to select and amplify the desired signal only. Thus, the addition of an RF amplifier to the detector not only increases sensitivity (ability to receive weak signals), but also provides for greater selectivity (ability to separate signals).

The detector stage is followed by one or more stages of AF amplification. If a headset is to be used, only one stage of audio amplification is necessary. If a speaker is to be used, two or more stages of audio amplification will be necessary.

The complete receiver, consisting of one or more RF amplifiers, a detector and one or more AF amplifiers, is called a TUNED RADIO FREQUENCY receiver, or simply, a TRF receiver. A block diagram of a TRF receiver, together with the waveform of the signal at each stage, is shown in Fig. 15-4.

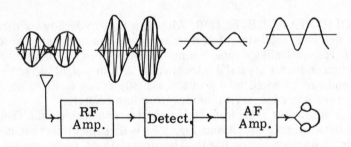

FIG. 15-4. BLOCK DIAGRAM OF A TRF RECEIVER.

THE RF AMPLIFIER. Fig. 15-5 illustrates an RF stage of amplification. It consists of a tuned circuit (L1, C1) that selects the desired signal, and a tube that amplifies the signal. The important operating characteristics of the amplifier are as follows:

(1) The RF amplifier tube is biased to operate as a Class A voltage amplifier. We do this because a Class A amplifier will amplify the signal without distorting it. It is important not to distort the signal at this point since it contains the audio intelligence.

(2) The tube used in the RF amplifier is generally a pentode because of its low interelectrode capacitances. If a triode, with its high interelectrode capacitances were used, there would be sufficient feedback from plate to grid at radio frequencies to cause the RF amplifier to oscillate. An oscillating amplifier would cause serious distortion, making satisfactory reception

288

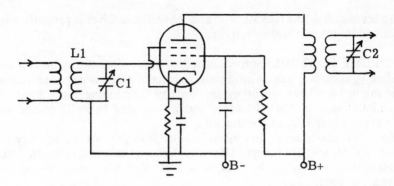

FIG. 15-5. RF STAGE OF AMPLIFICATION.

almost impossible.

(3) Cathode bias is almost always used. A cathode bias resistor and by-pass capacitor provide the bias for the tube.

(4) The RF transformers consist of a primary coil and a secondary coil. The secondary coil is designed to cover the desired frequency range when tuned by the capacitor across it.

At the height of their popularity, most TRF receivers used two or three RF amplifier stages ahead of the detector. Each stage is tuned to the same frequency. Since it would be impractical to tune each of the stages individually, all the tuning capacitors are mounted on a common shaft so that all the RF stages can be tuned simultaneously. Capacitors mounted on a common shaft in this manner are said to be "ganged".

In order that each stage be tuned to the exact same frequency at any setting of the ganged capacitors, the capacitors and coils in each stage should be identical. However, because of manufacturing tolerances and stray capacitances and inductances, this is not possible. In order to compensate for the small differences in value of the tuned circuit components, small variable capacitors, called trimmers, are placed across the tuning capacitors. These trimmers are mounted at the side of the tuning capacitors and their capacitances can be varied with an alignment tool. Fig. 15-6 illustrates a 3-gang tuning capacitor with its trimmers. We adjust the trimmers so that each one of the RF amplifier stages tunes to the same frequency at any particular setting of the station selector knob. The process of adjusting the

FIG. 15-6. A 3-GANG TUNING
CAPACITOR WITH TRIMMERS.

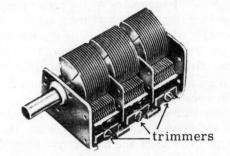

trimmers

trimmers is called "ALIGNMENT" and when the receiver is properly aligned, it has maximum gain and selectivity.

VOLUME CONTROL. Some method of controlling the volume of a radio receiver is necessary since the signals arriving at the receiver antenna vary in their intensity. There are many methods of controlling the volume. Some control the gain of the RF stages and are referred to as RF gain controls; others vary the output of the detector.

Fig. 15-7 illustrates a method of controlling the volume by varying the bias of an RF amplifier stage. The tube that is used is so constructed that its amplification varies as the bias is varied. We call this type of tube a variable-mu tube.

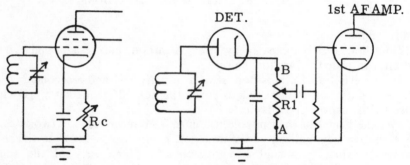

FIG. 15-7. VOLUME
CONTROL IN RF STAGE.

FIG. 15-8. VOLUME CONTROL
IN DETECTOR STAGE.

Fig. 15-8 illustrates another method of controlling the volume of a receiver. The variable resistor R1 is both the load of the diode detector and the volume control. The entire audio output of the detector is across R1. By sliding the arm of the potentiometer from A to B, we tap off varying amounts of audio and apply it to the grid of the first audio amplifier stage. In this way, we control the volume of the receiver. The technique in Fig. 15-8 is the one that is commonly used.

CAPABILITIES OF A TRF RECEIVER. A TRF receiver will operate in a satisfactory manner when it is used for a narrow, low frequency RF band. However, it is not satisfactory when used for high frequencies or over a wide range of frequencies. At the higher frequencies, a TRF receiver has difficulty picking one signal apart from another. In other words, its selectivity is poor.

Also, the amplification of the RF amplifier is low at the higher frequencies. This limits the reception of the TRF receiver. Not only are the gain and selectivity of the TRF poor, but they vary considerably from one frequency to another. It is difficult to design an RF amplifier whose gain and selectivity are constant over a wide tuning range.

The disadvantages of the TRF receiver led to the development of the superheterodyne type of receiver. The principles of the superheterodyne type of receiver and how it overcomes the disadvantages of the TRF receiver will now be fully discussed.

GENERAL THEORY OF THE SUPERHETERODYNE RECEIVER. The detector stage in a superheterodyne receiver is similar to the detector stage in a TRF receiver. The audio section is also the same. The differences between the two receivers lie in the stages preceding the detector.

In the TRF receiver, all the RF stages are tuned to the frequency of the incoming signal. This is not true in the superheterodyne receiver. Here, the incoming signal is first changed to a LOW, FIXED frequency and is then amplified and detected. The new frequency is called the Intermediate Frequency (IF). By amplifying the lower, fixed frequency, it is possible to use circuits that have greater selectivity and sensitivity than those used in TRF receivers.

THE SUPERHETERODYNE RECEIVER. Fig. 15-9 shows the block diagram of a typical superheterodyne receiver. The graphical form of the signal passing through the receiver is also shown. We will now study the operation of the superheterodyne receiver by following the signal through its stages.

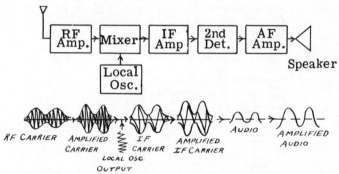

FIG. 15-9. BLOCK DIAGRAM OF A SUPERHETERODYNE RECEIVER.

From the antenna the incoming signal goes to the RF amplifier. Here it is selected and amplified in the same manner as in a TRF receiver. The signal is then passed on to the MIXER stage where it is "mixed" or heterodyned with a signal generated by the local oscillator. The mixer is called a CONVERTER and sometimes, a FIRST DETECTOR.

The mixing action of the mixer stage produces two new modulated RF signals, in addition to the original two signals. They are the sum and the difference of the signal frequency and the oscillator frequency. It is the difference or intermediate frequency in which we are interested. Therefore, the output of the mixer consists of an LC circuit, fixed-tuned to the intermediate frequency. All other signals are rejected. The new IF signal contains all the modulation characteristics of the original signal.

The IF signal is then fed to the IF amplifier stage where it is amplified. From here the signal goes to the detector, which is similar in operation to the detector of the TRF receiver. We sometimes refer to this stage as the second detector since we can consider the mixer stage as the first detector. After the audio is extracted from the modulated carrier, it is amplified by an

291

audio amplifier stage.

Thus, we have briefly traced a signal through a superheterodyne receiver. We shall now discuss in more detail, the operation of the various stages and circuits of the superheterodyne receiver.

FREQUENCY CONVERSION. The combined circuits of the mixer stage and oscillator stage form the frequency converter. As we previously pointed out, the purpose of the frequency converter is to convert the incoming signal to a low fixed frequency (the intermediate frequency) which is then fed to the IF amplifiers. There are a large number of possible combinations of tubes and circuits which may be used for frequency conversion. These various combinations may be broken down into two different types: (1) Circuits using a separate mixer tube and oscillator tube and (2) Circuits using one tube for both the oscillator and mixer stages. We shall now study each type in detail.

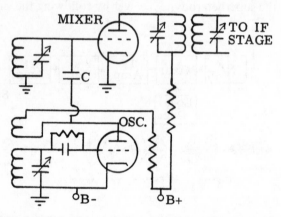

FIG. 15-10. FREQUENCY CONVERSION USING TWO TUBES.

Fig. 15-10 illustrates a frequency conversion circuit using a triode mixer stage and a separate triode oscillator stage. An Armstrong oscillator circuit is used. Practically any type of oscillator could be used.

The output of the oscillator is injected into the grid of the mixer through coupling capacitor C. This is called grid injection. The oscillator output can also be injected into the cathode of the mixer. The coil and capacitor in the mixer grid circuit are tuned to the frequency of the incoming signal. The coil and capacitor in the oscillator grid circuit are tuned to a frequency higher or lower than the signal frequency by an amount equal to the intermediate frequency. The plate circuit of the mixer stage is fixed tuned to the intermediate frequency. An example will clarify this point: If the incoming signal has a frequency of 1000 kHz and the IF is 456 kHz, the oscillator would then be tuned to 1456 kHz. The oscillator could also be tuned to 544 kHz, but practically all receivers tune the oscillator frequency above that of the incoming signal. The oscillator signal and the incoming signal mix together in the mixer tube and produce the intermediate frequency of 456 kHz.

answers to ensan text of
M.R.d.

Now let us assume that we wish to receive an incoming signal of 1200 kHz. We must tune the mixer grid circuit to 1200 kHz and, at the same time, we must tune the oscillator to 1656 kHz. These two frequencies will mix together in the mixer tube to produce the 456 kHz IF.

In order to tune the oscillator tank circuit and the mixer tank circuit at the same time, both tuning capacitors are on the same shaft. They are both rotated together when stations are changed. The two capacitors are said to be ganged. Fig. 15-11 shows a typical superheterodyne tuning capacitor. The smaller section is the oscillator capacitor and the larger section is the mixer capacitor.

FIG. 15-11. TYPICAL
SUPERHETERODYNE
TUNING CAPACITOR.

Fig. 15-12 illustrates our second type of frequency conversion. You will notice that only one tube is used for both the mixer and the oscillator. The tube has five grids and is called a pentagrid converter. The cathode, grid 1 and grid 2 act as the cathode, control grid and plate of the oscillator section respectively. The oscillator is a Hartley type of oscillator. L2 is the oscillator coil and C2 is the oscillator tuning capacitor. R1 and C3 are the oscillator grid-leak resistor and capacitor. Grid 4 acts as the mixer grid. It receives the incoming signal from the mixer tuned circuit, L1-C1. Grids 3 and 5 are connected together within the tube. They serve as the screen of the mixer and also as an electrostatic shield between the oscillator and mixer sections of the pentagrid converter.

The oscillator output is actually coupled to the mixer section by means of

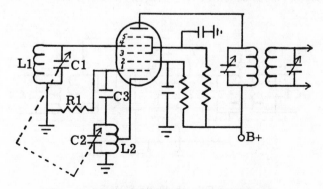

FIG. 15-12. THE PENTAGRID CONVERTER.

the tube's electron stream. We can consider the cathode and the first two grids as a composite cathode which supplies to the rest of the tube, an electron stream that varies at the oscillator frequency. The incoming signal voltage that is applied to grid 4, further controls the electron stream so that the plate current variations are a combination of the oscillator and the incoming signal frequencies. The plate circuit of the pentagrid converter is tuned to the difference of the two frequencies, the intermediate frequency.

IF AMPLIFIERS. The IF amplifier is a high gain Class A stage that is permanently tuned to the frequency difference between the incoming signal and the local oscillator. Pentode tubes are generally used as IF amplifiers because of their high gain and low interelectrode capacitances. Low interelectrode capacitances will prevent the IF amplifiers from oscillating.

The IF section of the superheterodyne receiver consists of one or more stages, with each stage tuned to the IF frequency. Since all incoming signals are converted to the same frequency, the IF amplifier operates at only one frequency. The tuned circuits, therefore, are efficiently designed for maximum gain and for the desired selectivity. It is in the IF section that most of the voltage gain and selectivity of the superheterodyne are achieved.

The diagram of an IF amplifier stage is shown in Fig. 15-13. Note T1 and T2. They are called IF transformers. The dotted lines around them indicate that the IF transformers are in metal cans. The cans act as shields and prevent undesired magnetic and electrostatic coupling between the transformers and adjacent circuits. The shields are made of low resistance conductors such as aluminum, copper and brass. When the magnetic field passes through the shield, an e.m.f. is induced in it, causing a current to flow. This current sets up its own magnetic field which opposes the original magnetic field and keeps it from spreading beyond the shield. The tuned circuits of Fig. 15-13 are adjusted to the exact IF frequency by means of the variable capacitors, C1, C2, C3 and C4. These capacitors are small trimmers located inside the transformer can. There are two holes in the transformer can that allow a small screwdriver to reach through the can and adjust the trimmers. In recent years, manufacturers have been using IF transformers that have fixed capacitors and variable inductors. The inductors use a powdered iron core and we tune the transformers by moving the core in and out of the coil. This is called PERMEABILITY TUNING.

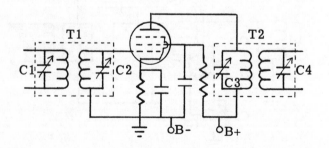

FIG. 15-13. IF STAGE.

The frequency to be used for the IF stages depends upon many factors. The lower the IF, the greater is the gain and selectivity. However, a low intermediate frequency results in image interference (discussed later in this lesson). If we use a high IF, we overcome this defect, but we lose gain and selectivity. A compromise IF of 456 kHz has been chosen by most receiver manufacturers, though some receivers have their IF's as low as 100 kHz and as high as 15,000 kHz.

SECOND DETECTORS. The "second detector" of the superheterodyne is the actual detector of the receiver. It is here that we extract the audio intelligence from the RF carrier. We call it a "second detector" because we sometimes refer to the frequency converter as the "first detector".

Fig. 15-14 illustrates the diagram of a second detector used in most superheterodynes. The second detector and the first audio frequency amplifier are combined in one tube. This is done to save tubes and space. The plate P1 and the cathode are the diode detector portion of the tube. The plate P2, the grid and the cathode represent the first AF portion of the tube.

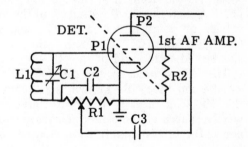

FIG. 15-14. SECOND DETECTOR AND FIRST AF STAGE.

The detector of Fig. 15-14 operates in the same manner as all diode detectors. L1-C1 is the secondary tuned circuit of the last IF transformer. It is also the tuned circuit of the detector. R1 is the detector load resistor across which the audio appears. By using it as a voltage divider to tap off various amounts of audio, we control the volume of the receiver. C2 is the capacitor that filters out the RF. C3 is an audio coupling capacitor that couples the audio from the detector to the grid of the first AF amplifier. R2 is the grid load resistor.

AUTOMATIC VOLUME CONTROL. Controlling the volume by varying the load resistor of the diode detector is a simple, satisfactory method. However, by itself, this method leaves a certain amount to be desired. For instance, every time we change from one station to another of different signal strength, we must reset the volume control. It would be far better to set the volume control at a desired level and have the audio output remain constant, regardless of the strength of the incoming signal. This can be accomplished by means of a system known as AUTOMATIC VOLUME CONTROL (abbreviated AVC). Fig. 15-15 shows a circuit using this system.

In the AVC system, we automatically reduce the strength of the strong signals and build up the strength of the weak signals. This is accomplished in

295

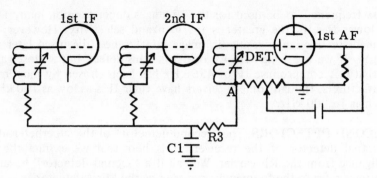

FIG. 15-15. AUTOMATIC VOLUME CONTROL CIRCUIT.

the following manner:

The audio output voltage of the diode detector is developed at point A. See Fig. 15-15. This voltage varies directly with the strength of the incoming signal. As the strength of the incoming signal increases, the audio voltage at point A increases; as the strength of the incoming signal decreases, the audio voltage at point A decreases. The audio voltage at point A is fed back through a filter (C1, R3) to the grids of the IF amplifiers. This voltage can also be fed to the grid of the RF amplifier, if the superheterodyne has one.

The tubes used in the IF and RF stages are variable-mu tubes. A variable-mu tube, also known as a "remote cut-off" tube, is constructed so that the wire turns of its control grid are closely spaced at the ends and widely spaced at the center. This is shown in Fig. 15-16. This construction allows the tube's amplification factor to vary inversely with its bias. As the bias on the grid of a variable-mu tube is made more negative, the amplification of the tube is decreased and, as the bias is made less negative, the amplification is increased.

We shall now see how all these factors operate to keep the output level of

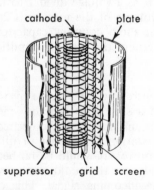

FIG. 15-16. CONSTRUCTION OF A VARIABLE-MU TUBE.

the receiver constant. Let us assume that we are listening to a certain station and have set the volume control to the desired audio output. We then change to a station whose incoming signal is stronger than the first station. This station will produce a larger audio voltage at point A (Fig. 15-15) than the previous station. This larger negative voltage will be fed back to the grids of the variable-mu amplifier tubes. The increased negative bias will reduce the amplification of the tubes and therefore, the gain of their stages will be reduced. This reduction in the gain of the receiver will compensate for the increased signal strength and will keep the audio output level constant.

Now, let us assume that we tune to a station whose signal strength is weak. There will be a low voltage at point A. The negative grid bias of the variable-mu tubes will decrease and the amplification of the tubes will automatically increase. This will increase the overall gain of the receiver and bring the audio output of this weak signal up to the output level of the other signals.

The function of R3, C1 is to filter out the audio variations and keep them from being fed back to the IF and RF stages. All that we want to feed back are the slower variations resulting from changes in the incoming signal strengths and not the audio variations themselves.

The AVC voltage at point A increases and decreases according to the strength of the incoming signal. This being the case, point A is a useful testing point for both troubleshooting and aligning the receiver.

A sensitive voltmeter, placed between point A and ground, with the negative test lead at point A, will read the AVC voltage. The meter should be at least a 20,000 ohm per volt type, or, a VTVM could be used. If there is a defect in the receiver up to the AVC test point, this AVC voltage will be affected. By injecting a signal, from a signal generator, at various points, the defective stage can be located. For instance, let us assume that there is a defect in the 1st IF stage of Fig. 15-15. When the signal generator is placed at the grid of the 2nd IF stage, the voltmeter at point A will read properly. When the signal generator is placed at the grid of the 1st stage, the voltmeter, which should show an increase in voltage, will now drop to a low value or to zero. We now know that there is something wrong in the 1st IF stage and we can localize the trouble to the bad component with the use of a volt-ohm-milliammeter.

By leaving the voltmeter on the AVC point (A), the IF and RF stages can be tuned up (aligned). We do this by injecting the signal generator at various points and adjusting the IF transformers and RF tuned circuits for a maximum reading of the voltmeter.

3 DELAYED AVC. One of the problems with ordinary AVC as described above is that the sensitivity of the receiver is reduced for weak signals. Even the weakest signal develops an AVC voltage that is applied back to the IF grids to reduce the gain of the receiver. To receive very weak signals, it is best to have no AVC. We want the receiver to operate at full gain. At the same time, we want the AVC to operate on medium and strong signals.

The way to accomplish this is through the use of a Delayed AVC circuit (DAVC). Fig. 15-17 illustrates a basic DAVC circuit. Unlike the AVC circuit of Fig. 15-15, the DAVC part of this circuit is completely separate from the detector circuit. The DAVC section consists of capacitor C4, a second diode plate (P3) in tube V3, resistors R3 and R4 and capacitor C3. A special bias voltage E_d is applied to the DAVC circuit through R4.

The negative bias voltage E_d prevents AVC operation on weak signals. The

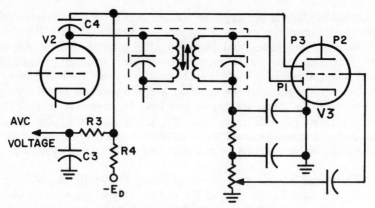

FIG. 15-17. A DELAYED AVC CIRCUIT.

RF and IF stages operate at maximum gain. As soon as a signal is strong enough to overcome the E_d bias, an AVC voltage develops and operates in the same manner as the AVC above.

3 **BEAT FREQUENCY OSCILLATOR.** The detectors that have been discussed thus far are able to detect only phone signals. They are not able to detect a C. W. signal. You will recall that a detector extracts audio from an RF carrier. However, a CW signal does not have any audio. It is all RF. If listen to a CW code signal with the detectors thus far described, all we will

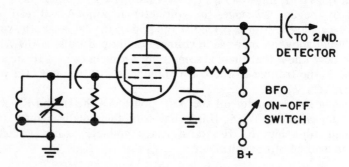

FIG. 15-18. CIRCUIT OF A BEAT-FREQUENCY OSCILLATOR.

hear are thumps and clicks.

The solution to this problem is to introduce a signal at the receiver that will heterodyne with the incoming CW signal to produce an audible signal. To accomplish this, the receiver contains an oscillator called a BEAT FREQUENCY OSCILLATOR (BFO). It is a simple oscillator, as shown in Fig. 15-18. It is connected to the detector. The oscillator generates a signal that is approximately 500 to 1000 Hz different from the incoming CW signal. The two signals beat together in the detector and the difference, which is audible to the human ear, is present in the output of the detector.

The amplitude of the Beat Frequency Oscillator should be greater than the incoming code signals in order to operate properly.

3 **RF AMPLIFIERS AND IMAGES.** The more expensive superheterodyne receivers contain one or two RF amplifiers ahead of the mixer. An RF amplifier will increase the gain and selectivity of the receiver. It will also reduce the reception of IMAGES. An image is an UNWANTED signal that differs in frequency from the local oscillator frequency by an amount equal to the intermediate frequency. For instance, if we are tuned to 1000 kHz and the IF is 456 kHz, then the oscillator frequency would be 1456 kHz. Assume there was a station at 1912 kHz. This signal would appear at the grid of the converter and beat with the oscillator to produce the IF of 456 kHz. This signal would be heard, in addition to the 1000 kHz signal that we are tuned to. We call 1912 kHz the image frequency. By adding a tuned RF amplifier ahead of the mixer, we reduce the reception of images. This is because the RF amplifier is tuned to the frequency of the station that we wish to listen to and it is difficult for the image frequency to get through the additional tuned circuits. Without the RF amplifier, the image frequency has only to get through the mixer tuned circuits.

We can also improve image rejection by designing the receiver with a higher IF frequency. For instance, in the above example, if the IF was 800 kHz instead of 456 kHz, the oscillator frequency would be 1800 kHz and the image frequency would be 2600 kHz. An image frequency of 2600 kHz is very difficult to pass through 1000 kHz tuned circuits because it is so far away in frequency. Thus we can see that image rejection is easier when the IF is higher.

3 **SPURIOUS RESPONSES IN A SUPERHETERODYNE.** In addition to images, there are other types of spurious signals that can be received or created in a superheterodyne receiver. One reason for spurious signals is the fact that a superheterodyne contains one or two local oscillators whose outputs can combine with other signals to create new spurious signals. For instance, the second harmonic of the local oscillator can combine with an undesired incoming signal to produce a frequency close to the IF frequency. The IF stages will amplify the new undesired signal, along with the desired signal, to produce interference.

A signal whose frequency is the same as that of the IF frequency can manage to get through the mixer stage and will cause interference. If two RF signals manage to get into the mixer and if their frequency difference is the same as the IF frequency, the IF stages will amplify the difference and cause interference.

Another source of spurious signals is the mixer stage. A mixer is a non-linear device that can generate harmonics of strong signals that reach it. These harmonics will combine with the local oscillator signal or with other signals to produce interfering signals.

Some of the methods by which spurious responses in a receiver can be reduced are: the use of an RF amplifier stage ahead of the mixer, proper choice of IF frequency, the use of IF filters, the use of high-pass filters at the antenna terminals and proper shielding.

3 **SINGLE-SIDEBAND SUPPRESSED-CARRIER (SSSC) RECEPTION.** A single-sideband receiver is similar to an AM receiver. The principal difference

between the two receivers lies in the detector circuit. In order to receive a SSSC signal, the carrier must be reinserted before the signal can be detected. In order to do this, we use a highly stable oscillator which produces a frequency approximately equal to the IF frequency. The output of this oscillator serves as a carrier of the signal. Once the carrier is reinserted, the signal is then detected in the usual manner. A beat frequency oscillator can be used as the stable oscillator.

Since no carrier is transmitted in SSSC transmission, the AVC of the superheterodyne will not operate in its usual manner. The manual RF gain control should be used for adjusting the level of the sideband signal.

In order to receive a SSSC signal, we first peak it with the main tuning dial. We then switch off the AVC and reduce the RF gain control. We bring up the audio with the audio volume control. The RF gain control is then advanced until the signal is barely heard. The beat frequency oscillator is then carefully adjusted until proper audio is heard. A certain amount of practice is necessary in order to tune single sideband signals with ease.

3 **SENSITIVITY OF A RECEIVER.** The sensitivity of a receiver is generally defined as the ability of a receiver to reproduce weak signals with satisfactory volume. It may be further defined as the minimum strength of a signal at the antenna that is required to produce a certain amount of audio power at the speaker. The sensitivity is largely determined by the number of amplification stages preceding the speaker. It is desirable to have as large a sensitivity as possible in order to receive signals from distant stations. However, there is a practical limit to the amount of amplification that a receiver can have. This limit is determined by the noise generated outside the receiver and by the noise generated inside the receiver. If we amplify the signal, we will be amplifying the noise as well, and may find that the noise at the output drowns out the signal.

There are several ways in which the sensitivity of a receiver can be expressed and comparisons between different receivers made.

(1) Sensitivity can be expressed in terms of the signal voltage required at the input of a receiver to achieve a given amount of output power at the speaker. For example, we can say that a particular receiver requires 1.5 microvolts of a signal, 30% modulated by a 400 Hz signal to develop one watt of power at the speaker. A receiver that requires 2 microvolts at the input to develop one watt of output power would be a less sensitive receiver.

(2) A second way of specifying receiver sensitivity is called the signal-to-noise ratio, expressed in decibels. The signal-to-noise ratio is the ratio of the signal power output to the noise power output at a specified value of modulated carrier voltage applied to the input of the receiver.

(3) A third way of expressing receiver sensitivity is the "noise figure" method. The noise figure may be defined as the ratio of the signal-to-noise ratio of an ideal receiver to the signal-to-noise ratio of the actual receiver. Noise figures are expressed in decibels and from the definition, we can see that the smaller the ratio, the better is the receiver sensitivity.

3 **RECEIVER NOISE.** Noise voltages affecting reception can be classified into two different categories: Internal and external. Internal noise can be

generated in the RF amplifier tubes or transistors, as well as tubes in the mixer, IF amplifier or audio amplifier stages. It can also be generated in wire conductors, resistors and other components. Some of the sources of internal noise are:

(1) Shot effect -- Noise generated by the fact that electrons in a tube do not flow in a smooth steady stream, but tend to strike the plate in bunches and in a random fashion. A random flow of electrons means that an extraneous signal will be present that was not present at the grid of the tube.

(2) Partition noise -- Partition noise occurs in modulated grid tubes. It is due to the arbitrary division or partition of electrons flowing to the grids and plate. The division of electron flow is random and therefore, a noise signal is produced.

(3) Induced grid noise – This is caused by electrons flowing past the control grid and inducing a voltage in it. As the frequency of the signal is increased, the induced grid voltage increases rapidly and hampers the effective use of the vacuum tube at the higher frequencies.

(4) Thermal agitation -- The random movement of electrons in any part of the circuit due to heat, produces small voltages which, when amplified, result in noise at the output.

(5) Microphonics – The mechanical vibrations due to a speaker or other sources of mechanical noise, cause a movement of the tube's elements or other components which generate random voltages, resulting in noise.

(6) Hum pickup -- The hum due to insufficient power supply filtering or pickup by sensitive circuits is amplified and heard in the output.

External noise, commonly called static, is caused by man-made devices and by natural sources. Noise is generated in man-made devices when electrical contacts are opened and closed. This occurs in lighting, power circuits, automobile ignition, corona discharge, motor commutators, etc. Noise from natural sources comes from lightning, rain and snow static and radiation from the sun and space. Aside from radiation, this type of noise is generated by the electrical arc that occurs in lightning and static.

3 **SELECTIVITY OF A RECEIVER.** The selectivity of a receiver is the ability of the receiver to select only the desired signal and to reject all others. Selectivity depends mainly on the quality of the tuned circuits. The selectivity of a receiver is expressed in the form of a response curve which shows the signal strength at the resonant frequency and the signal strength of the frequencies above and below the desired resonant frequency.

When a receiver is tuned to a certain frequency, it is desirable that signals above and below this frequency be rejected. Selectivity is specified by "band width". Bandwidth is the frequency range over which the received signal is above a certain level. For example, a bandwidth of 4 kHz at 6 db points, means that over a range of 4 kHz, signals will not be attenuated by more than 6 db. This is shown in the response curve drawn in Fig. 15-19. Note that below 9,998 kHz and above 10,002 kHz, the signal falls to more than 6 db below the peak. The distance between 9,998 kHz and 10,002 kHz is 4 kHz. We can therefore say that the bandwidth of a receiver, having the response curve of Fig. 15-19, is 4 kHz at 6 db points. The sharper the response curve, the greater is the selectivity. This means that the receiver will

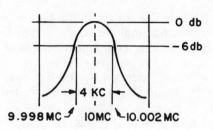

FIG. 15-19. FREQUENCY RESPONSE OF A RECEIVER.

respond to a narrow range of frequencies.

Many communication receivers utilize special bandpass filters that can narrow the bandwidth that a receiver will pass. They are usually placed in an IF stage and greatly improve the selectivity and sensitivity of the receiver. A switch on the front panel permits the operator to select a particular bandwidth. For instance, if CW were being received, the bandwidth should be as narrow as possible. A CW signal only occupies about 200 to 300 kHz. When the bandpass of the receiver is narrow, the signal-to-noise ratio is improved and interfering signals are rejected. A disadvantage of a narrow bandpass is that the signal will be lost if the signal or the receiver drifts slightly.

Since a single-sideband signal occupies approximately 3 kHz, the bandwidth should be set for approximately 3 kHz when listening to single sideband. When tuning ordinary AM, which occupies approximately 6 kHz, the bandwidth would be set for 6 kHz. If phone signals are tuned with too narrow a bandpass, some of the sidebands will be clipped and distortion will occur.

The bandpass filters are frequently sealed in order to prevent moisture and temperature changes from affecting their operation.

3 **ALIGNMENT.** In addition to the ganged variable capacitor, there are also a number of small variable capacitors (trimmers or padders) and variable inductors found in a superheterodyne. Their function is to correct for any variations that may exist in the tuned circuits. When the station selector knob is turned, the various RF stages must all tune to the same frequency and the local oscillator frequency must vary in such a manner that the frequency difference between the local oscillator and the RF stages is always equal to the intermediate frequency. When the circuits are adjusted in this manner, they are said to be TRACKING. It is also necessary to adjust the IF stages so that they all tune to the intermediate frequency. When all circuits are correctly tuned, we say that the receiver is properly aligned. Misalignment in any stage of the superheterodyne will cause a decrease in sensitivity or selectivity, or both.

With the aid of the block diagram of Fig. 15-20, we will see exactly how a superheterodyne receiver is aligned. In order to align a receiver, a calibrated oscillator or signal generator and some form of output indicator are required. The output indicator can be a V.T.V.M., an oscilloscope or the speaker of the receiver.

302

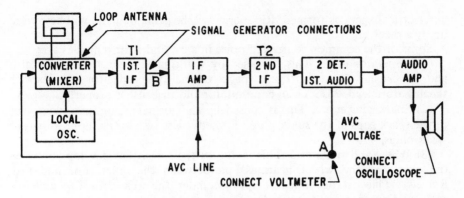

FIG. 15-20. ALIGNING AN AM SUPERHETERODYNE RECEIVER.

The primary objective of receiver alignment is to have all tuned circuits exactly tuned to the signals they are passing. In this way, the signal will receive maximum amplification. We must therefore inject signals at various points in the receiver and peak all adjustable tuned circuits for maximum indication.

Let us go through a typical alignment procedure on a step-by-step basis.

(1) Allow signal generator and receiver to warm up for at least fifteen minutes.

(2) Connect a VTVM set at − DC volts to AVC point A in Fig. 15-20.

(3) Set signal generator to receiver's IF frequency with modulation on.

(4) Temporarily short out oscillator variable capacitor.

(5) Connect signal generator through a small capacitor to the grid of the IF stage (point B).

(6) Keeping the output of the signal generator as low as possible, adjust trimmers on 2nd IF transformer (C8 and C9 in Fig. 15-21) for maximum indication on the VTVM.

(7) Connect signal generator to mixer grid and peak the trimmers on the 1st IF trannsformer for maximum VTVM reading. Continue to reduce the output of the signal generator to the minimum necessary to give an indication on the VTVM.

(8) Repeat steps 6 and 7.

(9) Adjust the signal generator to 1500 kHz modulated, and hook it to the antenna. If the receiver uses a loop, make a two-turn loop out of hookup wire and couple it to the receiver loop.

(10) Set the dial of the receiver to 1500 kHz and tune the mixer and oscillator trimmers (C2, C4 of Fig. 15-21) for maximum.

(11) Set the generator and receiver dial to 600 kHz and adjust the padder of the oscillator (C18 of Fig. 15-21) for maximum.

(12) Repeat steps 9 through 11. The receiver is now aligned.

3 NOISE IN A MOBILE RECEIVER. Unlike a home receiver, a mobile receiver is faced with the problem of noise. The mobile receiver is in the vicinity of a considerable number of noise-generating devices. Anytime that an electrical spark is formed, RF energy will be generated and will be picked up by a receiver.

Some of the common sources of noise in a car and their remedies are:

(1) Generator noise. This is caused by sparking between the commutator and the brushes. Remedy: Use a special coaxial type capacitor in series with the armature lead. Also, clean commutator and fit brushes properly.

(2) Spark plug noise. This is caused by the normal arcing that takes place in the spark gaps of the spark plugs. Remedy: Use resistor or suppressor-type spark plugs.

(3) Wheel and tire static. This is due to the static that develops between the axle and the wheel bearings and between the inner tube and tire. Remedy: Place static collector springs under the axle dust cap and put anti-static powder into the tube's valves.

(4) Voltage regulator noise. This is due to the sparking that occurs as the relay contacts open and close. Remedy: Place coaxial capacitors in the battery lead and armature lead at the frame of the regulator unit.

(5) Ignition coil and distributor noise. This is caused by high voltage discharges at desired and undesired points. Remedy: Use a coaxial type capacitor in series with the primary lead of the ignition coil. Place special suppressors in the center distributor arm and in each spark plug lead.

(6) Instrument and switch noise. This is due to the arc that occurs when the various switch and instrument contacts are opened and closed. Remedy: Place coaxial capacitors at the positions where the switches and gauges are mounted.

In addition to the remedies given above, shielded antenna transmission line and a noise limiter in the receiver can be used.

3 **A TYPICAL SUPERHETERODYNE RECEIVER.** The circuit diagram of a typical AC/DC superheterodyne is shown in Fig. 15-21. Each component part of the circuit is labeled. The table below, showing the function of each part, will serve as an excellent review of the theory of the superheterodyne receiver.

PART	VALUE	FUNCTION
V1		Pentagrid converter tube
V2		IF amplifier tube
V3		2nd detector, AVC and 1st audio frequency amplifier tube
V4		AF power amplifier tube
V5		Rectifier tube
T1		Input IF transformer
T2		Output IF transformer
T3		Audio output transformer
C1	15-350 pf	Converter tuning capacitor
C2	3-30 pf	Converter trimmer capacitor
C3	10-200 pf	Oscillator tuning capacitor
C4	3-30 pf	Oscillator trimmer capacitor
C5	100 pf	Oscillator grid leak capacitor

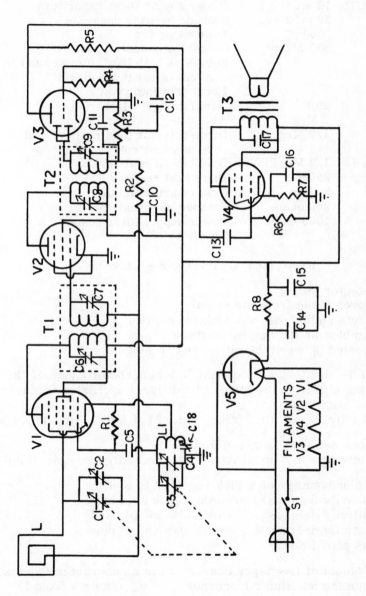

FIG. 15-21. A TYPICAL AC/DC SUPERHETERODYNE RECEIVER.

305

C6, C7	3-30 pf	IF transformer trimmer capacitors -
C8, C9		used in alignment of IF stages
C10	0.5 mf	AVC filter capacitor
C11	100 pf	Detector RF filter capacitor
C12, C13	.01 mf	Audio coupling capacitors
C14, C15	16 mf 150 V.	Power supply filter capacitors
C16	20 mf 20 V.	Cathode by-pass capacitor
C17	1000 pf	Tone capacitor
C18	200-500 pf	Oscillator padder capacitor
L		Serves as both loop antenna and coil
		of converter tuned circuit
L1		Local oscillator coil
R1	25 K	Oscillator grid-leak resistor
R2	2 Meg.	AVC filter resistor
R3	1/2 Meg.	Diode detector load resistor and
		volume control
R4	1/2 Meg.	Grid return resistor
R5	250 K	Plate load resistor
R6	5 Meg.	Grid return resistor
R7	200 ohms	Cathode bias resistor
R8	1000 ohms	Power supply filter resistor
S1		On-off switch

PRACTICE QUESTIONS - LESSON 15

1. A detector stage:
a. removes noise from the signal
b. extracts audio from a modulated carrier
c. resembles an RF amplifier stage
d. is located between the mixer and IF stage

2. What is the image frequency in a superheterodyne, if the incoming signal is 104 MHz and the local oscillator frequency is 114.7 MHz? (3)
a. 93.3 MHz   b. 10.7 MHz   c. 21.4 MHz   d. 125.4 MHz

3. A diode detector is known for its:
a. selectivity   b. sensitivity   c. noise figure   d. fidelity

4. The disadvantage of a TRF receiver is that:
a. sensitivity decreases towards high end of band
b. sensitivity decreases towards low end of band
c. selectivity decreases towards high end of band
d. it has poor fidelity

5. The object of frequency conversion in a superheterodyne is to:
a. change the oscillator frequency   c. obtain a fixed IF
b. double the IF   d. increase the fidelity

6. A beat frequency oscillator introduces a signal that is separated from the incoming signal by approximately: (3)
a. 20 Hz   b. 456 kHz   c. 600 Hz   d. 1600 kHz

7. In order to improve the sensitivity of a receiver, we can add: (3)
a. automatic volume control   c. AF amplifiers
b. delayed AVC   d. beat frequency oscillator

8. Random noise in a receiver is not produced by: (3)
a. electrons flowing in a tube in a random manner
b. random partition of electrons flowing to grids and plate
c. induced grid noise   d. poor voltage regulation

9. With reference to Fig. 9, what is this circuit a part of?
a. a superheterodyne   c. a low power transmitter
b. a public address system   d. a TRF receiver

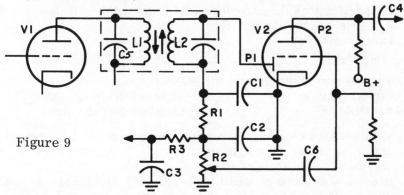

Figure 9

10. With reference to Fig. 9, P1 is the plate of the:
a. noise limiter   b. detector   c. audio amplifier   d. modulator

11. With reference to Fig. 9, R3, C3 is a part of the:
a. detector circuit   c. modulator circuit
b. AVC circuit   d. IF circuit

12. With reference to Fig. 9, which of the following would not happen if L1 were open?
a. the plate voltage on V1 would drop
b. the voltage across L2 would drop
c. the resistance across C5 would rise
d. the voltage across L2 would rise

13. With reference to Fig. 9, which of the following would occur if C1 were to open?
a. the signal across R2 would increase
b. the voltage across C3 would increase
c. signal across R2 would be lost   d. none of the above

14. One of the main purposes of trimmer and padder capacitors in a receiver is:
a. to improve oscillator stability
b. tracking of oscillator and RF tuning circuits
c. to improve stability of IF circuits
d. to improve the signal-to-noise ratio

307

15. The carrier and one set of sidebands are eliminated in: (3)
   a. frequency modulation   b. phase modulation
   c. single-sideband, suppressed-carrier transmission
   d. double-sideband, suppressed-carrier transmission

16. The Intermediate Frequency:
   a. is the difference frequency between the carrier frequency and the local oscillator frequency
   b. is always one-half the local oscillator frequency
   c. depends upon the station tuned to
   d. is twice the carrier frequency

17. A specification that provides us with a meaningful idea of a receiver's sensitivity is: (3)
   a. image rejection   c. shape factor
   b. spurious rejection   d. signal-to-noise ratio

18. Fixed tuned IF stages mean: (3)
   a. high fidelity   c. high selectivity, high gain
   b. variable IF   d. constant power output

19. Which of the following will not improve a receiver's sensitivity? (3)
   a. add a low noise preamplifier
   b. use a low noise mixer tube
   c. use a low Q tuned circuit between the RF amplifier and mixer
   d. use a high Q tuned circuit in the RF stage

20. The IF of a superheterodyne receiver is:
   a. the sum of the local oscillator frequency and the incoming signal frequency
   b. the sum of the audio frequency and the local oscillator frequency
   c. twice the local oscillator frequency, plus the incoming signal frequency
   d. the frequency difference between the local oscillator and incoming signal

LESSON 16
FREQUENCY MODULATION

FUNDAMENTAL CONSIDERATIONS OF MODULATION. Modulation is defined as the process wherein an audio voltage is superimposed upon an RF carrier wave in such a manner as to change one of the characteristics of the carrier. The characteristics of the carrier that can be changed are its amplitude, its frequency or its phase. In the system of amplitude modulation that has previously been discussed, the audio signal causes the amplitude of the carrier to vary. The variations in carrier amplitude follow the variations in the audio modulating voltage. At the receiver, the detector extracts the amplitude variations which represent the audio and pass them on to the audio amplifier.

The degree of modulation of an AM signal is directly dependent upon the strength of the audio modulating voltage. A larger audio signal causes a larger variation in carrier amplitude, and a smaller audio voltage causes a smaller variation in carrier amplitude.

AM DEFICIENCIES. If we modulate too heavily, we will have overmodulation. This, as we have previously seen, produces distortion. Another problem in AM is the fact that the frequency of the modulating system is limited. During modulation, sidebands are produced and they are equal to the carrier frequency, plus and minus the audio frequencies. Thus, if we modulate a carrier with high audio frequencies, the bandwidth occupied by the RF signal will be quite wide and will interfere with neighboring channels. In order to stay within the channel limits, the FCC has imposed a limit on the audio frequency that is used to modulate the carrier.

Interference, such as lightning, static, man-made, etc., generally causes the amplitude of a signal to vary. It impresses itself on the carrier as additional amplitude modulation. In the AM system of modulation, we therefore have the interference, as well as the audio, creating amplitude variations. When we detect the signal at the receiver, the interference will still be present.

These basic problems that are inherent in amplitude modulation are overcome in frequency modulation. In frequency modulation, the audio modulating signal causes the FREQUENCY of the carrier to vary in accordance with the strength of the audio signal. The amplitude of the RF carrier remains constant. This is shown in Fig. 16-1 where AM and FM are compared.

In FM, the frequency of the carrier varies in accordance with the amplitude of the audio signal. The higher the audio amplitude, the greater is the amount of frequency shift away from the center or resting frequency. The smaller the audio amplitude, the smaller is the frequency shift away from the center frequency. The amplitude of the carrier remains constant;

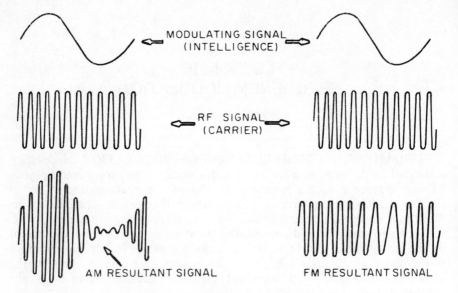

MODULATING SIGNAL
(INTELLIGENCE)

RF SIGNAL
(CARRIER)

AM RESULTANT SIGNAL

FM RESULTANT SIGNAL

FIG. 16-1. AM AND FM COMPARED.

only the frequency varies.

Note in Fig. 16-1 that the positive alternation of audio causes the carrier frequency to increase and the negative alternation causes the carrier frequency to decrease. The amount of frequency shift of the carrier above or below the resting frequency is known as the frequency deviation. The total variation between the minimum and maximum frequency values is known as the CARRIER SWING. While the extent of the frequency deviation is determined by the amplitude of the audio, the number of frequency deviations per second, or the rate of swing, depends upon the frequency of the modulating audio.

PERCENTAGE OF MODULATION. In AM, the percentage of modulation tells us the extent to which the audio has altered the amplitude of the carrier. We define 100% modulation as the point where the amplitude of the carrier rises to twice the normal amplitude at its maximum, and falls to zero at its minimum. Anything above 100% modulation is undesirable because it causes distortion.

The situation in FM is quite different. The FCC places a limit on the amount of frequency deviation so that the band occupied by the station is not too great. In the case of FM broadcast stations, the frequency deviation is plus or minus 75 kHz. When we modulate an FM carrier so that 75 kHz deviation is reached, we say we have 100% modulation. If we modulate above 100%, we will not cause distortion as in AM. We are merely exceeding the legal limit of 75 kHz. The lower the percentage of modulation, the lower is the amount of frequency swing or deviation. For instance, if we modulate 50%, the frequency deviation will be plus and minus 37.5 kHz (50% of 75 kHz is 37.5 kHz). Changing the frequency of the audio signal will not alter the frequency deviation. Only the amplitude of the audio modulating signal will control the frequency deviation of the carrier.

310

FM SIDEBANDS. We have previously learned that when amplitude modulation takes place, sidebands are produced. The sideband frequencies are equal to the carrier frequency, plus and minus the audio frequency. Thus, if we modulate a 1000 kHz carrier with a 2 kHz signal, we will have a sideband at 1002 kHz and a sideband at 998 kHz.

In FM, the situation is quite different. Upon modulation, the carrier frequency is shifted back and forth about the resting frequency. Many additional sidebands are formed even though we modulate with a single audio frequency. There are a large number of additions and subtractions of frequencies. Theoretically, the number of sidebands produced is infinite and the strength of the sidebands is reduced as we get further away from the carrier frequency. This is shown in Fig. 16-2. Note that the sidebands occur above and below the carrier. The spacing between sidebands is equal to the frequency of the modulating signal. Thus, if we modulate with a 2 kc. audio signal, sidebands occur every 2 kc. above and below the carrier frequency. However, only a small number of sidebands are significant in amplitude.

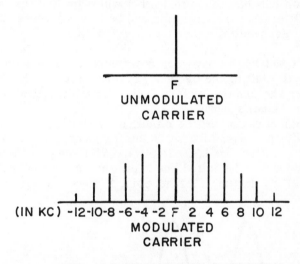

FIG. 16-2. SIDEBANDS OF AN FM SIGNAL.

3 The number of sidebands that occur in FM depends upon the relationship between the modulating frequency and the frequency deviation. This relationship is expressed by a term called the MODULATION INDEX. Modulation index is the ratio between the frequency deviation in Hz and the modulation frequency in Hz. Its formula is:

$$\text{Modulation index} = \frac{\text{carrier frequency deviation}}{\text{audio frequency causing this deviation}}$$

The higher the modulation index, the more are the number of sidebands, and vice versa. From the formula, we can see that if the frequency deviation is kept constant, the number of sidebands produced varies inversely with the

311

audio modulating frequency. We also can see, from the formula, that the Modulation Index varies directly with the frequency deviation. This means that the number of sidebands is proportional to frequency deviation, which is, in turn, proportional to the amplitude of the modulating voltage or the percentage of modulation.

EXAMPLE: What is the modulation index in an FM transmitter when an audio frequency of 400 Hz causes the carrier to shift 2 kHz to either side of the center frequency?

$$\text{Modulation Index} = \frac{2000}{400} = 5.$$

The DEVIATION RATIO is equal to the maximum carrier frequency deviation divided by the highest modulating frequency. The deviation ratio is useful in determining the bandwidth of emission because the maximum frequency deviation tells how much the carrier will swing and the modulating frequency tells us what the separation will be between sidebands. Both factors affect the total bandwidth.

PHASE MODULATION. We have seen how frequency modulation can be produced by directly shifting the frequency of a carrier above and below a resting frequency. The amount of frequency shifting depended upon the amplitude of the modulating signal.

Frequency modulation can also be produced by shifting the phase of a signal. If we shift the phase of a signal, its frequency is automatically changed. This is shown in Fig. 16-3. Sine wave #1 represents the original frequency. Sine wave #2, the dotted line, represents the same signal which has been shifted 40° by the time it reaches point A. Since sine wave #2 takes

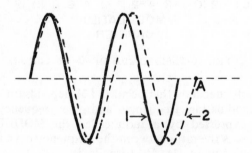

FIG. 16-3. SHIFTING THE PHASE.

longer than #1, it is obvious that the frequency has been reduced. If we shifted the phase angle in the opposite direction, the two cycles would be completed sooner and the frequency would have been increased. Thus, it is obvious that phase shift produces frequency changes.

In actual practice, an audio signal is used to alter the phase of a carrier. The higher the amplitude of the audio signal, the greater is the phase shift,

312

resulting in a greater frequency swing. The lower the amplitude of the modulating signal, the lower is the phase shift, resulting in a reduced frequency swing of the carrier.

We refer to frequency modulation that results from the phase shift method as INDIRECT FM. The audio does not directly alter the frequency of the carrier; it changes the phase of the carrier which brings about the change in the frequency.

The frequency of the modulating signal determines the amount of shifting per second that the carrier will experience. However, if we shift the carrier faster or slower, this in itself also causes the carrier's frequency to vary. Thus we find that the frequency of the carrier is also affected by the frequency of the modulating signal.

To summarize; the amount of indirect FM produced as a result of phase modulation depends upon (1) the amplitude of the modulating signal and (2) the frequency of the modulating signal.

PREDISTORTION. A serious problem arises from the fact that the frequency deviation resulting from phase modulation depends upon the frequency as well as the amplitude of the audio modulating signal. We only want the amount of frequency deviation to be dependent upon the amplitude of the modulating signal. This is because the FM receiver produces amplitude variations that are dependent upon the frequency deviation. If the FM signal contained frequency deviations that were the result of frequency variations of the modulating signal, the FM receiver wouldn't know it. It would produce amplitude variations that never existed at the microphone of the transmitter.

To overcome this problem, a predistortion circuit is inserted in the audio stages of the transmitter. It distorts the audio signal so that its amplitude varies inversely with the frequency. In other words, when the frequency of the audio signal increases, the audio amplitude is reduced, and vice versa. This compensates for the opposite effect that takes place during phase modulation. Thus, the output frequency deviation of a phase modulated transmitter varies only with the amplitude of the modulating signal.

NARROW-BAND AND WIDE-BAND FM. The terms "narrow-band" and "wide-band" refer to the amount of frequency deviation present for a given signal. This, in turn, determines the amount of bandwidth in the frequency spectrum that the signal will occupy.

Since frequency space is at a premium, we must limit the bandwidth that a station occupies. In the 150 to 175 MHz range, the police and fire services are permitted a maximum channel width of 10 kHz (a frequency deviation of ±5 kHz). This is known as NARROW-BAND FM. A technical definition of narrow-band FM states that narrow band FM does not occupy a channel wider than AM would occupy having the same audio frequencies.

Above 470 MHz, the voice communication services use a frequency deviation of ±15 kHz. This is known as WIDE-BAND FM.

Some of the advantages of narrow-band FM over wide-band FM are:
(1) The equipment for receiving and transmitting is less expensive;
(2) for a given number of stages, the gain and selectivity of a narrow band

313

receiver is greater;

(3) an AM detector can be used (when this is done, it is referred to as slope detection);

(4) the readable transmission distance is greater.

The FM broadcast stations are 150 kHz wide (2 x ±75 kHz). The FCC assigns them a channel width of 200 kHz. This allows for a guard band of 25 kHz on each side (150 kHz + 25 kHz + 25 kHz = 200 kHz). It is obvious to see that FM stations could not operate in the AM broadcast band. Aside from the technical consideration, there isn't enough room in the AM broadcast band. The broadcast band is 1070 kHz wide (535 kHz to 1605 kHz). Only 5 FM stations could fit in. On the other hand, the FM broadcast band extends from 88,000 kHz to 108,000 kHz, a width of 20,000 kHz. Theoretically, 100 FM stations could fit into the FM broadcast band (100 x 200 kHz = 20,000 kHz).

FM TRANSMISSION. There are a number of methods by which FM may be produced. One of the simplest is shown in Fig. 16-4.

The method used in Fig. 16-4 is a crude, elementary one. However, its action will help us understand how FM is produced.

An ordinary Armstrong oscillator is used and an additional capacitor is placed across the tuned circuit. The capacitor is actually a microphone with plate A free to move back and forth. Plate B is stationary. The frequency of the oscillator is primarily determined by the values of the inductance and the capacitance in the tank circuit. The capacitance of the tank circuit is the sum of C2 and the microphone capacitor C1.

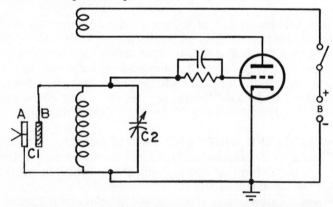

FIG. 16-4. AN ELEMENTARY METHOD OF PRODUCING FM.

Before speaking into the microphone, the oscillator produces a steady output frequency. When we speak into the microphone, we cause plate A of C1 to move back and forth in accordance with the speech. This causes the capacitance of C1 to vary, which in turn causes the output frequency of the oscillator to vary. If we speak louder into the microphone, C1's capacitance will vary by larger amounts and the output frequency will vary by larger amounts. If we speak in a lower volume, C1's capacitance will vary slightly and the output frequency will vary slightly. Thus, we have succeeded in converting audio into FM.

314

This method of frequency modulation is unsatisfactory because of the varying response of the capacitor microphone to different voices and because of the poor linearity of the microphone response. Furthermore, the microphone must be close to the oscillator to prevent the pickup of stray signals by the microphone leads.

REACTANCE TUBE MODULATOR. The reactance tube modulator of Fig. 16-5 is a satisfactory method of producing FM. V2 is the oscillator. L and C1 are the inductance and capacitance of the tuned circuit of the oscillator. V1 is the reactance tube.

The reactance tube modulator operates in the following manner: The resistance of R1 is very high, compared to the capacitive reactance of C2. The circuit R1C2 is therefore a resistive circuit. The current, I1, that flows through R1C2, is practically in phase with the voltage E, which is across R1C2. This is so because current and voltage tend to be in phase in a resistive circuit. However, Ec, which is the voltage across C2, is out of phase with I1. In fact, Ec lags behind I1 by 90° because the voltage across a capacitor lags behind its current by 90°. This is shown vectorially in Fig. 16-6.

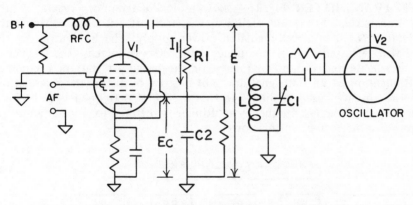

FIG. 16-5. A REACTANCE TUBE MODULATOR.

By looking at Fig. 16-5, we note that Ec also happens to be the grid voltage of V1. Since the plate current variations of a tube are the direct result of the grid voltage variations, we can say that the plate current Ip is in phase with the grid voltage Ec. This is also noted in Fig.16-6 by drawing Ip alongside of Ec. We can put E on the same line as I1, since we previously proved that I1 and E were practically in phase. By looking at the vectorial diagram, we note that Ip, the plate current of V1, is 90° behind E, the plate voltage of V1. Thus, we have a circuit in which the plate current lags behind the plate voltage by 90°. In our discussion of inductances, we learned that

FIG. 16-6. VECTOR ANALYSIS
OF PRODUCING FM.

315

the current through an inductance lags behind the voltage across the inductance by 90°. Thus, V1 behaves the same as an inductance. As far as the tuned circuit of the oscillator is concerned, it "sees" V1 as an inductor.

If an audio signal is applied to grid #3 of V1, the plate current varies. This is the same as though the "acting" inductance were to vary because a varying inductance would also cause the current to vary. If the acting inductance varies, there will be a change in frequency. Thus, we see how FM can be produced in a very practical manner.

One important difference between AM and FM is that AM requires a considerable amount of audio power for proper modulation, whereas FM requires very little power. In an AM transmitter, the modulator must supply approximately 50% of the unmodulated carrier power for 100% modulation. In FM, the audio power required for 100% modulation is negligible. The FM modulation process involves a voltage imposition rather than power. During FM modulation, the transmission line current and the antenna current are the same as they were with no modulation present. Only the frequency is varied.

FM TRANSMITTER. Fig. 16-7 shows a block diagram of a reactance tube FM transmitter. For good stability, we start off with a low frequency oscillator that uses a well-regulated power supply. The FM output of the oscillator is passed through frequency multipliers to increase the frequency up to the desired output frequency of the broadcast station. Frequency multiplication of an FM signal does not destroy or distort the modulation, and the circuitry used is similar to that used in AM frequency multipliers. The output of the last frequency multiplier is then fed to a power amplifier to produce the correct output power.

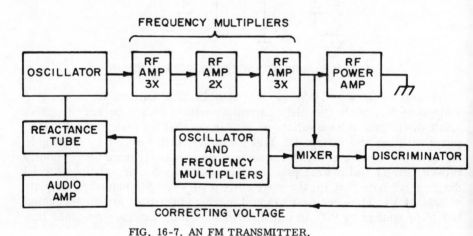

FIG. 16-7. AN FM TRANSMITTER.

If we wish to transmit an FM signal of 90 MHz, the oscillator would have to generate a 5 MHz signal. This is because the frequency multipliers multiply the oscillator signal a total of 18 times (3 x 2 x 3 = 18). 5 MHz x 18 = 90 MHz.

Not only will the center frequency be multiplied 18 times, but the carrier swing will also be multiplied 18 times. If we intend to modulate 100%, the transmitter's output will be 90 MHz ±75 kHz. The oscillator output will be 5 MHz ±75 kHz/18 or 5 MHz ±4.1 kHz.

Since the oscillator is not crystal controlled, we use an automatic frequency control system (AFC) to keep the carrier frequency constant. This is shown in Fig. 16-7. In the AFC system, the output of the frequency multiplier is compared with the output of a crystal oscillator. If the master oscillator has erroneously shifted, a voltage will be produced in the converter-discriminator stages, which is fed back to the reactance tube modulator. This, in turn, corrects the oscillator and sets it to its correct center frequency.

The FM transmitting antenna should be of the high gain type and it should be horizontally polarized. The FM broadcast band is from 88 to 108 MHz. Propagation at these frequencies is strictly via the ground wave. Any energy that travels upward is not reflected back to earth. It is therefore important that all the energy be radiated in a horizontal rather than vertical plane. High gain antennas should be used because the signal traveling in a horizontal plane along the ground is rapidly attenuated and absorbed by the ground.

3 PHASE MODULATED TRANSMITTER. The general principles of deriving frequency variations from phase shifting have been discussed in an earlier part of this lesson. We will now concern ourselves with the actual mechanics of creating frequency modulation by shifting the phase of a carrier. There are several methods of doing this. They all involve the combining of two signals that are out of phase. The two out-of-phase signals develop a resultant signal whose phase depends upon the amplitude of the two signals that produced it.

Fig. 16-8 illustrates a simplified schematic of one type of phase modulation. Its operation is as follows:

The output of the crystal controlled oscillator takes two paths. One part goes to the grid of the phase modulator tube. Here it is amplified in the usual

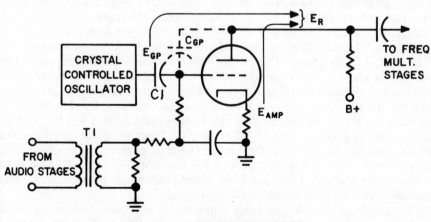

FIG. 16-8. A PHASE MODULATOR.

317

manner, and we refer to this signal as Eamp. The other path goes to the plate through the grid-to-plate capacitance. We refer to this signal by the term Egp. At the plate of the phase modulator, the two signals are out of phase. This is shown in Fig. 16-9. They are out of phase because the tube inverts the phase of one of the signals by 180° and the combination of C1 and Cgp changes the phase of the other signal. The two out-of-phase signals combine to produce a resultant signal labeled E_R. This is shown vectorially in Fig. 16-9A.

The audio is applied to the grid through transformer T1. As the amplitude of the audio signal varies, the transconductance of the tube varies. This causes Eamp to vary in its amplitude. This is shown in Fig. 16-9B. If we now combine Eamp with Egp, we get a new resultant voltage whose phase angle A is different from what it was previously. In other words, as the audio varies, Eamp varies and as Eamp varies, the phase angle A of the resultant voltage varies. From our previous discussion, we have learned that a change in phase causes a change in frequency. Thus we have succeeded in producing frequency modulation by the phase method.

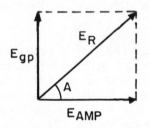 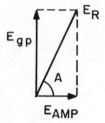

FIG. 16-9. VECTOR ANALYSIS OF PHASE MODULATION.

Another method used to accomplish phase modulation is by the use of a balanced modulator. This is shown in Fig. 16-10. The signal from the crystal controlled oscillator divides itself into two parts. One part is fed to a buffer amplifier VT3. The other part is fed to the grids of VT1 and VT2. The two control grids are connected in parallel. The screen grids are connected in push-pull and receive the audio modulating signal. The plates of the balanced modulator are also connected in push-pull. With no audio present, the currents in L1 and L2 are equal and opposite and cancel each other out. This, in effect, cancels out the carrier. When the audio signal is applied, the two screen grids receive opposite voltages. This causes the two tubes to be unbalanced. Unequal currents will flow in their plate circuits. The difference between the currents in L1 and L2 will induce a voltage in L3. The values of the components are so chosen that the voltage induced in L3 is 90° out of phase with the plate currents in VT1 and VT2. Since the plate tuned circuits are resonant to the oscillator frequency, the plate currents are in phase with the oscillator voltage. The voltage in L3 is therefore 90° out of phase with the oscillator voltage. Thus, we have accomplished the phase shift that is necessary before we can combine the two signals.

VT4 amplifies the 90° sideband components and passes them on to an amplifier where they combine with the signal coming from the crystal

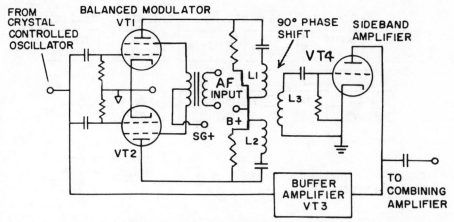

FIG. 16-10. PHASE MODULATION USING A BALANCED MODULATOR.

oscillator. They combine in the manner shown in Fig. 16-9. As the audio varies, the output of the balanced modulator will vary, and this will change the phase of the resultant signal. Changing the phase will, as we have learned, cause frequency modulation.

The output of the combining amplifier is then fed to frequency multipliers and frequency converters to bring the basic carrier frequency up to the level at which the signal will be transmitted.

It is important for both halves of the circuitry of the balanced modulator to be perfectly balanced. This includes the tubes. If the stage is not perfectly balanced, modulation will cause one half of the sidebands to be stronger than they would normally be, and the other half of the sideband to be weaker then they would normally be. This would cause the average frequency output of the transmitter to shift. Other causes of frequency shift during modulation are:

(1) Poor regulation of the power supply —— unless the regulation of the power supply feeding the oscillator is excellent, the varying load conditions during modulation would be fed back to the oscillator to cause its frequency to shift.

(2) Undesirable feedback between the modulator and oscillator would cause the oscillator's frequency to shift when the modulator is activated.

(3) Any other changes of the load of the oscillator will be reflected back into the oscillator and cause its frequency to change.

Fig. 16-11 shows a block diagram of a phase modulated FM transmitter. The principles discussed above are used in this transmitter.

The blocks labeled CRYSTAL OSC, BUFFER AMPL, 90° PHASE SHIFT AMPL and BAL MOD have been fully discussed in previous paragraphs. That part of the block labeled PRE-DISTORTER has been discussed in an earlier part of this lesson. The limiter section of this block provides a means of limiting the amplitude of the audio signal so that it doesn't over-modulate. It contains a control that sets a level above which an increased audio signal at the microphone will not produce a larger signal. The proper setting for the control is determined by observing the FM modulation meter which indicates the amount of modulation present at the output of the FM

319

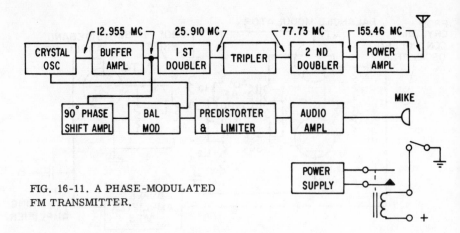

FIG. 16-11. A PHASE-MODULATED
FM TRANSMITTER.

transmitter. The switch and relay at the mike represent a press-to-talk switch located at the microphone housing. This switch turns the transmitter on prior to transmitting.

The purpose of the doubler stages and tripler is to increase the crystal frequency to the carrier frequency. For stability and practicality, the frequency of the crystal must be low. Once we have achieved a good stable signal, we use frequency multipliers to boost the frequency.

The purpose of the power amplifier is to boost the power of the transmitter up to its authorized power rating.

Fig. 16-12 illustrates a typical simple power amplifier for an FM transmitter. This power amplifier is similar to the power amplifiers that are used in AM transmitters. The amplifier is neutralized because a triode is used. The grid bias for the stage is supplied from a grid bias power supply. Its voltage is fixed and must remain so. If, by chance, the bias voltage should vary, the power output along with the antenna current would vary. Normally, an increase in bias voltage causes a decrease in output power with a subsequent decrease in antenna current. A decrease in bias causes an increase in power output and antenna current.

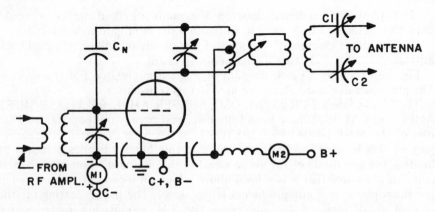

FIG. 16-12. A POWER AMPLIFIER WITH VARIABLE LINK COUPLING.

Meter M1 reads the grid current and meter M2 reads the plate current. The amount of power that can be transferred from the stage to the antenna coupling system can be adjusted by the variable link coupling. Proper impedance matching of the antenna is obtained by adjusting capacitors C1 and C2.

Push-pull amplification can be used in place of the single-ended stage of Fig. 16-12.

3 RF ALIGNMENT OF A PHASE MODULATED TRANSMITTER.

Generally speaking, a transmitter should be re-tuned after repairs have been made to any part of the RF section. The total capacity of a circuit is altered whenever a tube, transistor or other part is changed. Also, if the dress of the leads is altered, the capacity will be changed. This necessitates a re-tuning of the section where the changes have been made. Repairs to the audio or power circuits do not require re-tuning.

The tuning and alignment of the RF section of a phase modulated transmitter is really no different from that of an AM transmitter. We start at the low level stages and we tune each stage until we reach the final amplifier. We then tune up the final amplifier and the antenna circuit.

In order to tune up the tranmitter of Fig. 16-11, the following steps must be taken in the order given below:

(1) Remove the plate and screen voltages from the final amplifier. This is important since we can damage the final tube if the tuned circuits are not properly adjusted when the power is on.

(2) Insert the ammeter (a milliammeter is actually used) into the grid circuit of the buffer amplifier.

(3) With the power of the low level stages on and the proper crystal in place, adjust the plate tank capacitor of the oscillator for maximum reading. The oscillator tuning can also be accomplished by inserting a milliammeter into the plate circuit of the oscillator and tuning for a dip, as described in Lesson 12.

(4) Loosely couple the wave meter to the output of the oscillator. This is done to make certain that we are tuned to the correct frequency and not to a multiple of what the oscillator's output should be. In other words, it is possible for the output tank circuit of the oscillator to resonate at 26 MHz instead of 13 MHz. If the oscillator's tank circuit were resonant to 26 MHz, it would produce an indication in the grid circuit of the buffer stage. However, the milliammeter would not tell us that the frequency is wrong. This is the reason that we need a wavemeter check.

(5) Loosely couple the heterodyne frequency meter to the output of the oscillator to make certain that the crystal frequency is exact. The law requires that the transmitter frequency be exactly as stated in the station license.

(6) Place the milliammeter in the grid circuit of the first doubler and adjust the buffer tuned circuits for maximum reading.

(7) Couple the wave meter to the output of the buffer amplifier to check that the buffer tuned circuits are set to the correct frequency and not to an incorrect harmonic. The wave meter gives a rough indication - that is all we are interested in at this time. Once the oscillator's output frequency is exact,

the output frequency of the transmitter will be exact, provided that the frequency multipliers do the correct multiplying.

(8) Place the milliammeter in the grid circuit of the tripler stage and adjust the first doubler tuned circuits for maximum reading. Use the wave meter to check that the plate tank circuit of the first doubler is tuned to the correct harmonic frequency (approximately 26 MHz).

It is important to tune the tank circuits of the multiplier stages as accurately as possible. If they are slightly de-tuned, the frequency will still be correct but the output of the stage will not be as high as it should be. This will reduce the drive to the following stage. As de-tuning becomes worse, additional unwanted phase modulation takes place. This results in spurious signals that may cause interference at the receiver. If the tuning is too far off, the tank circuit might be resonant to a wrong harmonic. This would cause radiation at incorrect frequencies and damage to the transmitter.

(9) Place the milliammeter in the grid circuit of the second doubler stage and adjust the tuned circuits of the tripler stage for maximum reading. Use the wavemeter to make certain that the output frequency from the tripler stage is approximately 77-78 MHz.

(10) Place the milliammeter in the grid circuit of the power amplifier stage and peak the tuned circuits in the second doubler stage and the tuned circuit (if there is one) in the grid section of the power amplifier stage, for maximum reading. Use the wavemeter to verify that the output frequency of the doubler is approximately 155-156 MHz.

(11) Connect the output antenna circuit to a dummy load. We connect this to a dummy load rather than to an antenna because we do not want to transmit a signal while tuning up the transmitter.

(12) Adjust the antenna coupling to minimum and insert the milliammeter (or ammeter) into the cathode section of the power amplifier. Turn the plate and screen voltages of the power amplifier on and QUICKLY adjust the plate tank circuit for minimum cathode current. We do this quickly because a high current flows in the tube until the plate tank circuit is brought into resonance.

(13) Check the tube manual for the proper plate current. Subtract the approximate screen and control grid currents from the cathode current that is being read to arrive at the true plate current. Adjust the antenna tuned circuit for the maximum current permitted by the tube manual.

(14) Re-adjust the plate tank capacitor for a dip in the cathode current. Continue to adjust the antenna coupling and the plate tank capacitor until the current, at its "dip" point, is in accordance with the tube manual.

(15) Repeat step 10 once again. However, do not exceed the maximum grid current as shown in the tube manual.

(16) Repeat step 13 again.

(17) Disconnect the power and remove the dummy load. Connect the antenna to the transmitter.

(18) Turn on the power and repeat step 13 because the antenna may not present the exact same load to the transmitter as the dummy load did.

FM RECEIVERS. The FM receiver is similar to the AM receiver. Fig. 16-13 shows block diagrams of an AM receiver and an FM receiver. A superhetero-

322

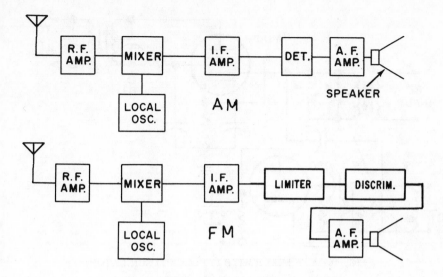

FIG. 16-13. AM AND FM RECEIVERS.

dyne circuit is used for both. The chief difference between the two receivers lies in the limiter-discriminator stages which are found in the FM receiver, but not in the AM receiver.

The FM receiver must have a bandwidth sufficient to pass the range of frequencies sent out by the FM transmitter. The IF bandwidth is an important factor as it must pass a band of frequencies 150 kHz wide with no appreciable attenuation. The RF and mixer stages must have the same band pass characteristics.

The FM receiver must be capable of converting frequency variations into amplitude variations. In other words, a detector which operates on frequency variations, rather than amplitude variations, must be used. This type of detector is called a DISCRIMINATOR.

In order to realize the full noise reducing capabilities of FM reception, a limiting stage is required to eliminate amplitude variations before they reach the discriminator.

We will now discuss each stage of a typical FM receiver in detail.

MIXER-OSCILLATOR CIRCUIT. Fig.16-14 illustrates a typical mixer-oscillator circuit.

The tube of the RF amplifier is fed to T1 which is in the mixer grid circuit. From T1 it is applied to the grid of the mixer. The local oscillator uses a conventional Hartley oscillator circuit. The oscillator circuit generates a signal and injects it into the mixer stage through Cc. The two signals beat with each other to produce the IF, which appears in the plate of the mixer. The IF is then fed to the IF amplifier stage where it is amplified.

Capacitor C1 is a temperature compensating capacitor having a negative temperature coefficient. Its purpose is to counteract the changes that temperature has on the various capacities in the circuit. It thereby maintains a stable oscillator frequency.

323

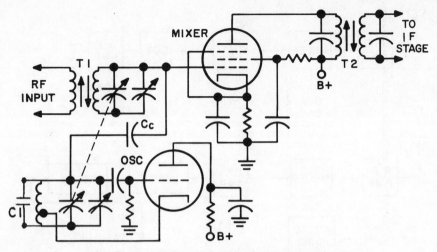

FIG. 16-14. A MIXER WITH ITS LOCAL OSCILLATOR.

IF AMPLIFIER STAGE. Fig.16-15 shows a typical IF amplifier stage that is used in an FM receiver. The stage operates as a Class A amplifier using cathode bias. Class A amplifiers must be used since we do not want to distort the signal. A pentode is used because external neutralization would be necessary if a triode were used. Resistors R1 and R2 broaden the response curve of the stage to accommodate wideband signals. In the case of an FM broadcast station, the bandwidth is 150 kHz wide.

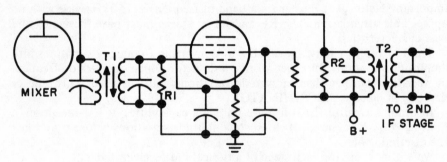

FIG. 16-15. IF AMPLIFIER STAGE.

LIMITER STAGE. We have learned that noise superimposes itself on to the amplitude of a signal. The purpose of the limiter stage is to clip or cut all amplitude variations from the FM signal. In this way, we will get rid of noise and any other amplitude variations which were not present in the original signal at the transmitter. The limiter is between the IF stage and the detector. It removes the amplitude variations before the signal reaches the detector.

Fig.16-16 shows a typical limiter stage. It resembles an ordinary IF stage. However, it differs from the ordinary IF stage in the following manner: In addition to using a sharp cutoff tube, grid leak bias is used. The limiter tube operates with a low plate voltage (40 to 80 volts) and a low screen voltage

The low plate and screen voltages cause the tube to saturate quickly and the limiter stage will not respond to input voltages above a certain value. To insure proper limiting, the input signal to the limiter must be large enough to

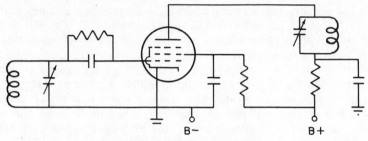

FIG. 16-16. A LIMITER STAGE.

cause the tube to reach saturation. The grid leak bias responds quickly to sudden amplitude variations and tends to counteract them. For instance, if the input signal suddenly increases, the bias would increase and the gain of the stage would decrease.

Thus, we see how amplitude modulation, arising from any cause, is "clipped" from the signal. The limiter does not interfere with the frequency modulation because its action does not affect the instantaneous frequency of the signal.

DISCRIMINATOR. Fig. 16-17 illustrates a basic discriminator. It is known as a TRAVIS DISCRIMINATOR. The primary and secondary of T1 are inductively coupled. The primary tuned circuit is tuned to the center frequency of the incoming IF signal. The secondary is a double tuned circuit. S1C1 represents one tuned circuit and S2C2 represents the other tuned circuit. S1C1 is tuned to one side of the IF center frequency, while S2C2 is tuned to the other side of the IF center frequency. The resonant frequency of each secondary tuned circuit is spaced slightly more than the expected transmitter swing.

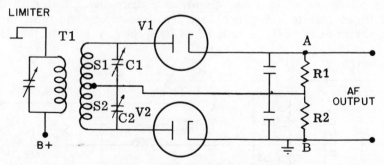

FIG. 16-17. A TRAVIS DISCRIMINATOR

The operation of the Travis discriminator is as follows: When there is no modulation, the center carrier frequency appears across the primary tuned circuit. Since S1C1 is resonant to a frequency away from the IF center

325

frequency, a small amount of voltage will appear across S1C1. This will be rectified and a small DC voltage appears across R1. S2C2 is resonant to a frequency on the other side of the IF center frequency. The difference in frequency between S2C2 and the primary tuned circuit is the same as that between the primary tuned circuit and S1C1. Therefore, the same amount of voltage that appears across S1C1 will appear across S2C2. This RF voltage is rectified by D2 and a DC voltage appears across R2. The voltage across R2 is equal to the voltage across R1. However, the two voltages are opposite to each other, as can be seen from Fig.16-17.Since they are equal and opposite, the output of the discriminator (with no modulation present) is zero.

Now let us assume that modulation is present and that the IF frequency increases. Let us further assume that S1C1 is tuned above the resting frequency and S2C2 is tuned below the resting frequency. When the incoming frequency increases, the voltage developed in the S1C1 tuned circuit will be large because the incoming signal will be close to its resonant frequency. At the same time, the voltage developed across S2C2 will be extremely small. R1 will therefore have a large DC voltage across it and R2 will have a small voltage across it. The difference will therefore be a positive voltage.

When the incoming frequency goes below the resting frequency, S2C2 will have a high voltage across it and S1C1 will have a low voltage across it. The voltage across R2 will be large and the voltage across R1 will be small. The voltage across the output of the discriminator will now be negative. We can therefore see how frequency variations applied to a discriminator cause positive and negative voltages at the output of the discriminator. Since the frequency variations were originnally due to audio signals, the output of the discriminator produces a replica of the original audio signal.

The discriminator of Fig.16-17 is not popular because it has three tuned circuits and alignment is critical and difficult. However, the study of this discriminator helps us understand the basic operation of all FM discriminators.

FOSTER-SEELEY DISCRIMINATOR. Fig. 16-18 illustrates the Foster-Seeley discriminator. It is also known as a phase discriminator. In it, the three tuned circuits of Fig.16-17 have been replaced by two tuned circuits. Also, the primary of T1 is coupled to its secondary by induction and by

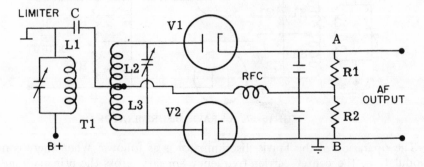

FIG. 16-18. THE FOSTER-SEELEY DISCRIMINATOR.

capacitor C. The operation of the Foster-Seeley discriminator is as follows:

The primary tuned circuit and the secondary tuned circuit are tuned to the center frequency of the incoming IF-FM signal. From an RF point of view, the primary tuned circuit is in series with each half of the secondary coil. Thus, the voltage across L1 and the voltage across L2, are applied to V1; the voltage across L1 and the voltage across L3 are applied to V2.

When there is no modulation present, the voltage induced in the secondary (E_{IND}) is 180° out of phase with the voltage across the primary (E_{L1}). This is shown in Fig. 16-19. One half of the secondary voltage appears across L2 and one half appears across L3. When the carrier frequency is injected into the circuit, the total voltage applied to the V1 circuit is equal to the vector sum of E_{L1} and E_{L2}. The total voltage applied to the V2 circuit is equal to the vector sum of E_{L1} and E_{L3}. This is shown

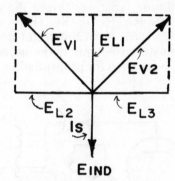

FIG. 16-19. VECTOR ANALYSIS
OF FOSTER-SEELEY DISCRIMINATOR
WITH NO MODULATION.

in Fig. 16-19. It can be seen that the resultant voltages E_{V1} and E_{V2} are equal to each other. The rectified voltage across R1 will be equal and opposite to the rectified voltage across R2. The output of the discriminator (the difference between the two voltages) will therefore be zero.

When modulation is applied, the incoming frequency shifts above and below the resting frequency. The tuned circuits are no longer resonant to the incoming frequency. The secondary tuned circuit becomes inductive or capacitive, depending on which way the signal shifts from the center frequency. When the tuned circuits become reactive, the phase relationships between current and voltage change. The 90° phase relationship between the

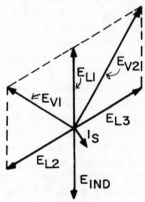

FIG. 16-20. VECTOR ANALYSIS OF
FOSTER-SEELEY DISCRIMINATOR
WITH MODULATION.

primary and secondary voltages is no longer true. Fig. 16-20 illustrates one of the new phase relationships. Note that while the voltages remain the same, the phase angles change. The resultant voltage applied to V1 is now different from that applied to V2. The rectified voltage across R1 will not be equal to the rectified voltage across R2. The difference between these two voltages will no longer be zero and thus, we will have a voltage at the output of the discriminator. As the frequency varies above and below the resting frequency, varying voltages will appear at the output of the discriminator. Thus, we have succeeded in converting frequency variations to audio.

RATIO DETECTOR. The major fault of the two discriminators described above is that they are sensitive to amplitude variations in addition to frequency variations. They therefore require a limiter stage to remove the amplitude variations before the signal reaches the discriminator stage. The use of a RATIO DETECTOR in an FM receiver eliminates the necessity of a limiter stage. A ratio detector does not respond to amplitude variations. In eliminating the limiter, the necessity for large amounts of RF and IF gain that is required for proper limiter operation is also eliminated.

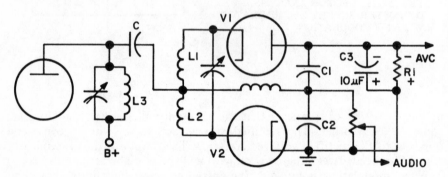

FIG. 16-21. A RATIO DETECTOR.

Fig. 16-21 illustrates a typical ratio detector. It is similar to the Foster-Seeley discriminator of Fig. 16-18 except for the following differences:

(1) The diodes in the ratio detector are in series and their DC output voltages add up. In the discriminator, the diodes are connected so that their DC output voltages are in opposition to each other.

(2) The output section of the ratio detector stage contains a large capacitor (C3) across a resistor instead of the two equal resistors that the Foster-Seeley discriminator contains.

The explanation for the signal voltages developed in the V1 and V2 circuits is similar to that of the Foster-Seeley discriminator. In other words, at the resting frequency, the voltage applied to the V1 section is equal to the voltage applied to the V2 section. As the incoming signal frequency goes above and below the resting frequency, the phase variations are such that the amount of resultant voltage applied to the two sections varies. The outputs of the two sections appear across C1 and C2. The output for the ratio detector is taken across C2. The output voltage will vary up and down as the frequency varies up and down. This voltage varies with the ratio of the output of the two diodes; hence the name, RATIO DETECTOR. The voltage across R1 is constant for a given carrier level. This is because C3 is a very large capacitor and will not permit momentary variations. Since the voltage across R1 is equal to the sum of the voltages across C1 and C2, the amplitude variation of the incoming signal will have no effect on the voltages across C1 or C2. These voltages will vary only in accordance with the frequency variations at L1 and L2. If the carrier strength changes (such as tuning in a stronger station), a new voltage will establish itself across R1. But, it will not vary in accordance with any instantaneous amplitude variations in the signal. Thus we see how the combination of R1 and C3 accomplishes the limiting action of a ratio detector.

PRE-EMPHASIS AND DE-EMPHASIS. A good deal of the noise that is generated in transmitter and receiver circuits occur at the higher audio frequencies. This noise interferes with and masks the higher audio frequencies that are a part of the audio signal. Good fidelity of the audio thus becomes difficult.

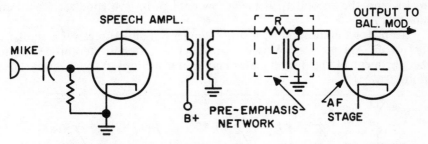

FIG. 16-22. SPEECH AMPLIFIER INCLUDING A PRE-EMPHASIS CIRCUIT.

To overcome this undesirable effect, the higher audio frequencies are deliberately boosted at the transmitter. The circuit that does this is known as a PRE-EMPHASIS CIRCUIT. It is nothing more than a form of high-pass filter. A high-pass filter, as we have learned, favors the higher frequencies while attenuating the lower frequencies. This pre-emphasis circuit, of course, causes an inaccurate audio signal to be sent out. At the receiver end, this inaccurate signal, together with a high noise content at the higher audio frequencies, is present at the output of the detector. A circuit is installed here which cuts down the high frequencies. In doing so, it reduces the noise considerably and it also reduces the higher audio frequencies. However, the higher audio frequencies were previously increased. Thus, in reducing them, we restore the audio signal back to its normal status. The circuit at the receiver end that reduces the high frequencies is known as a DE-EMPHASIS CIRCUIT and it is a form of low-pass filter.

Fig. 16-22 shows a simple speech amplifier with a pre-emphasis network. The pre-emphasis network consists of R and L. As the higher audio frequencies pass through the pre-emphasis network, they develop a higher reactance at L. This causes a higher voltage to be applied to the grid of the following stage when the frequencies are higher. A lower audio frequency causes a lower reactance across L and this means a lower voltage will be applied to the grid of the following stage.

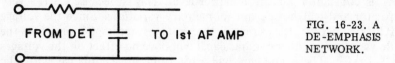

Fig. 16-23 shows a simple de-emphasis circuit. Note that it is nothing more than a low-pass filter. The higher audio frequencies develop a lower reactance across C, thereby tending to short themselves out. The lower frequencies develop a higher reactance across C. This means a higher voltage drop for the low frequencies across C. Thus, the amplitude of the higher frequencies are reduced.

ALIGNMENT. Fig. 16-24 illustrates a block diagram of a double-conversion FM superheterodyne receiver. Double-conversion can be used in AM as well as FM. Two mixing operations are performed. The chief advantage of double conversion is that the first IF is made high enough to eliminate images and the second IF is made low enough to give good selectivity and sensitivity.

Except for the discriminator, the alignment of an FM receiver is similar to that of an AM receiver. We will now describe a step-by-step procedure for the alignment of the discriminator and limiter sections of the receiver shown in Fig. 16-24.

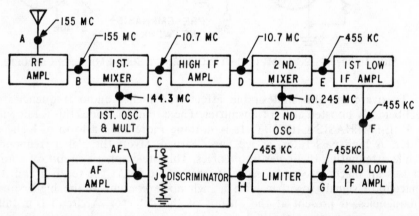

FIG. 16-24. BLOCK DIAGRAM OF AN FM DOUBLE CONVERSION RECEIVER.

The first stage to be aligned in an FM receiver is the discriminator. We will assume that the discriminator is of the Foster-Seeley type. A signal generator, set at 455 kHz, unmodulated, is fed to the grid of the limiter (point G) through a small capacitor. A VTVM, with a center zero scale, is connected between point J of the discriminator and ground. The "hot" lead of the VTVM is at point J. As in most alignment procedures, the output of the signal generator is set as low as possible. The VTVM is set at its lowest scale so that it can pick up the weakest output of the signal generator. The primary of the discriminator transformer, at point H, is peaked for maximum reading of the VTVM. The hot lead of the VTVM is then moved from point J to point I. The secondary of the discriminator transformer at point H is adjusted for center zero on the VTVM. The linearity of the discriminator is checked by varying the signal generator frequency equal amounts on both sides of 455 kHz. The meter reading should vary equal amounts on both sides of center zero. If the linearity is off, the primary of the discriminator transformer can be touched up.

The VTVM is now placed across the limiter's grid resistor. The signal generator, using the lowest possible output at 455 kHz is fed to point F, the grid of the second low IF amplifier. The primary and secondary of the IF transformer at point G are adjusted for maximum reading.

The VTVM remains across the limiter's grid resistor and the rest of the alignment is similar to the alignment of the AM superheterodyne described in lesson 15. The signal generator is moved back one stage at a time, to point A, as each transformer or adjustment is peaked. The signal generator frequencies are indicated in Fig. 16-24.

3 FM DEVIATION METER. Every FM broadcast station must have a modulation meter to indicate its frequency deviation or percentage of modulation. Fig. 16-25 is a block diagram of an FM deviation meter. It is similar to an FM receiver. Instead of an audio section, the FM deviation meter contains a Peak Reading Voltmeter.

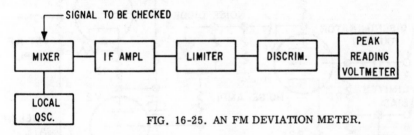

FIG. 16-25. AN FM DEVIATION METER.

The station signal is picked up in the mixer and beat with a signal from the local oscillator. The IF amplifier, limiter and discriminator operate in the same manner as they do in a conventional FM receiver. The output of the discriminator contains the audio that modulated the RF signal. This audio is then passed on to a peak reading voltmeter. It reads the amplitude peaks of the audio signal. The audio peaks vary directly with the frequency deviation. The greater the deviation, the higher the peak voltmeter will read. This meter is actually calibrated in frequency deviation since we know how much frequency deviation will cause a certain amount of peak voltage and we also know how much the meter needle will move for a given amount of voltage.

3 SQUELCH. In tuning a receiver, a hash or hiss noise is heard between stations. It is not heard when a station is tuned in because the station "drowns out" the noise. The hash is especially strong in FM receivers because the gain is high in order to feed the limiters with a strong signal. It is especially offensive to an operator who must monitor a station where there is no signal during most of the time. This situation is true of most two-way radio operators such as policemen, volunteer firemen, etc. In order to eliminate the noise or hiss, a SQUELCH circuit is incorporated into the receiver design.

Fig. 16-26 illustrates a differential squelch circuit. It operates as follows:

The output of the discriminator is fed to points A and C. The negative limiter bias is fed to point B. During the period of no signal reception, the noise output of the discriminator will appear at point A. The values of C1 and R1 are so chosen that they favor the noise and tend to reject the signal. The noise then appears at the grid of the noise amplifier, V1, where it is amplified. The amplified noise then goes to the noise diode where it is rectified. The rectified DC resulting from the noise appears as a positive voltage on the grid of the squelch gate tube, V2. This causes heavy plate current to flow through V2 and R3. Since R3 is the cathode bias resistor for V3, the heavy current will cause a large bias voltage to develop across R3. This heavy bias voltage makes V3's grid highly negative and cuts off V3. Since V3 is the first audio amplifier, nothing will get through the audio system to the speaker. Thus we see how the receiver is squelched when no signal is being received.

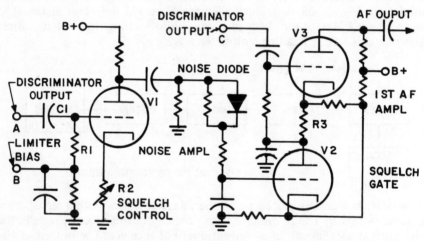

FIG. 16-26. A DIFFERENTIAL SQUELCH CIRCUIT.

When a signal is received, the limiter stage operates to cut down the noise and the amount of noise appearing at V1 is negligible. In addition to this, the incoming signal creates a strong negative limiter bias which appears at point B. The high negative voltage at point B appears on the grid of V1, through R1, and cuts V1 off. Thus the output of V1 is zero and the voltage appearing at the grid of V2 is also zero. Under these circumstances, the cathode bias at V2 is such that very little current flows through V2. The large voltage that appeared previously across R3 disappears and V3, which is the first audio amplifier, operates in a normal manner. It receives the discriminator output from point C. Thus we see how the receiver operates normally when a signal is received.

3 **FREQUENCY SHIFT KEYING.** CW transmission and reception were discussed in Lesson 13. Dots and dashes were formed by turning a transmitter's output on and off. A dot was formed by keeping the transmitter on for a short time. A dash was formed by keeping the transmitter on for a longer time. No signal was transmitted during the spaces between the dots and dashes.

The disadvantages of ordinary CW are: (1) It is not too suitable for teletype reception and (2) it is subject to interference from noise. A more sophisticated type of keying that overcomes these objections is known as "FREQUENCY SHIFT KEYING" (FSK). In this method, the carrier is kept on at all times. When the key is pressed for dots and dashes, the frequency of the carrier is shifted by approximately 850 Hz. When the key is up, the carrier returns to its "resting" frequency.

One way of accomplishing Frequency Shift Keying is to key a reactance tube that is placed across a Variable Frequency Oscillator (VFO) tank circuit. The keying changes the plate resistance of the reactance tube, which changes the reactance across the VFO tuned circuit. This causes the frequency of the VFO to vary.

Another way of producing FSK is to key a capacitor in parallel with the crystal of a crystal-controlled oscillator. By keying the capacitor in or out of the circuit, the frequency of the oscillator is changed.

The receiver contains a beat frequency oscillator that "beats" or heterodynes with the two incoming signals to produce two audio tones at the detector output.

An FM limiter-discriminator circuit then separates the two tones. The tone representing the dots and dashes can be applied to headphones for aural code reception while the other tone can be ignored. In the case of teletype signals, both tones are used to operate the radioteletype printer.

Noise is eliminated from the signal because an FM limiter-discriminator circuit is used to detect the FSK signal.

PRACTICE QUESTIONS – LESSON 16

1. The purpose of a "squelch" circuit is to: **(3)**
a. reduce the signal strength of the incoming signal
b. render the receiver inoperative when no carrier wave is present
c. increase the strength of all incoming signals
d. turn off the transmitter when safe voltage is not maintained
(3)
2. In aligning a phase modulated transmitter, we use a wavemeter:
a. to measure the frequency
b. to make certain we have the correct harmonic
c. because a milliammeter is not accurate enough
d. because a wavemeter is inexpensive

3. What is the Modulation Index when an audio frequency of 500 Hz causes a 90 MHz signal to shift ±4 kHz? **(3)**
a. 22.5   b. 16   c. 20   d. 8

333

4. A ratio-detector can be recognized by:
a. a tapped secondary coil
b. two series capacitors in the output
c. a large capacitor in the output
d. an RF choke between the coil and capacitors

5. In frequency shift keying: (3)
a. the dots appear at a high frequency and the dashes at a lower frequency
b. the dots appear at a low frequency and the dashes at a higher frequency
c. the dots and dashes appear at one frequency and the spaces appear at another frequency
d. the dots, dashes and spaces all appear at different frequencies

6. A de-emphasis circuit is similar to a:
a. low-pass filter   c. high-pass filter
b. M-derived filter   d. band-pass filter

7. In the alignment of a Foster-Seeley discriminator, the secondary of the transformer is tuned for a:
a. peak reading on the VTVM
b. center zero on the VTVM
c. minimum reading on the VTVM
d. linear reading on the VTVM

8. In aligning a Foster-Seeley discriminator:
a. two equal resistors are added to the output
b. the primary of the discriminator transformer is adjusted for minimum output
c. the secondary of the discriminator transformer is adjusted for minimum output
d. the meter is placed between the center of the output resistors and the primary of the discriminator transformer

9. Overmodulation in an FM system causes:
a. carrier shift   c. a wider bandwidth
b. distortion   d. instability

10. What type of modulation is mainly contained in "static" radio waves?
a. frequency modulation   c. pulsed frequency modulation
b. amplitude modulation   d. vestigial sideband modulation

11. The principal merit of frequency-modulated transmission is:
a. the reduction of the FM receiver's noise level
b. simpler circuits in both the transmitter and receiver
c. the need for less bandwidth
d. simpler alignment procedures

12. FM can be produced by a:
    a. reactance tube modulator   c. pre-emphasis circuit
    b. predistortion circuit   d. AFC circuitry

13. What arrangement of multiplier stages is necessary to bring an oscillator frequency swing of 3 kHz up to an output carrier swing of 54 kHz?
    a. two doublers and a tripler
    b. a tripler and a quadrupler
    c. a doubler and two triplers
    d. a doubler, a tripler and a quadrupler

14. The chief difference between the IF stage in an AM broadcast receiver and an FM broadcast receiver is:
    a. amount of gain   c. bandwidth
    b. selectivity   d. bias

15. In an FM radiocommunication system, "deviation ratio" means:
    a. the standard deviation of the various components
    b. the deviation from accepted modulation practices
    c. the ratio of the maximum permissible frequency deviation to the maximum permissible audio modulating frequency
    d. the ratio of deviation between power input and power output

16. FM stands for:
    a. frequency monitoring   c. frequency modulation
    b. fundamental   d. fading motorboating

17. Which of the following is not used in an FM limiter stage?
    a. low plate voltage   c. cathode bias
    b. low screen voltage   d. sharp cutoff tube

18. A type of FM detector that does not require a limiter is the:
    a. ratio detector   c. Armstrong detector
    b. Foster-Seeley detector   d. impedance detector

19. An AM system:
    a. requires critical receiving antenna specifications at broadcast frequencies
    b. requires more complicated transmitter circuits than does an FM system
    c. does not have the stability of an FM system
    d. requires less bandwidth than does an FM system

20. An advantage of narrow-band FM over wide-band FM is not:
    a. slope detection can be used
    b. greater audio frequency range can be utilized
    c. less expensive receiving equipment can be used
    d. allows for greater gain

335

21. In phase modulation, two signals are combined: (3)
a. 90° out of phase with each other
b. 180° out of phase with each other
c. less than 90° out of phase with each other
d. more than 90° out of phase with each other

22. In a phase modulated system, we make the frequency modulation depend only upon the audio amplitude by using:
a. a de-emphasis circuit   c. a and b
b. a pre-emphasis circuit   d. a pre-distortion circuit

23. A tube can act as a variable inductance in a:
a. reactance tube modulator   c. Foster-Seeley discriminator
b. ratio detector   d. Heterodyne Frequency meter

24. The amount that an FM carrier shifts, above or below its resting frequency, is called: (3)
a. deviation ratio   c. frequency deviation
b. modulation index   d. deviation index

25. Our standard broadcast band could not accommodate FM stations because:
a. it is impossible to frequency-modulate a carrier in the broadcast band
b. FM stations occupy a large amount of frequency space
c. large amounts of power are required in the broadcast band
d. the noise level in the broadcast band would be too high for FM reception

26. The space between FM sidebands is equal to the: (3)
a. modulation index   c. audio frequency
b. deviation index   d. deviation ratio

27. The amount of frequency shift resulting from phase modulation depends upon: (3)
a. the phase angle   c. the frequency of the audio
b. the amplitude of the audio d. b and c

28. The output of an FM deviation meter uses a/an:
a. VTVM   c. RF voltmeter
b. speaker   d. peak reading voltmeter

LESSON 17
ANTENNAS AND TRANSMISSION LINES

PROPAGATION OF RADIO WAVES. Radio waves that leave a transmitter take two general paths. One path is along the surface of the earth and is called the GROUND WAVE. The other path is toward the sky and is called the SKY WAVE. See Fig. 17-1.

In traveling along the surface of the earth, the ground wave quickly loses its strength until it is completely diminished. On the other hand, the sky wave can travel for thousands of miles.

Some distance above the earth, the sky wave strikes a gaseous mass called the IONOSPHERE. Here the wave is refracted back to the earth. If a receiver is located between the end of the ground wave and the point where the sky wave returns to earth, it will not pick up the transmitted signal. This area is called the SKIP ZONE. After the wave strikes the earth, it may be reflected up to the ionosphere and back to the earth. In this way, a signal can travel all around the world.

Frequencies above 50 MHz (FM and TV), generally do not refract from the ionosphere. They penetrate the ionosphere and never return to earth. Thus, for these frequencies, we must depend upon the ground wave.

3 **THE IONOSPHERE.** The ionosphere is a region in the upper atmosphere that extends approximately 30 to 300 miles above the earth. It consists of several layers of ionized particles. The ionization is caused by the air particles being bombarded by the sun's ultra violet rays and cosmic rays. The layers which form the ionosphere undergo considerable variations in altitude, density and thickness due to the varying degrees of solar and sunspot activity. Every eleven years, the concentration of solar radiation (sunspot

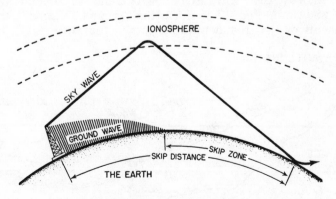

FIG. 17-1. PROPAGATION OF RADIO WAVES.

337

activity) into the earth's atmosphere, reaches a peak. We refer to this as the SUN SPOT CYCLE. During periods of maximum sunspot activity, the ionized layers are more dense and occur at higher altitudes. This allows for communication over greater distances. The opposite happens during minimum sun spot activity.

It can be seen from Fig. 17-1 that if the angle of radiation (the angle between the sky wave and the earth) is increased, the skip distance will be decreased and the signal will return to earth at a point closer to the transmitter. By the same token, if the angle of radiation is decreased, the skip distance will increase.

If the ionosphere is more dense, the refraction is greater and the signal bending is also greater. Hence, the signal will return to earth sooner and the skip distance will be reduced. If the altitude of the ionosphere increases, the skip zone will increase. This is shown in Fig. 17-2.

In general, the higher the frequency, the longer will be the skip distance. This is because the higher frequencies are not refracted as easily as the lower frequencies and go further into the ionosphere before being returned to earth. This results in a situation similar to that shown in Fig. 17-2. If the frequency is increased above a critical value, known as the MAXIMUM USABLE FREQUENCY (MUF), the signal penetrates the ionized region completely and never returns to earth.

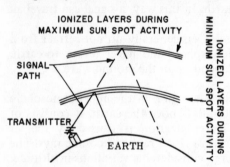

FIG. 17-2. PROPAGATION VERSUS SUN SPOT ACTIVITY.

3 **GROUND WAVE.**The term GROUND WAVE includes the SURFACE WAVE, the GROUND REFLECTED WAVE and the DIRECT WAVE. These are all shown in Fig. 17-3. Since the "ground reflected" and "direct" components of the ground wave are lost as the earth curves, the "surface

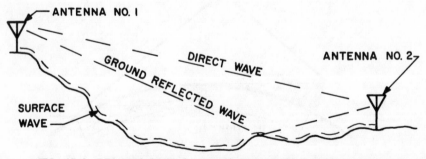

FIG. 17-3. RELATIONSHIP OF RADIO SIGNAL TO EARTH'S SURFACE.

338

wave" is the important part of the ground wave. It diminishes rapidly as the frequency increases. Its energy is absorbed into the earth. The methods used to overcome losses that a ground wave encounters, if one must depend upon ground wave for communication, are:

(1) Increase the power of the transmitter.

(2) Increase the height of the antenna and

(3) Use a high efficiency antenna.

3 **RADIO PROPAGATION AND FREQUENCY.** It has been pointed out that radio propagation varies from frequency to frequency. The following is a brief summary of the ground wave and sky wave propagation characteristics of several different frequency bands. Since there are many factors and variables that influence propagation, this chart can only serve as a guide.

FREQUENCY	GROUND WAVE	SKY WAVE
Low Frequency (50 kHz - 500 kHz)	Communications are possible up to 1,000 or more miles, day or night, with high power transmitters.	Communications are generally reliable, day or night, over most of the band. They are slightly better at night. At the upper end of the band, the sky wave is useful only at night. Depending upon the time of day, the seasons and other factors, useful reception can be had for distances up to 8,000 miles.
Broadcast Frequencies (500 - 1600 kHz)	Reception can be had up to 50 to 100 miles, day or night.	There is no sky wave reception in the day time. At night, reception can be had up to 3,000 miles.
Short Wave (7.0 - 7.4 MHz)	Communications are good only up to about 20 miles.	During the day, useful communications can be had up to 750 miles. At night, communication is possible up to 10,000 miles.
Ultra High Frequency (30 - 300 MHz)	There is little or no ground wave propagation. The only communication is through the direct, line of sight wave, from the transmitter antenna to the receiver antenna.	There is generally very little reflection from the ionosphere, day or night. Occasionally, there is some sporadic reception for short periods of time in limited localities.

PRINCIPLES OF RADIATION. The currents flowing in the antenna create an electromagnetic field which is pushed out from the antenna and into space. The radiated wave consists of a magnetic field and an electrostatic field whose planes are at right angles to each other. Both fields are at right angles to the direction in which the wave is traveling. This is illustrated in Fig. 17-4. The direction of the radiated wave is from the page toward the reader.

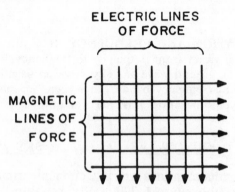

FIG. 17-4. FIELDS OF A RADIATED WAVE.

The wave travels through space at a constant velocity, regardless of the frequency at which it is being transmitted. This velocity is 186,000 miles per second, which is equal to 300,000,000 meters per second. This is also the velocity of light energy.

Since the radiated signal is an alternating current of a specific frequency, each signal has a specific wavelength associated with it. Wavelength is defined as the distance between adjacent AC peaks, or the distance the wave travels through space during one cycle. An equation which ties together the wavelength, frequency and velocity of an electromagnetic wave is:

(1) $V = F\lambda$ where: V is the velocity of the wave which is constant at 300, 000, 000 meters per second, F is the frequency in Hz and λ is the wavelength in meters.

If the frequency is in kHz, the formula becomes:

(2) $F \text{ (kHz)} \times \lambda \text{ (meters)} = 300,000$.

If we wish to solve for the wavelength, the formula becomes:

(3) $\lambda \text{ (meters)} = \dfrac{300,000}{F \text{ (kHz)}}$

If we wish to solve for the frequency, the formula becomes:

(4) $F \text{ (in kHz)} = \dfrac{300,000}{\lambda \text{ (meters)}}$

340

PROBLEMS: (a) Find the wavelength of the distress frequency, 500 kHz.

SOLUTION: Use formula (3):

$$\lambda \text{ (meters)} = \frac{300,000}{F\text{ (kHz)}} = \frac{300,000}{500} = 600 \text{ meters}$$

(b) Find the frequency of the signal whose wavelength is 300 meters.

SOLUTION: Use formula (4):

$$F \text{ (kHz)} = \frac{300,000}{\lambda\text{ (meters)}} = \frac{300,000}{300} = 1000 \text{ kHz.}$$

The velocity of a radio wave changes from 300,000,000 meters per second to a smaller value if it travels in a solid or medium other than free space. From formula (3) above, it can be seen that if this happens, the wavelength will also decrease since the frequency is fixed and remains the same. Thus, when a signal travels through metal or through a transmission line, its velocity as well as its wavelength, changes.

FUNDAMENTAL ANTENNA CONSIDERATIONS Fig. 17-5 shows a wire or antenna connected to an RF source. The signal travels along the wire from point A to point B. At point B, it is reflected back to point A.

It has been stated that a signal travels a distance of one wavelength in one cycle. If the wave travels the length of the wire and back during the period of one cycle, it is evident that the wire must be equal in length to one-half the wavelength of the signal being applied. The wire is then said to be resonant to the frequency of the applied voltage.

During the negative alternation of the RF generator, electrons will move along the wire away from point A towards point B. The electrons are stopped and accumulate at point B, which becomes a high potential or voltage point. During the positive alternation, electrons move away from point B and crowd together at point A, which also represents a high voltage point. In the center of the antenna, there is, at all times, a maximum movement of electrons. Therefore, the center of the antenna is a high current, low voltage point. Fig. 17-6 illustrates the voltage and current distribution on this fundamental half-wave antenna. The points of minimum current and voltage are known as current and voltage nodes, respectively.

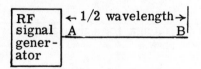

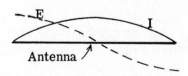

FIG. 17-5. HALF-WAVE ANTENNA.   FIG. 17-6. DISTRIBUTION OF VOLTAGE
AND CURRENT ON HALF-WAVE ANTENNA.

Since the waves traveling back and forth in the antenna reinforce each other, a maximum radiation of electro-magnetic waves into space results. If the antenna were not resonant to the signal voltage, the waves would cancel each other, thus dissipating their energies in the form of heat loss. A resonant antenna connected to an RF generator dissipates power by converting all of the energy into electro-magnetic radiation.

ANTENNA IMPEDANCE. Since voltage and current vary along the length of an antenna, each point on the antenna has a definite impedance value. From Ohm's law we know that the impedance is simply the voltage at a particular point, divided by the current at that point. Thus, the lowest impedance occurs where the current is highest and the highest impedance occurs where the current is lowest.

THE HERTZ ANTENNA. A Hertz antenna is any length of wire far enough from ground so that it will not be influenced by grounded objects. Therefore, its physical length will directly determine the wavelength to which it will tune. A short antenna will be resonant to a short wavelength or high frequency; a long antenna will be resonant to a long wavelength or low frequency. Therefore, the resonant frequency of a Hertz antenna can be changed by varying its physical length. An antenna is resonant to a frequency when its length is an integral multiple of a half wavelength of that frequency.

Fig. 17-7 illustrates a full-wave antenna with a current and voltage graph superimposed on the antenna. We can see that the current is low at the middle and at the ends, whereas the voltage is high at the middle and at the ends. Fig. 17-8 illustrates a center-fed Hertz half-wave antenna. This antenna is somewhat more practical than a full-wave antenna because it is only half the length and occupies half the space. Since the center of a half-wave antenna is a high current point, we say that the antenna is current fed by the transmitter. The impedance at the center of this Hertz antenna is about 73 ohms. The impedance rises uniformly towards each end of the antenna where it is about 2400 ohms.

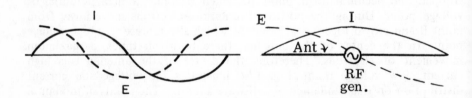

FIG. 17-7. FULL WAVE ANTENNA
WITH E AND I GRAPH.

FIG. 17-8. CENTER-FED
HERTZ ANTENNA.

In order to find the length of a half-wave antenna for a given frequency, we first use the wavelength formula (3) given above.

$$\lambda = \frac{300,000}{F}$$ where: λ is the wavelength in meters
F is the frequency in kHz.

The result gives us the full wavelength of the frequency. This is cut in half to arrive at the half wavelength. For example, let us find the length of a half wave antenna to resonate at 30,000 kHz. We substitute in the formula as follows:

$$\lambda = \frac{300,000}{F} = \frac{300,000}{30,000} = 10 \text{ meters}$$

We then take one-half of 10 meters, or 5 meters. 5 meters is the theoretical or electrical length of the half wave antenna.

We used the term "theoretical" length because in practice, there is a correction factor that must be used for the actual or physical length of an antenna. The theoretical antenna is an antenna far out in space where there are no effects from the earth or other nearby objects. However, the practical antenna is close to the earth, the antenna's supporting structure and other objects. There is capacity between the ends of the antenna and the earth or other objects. We refer to these capacities and similar effects as "end effects". Because of these end effects, a practical antenna should have a physical or actual length that is approximately 5% less than the electrical length. Thus the above antenna should be 5 meters less 5% or 4.75 meters.

A reasonable, practical formula for a half-wave antenna that takes into account all of the extraneous factors is:

$$L = \frac{468}{F} \quad \text{where: L is the length of the half-wave antenna in feet and F is the frequency in MHz.}$$

There are times when we wish to express the physical height of a vertical antenna in terms of wavelength. An example will show how this is done:

QUESTION: An antenna is 500 feet high (long) and is operated at 1000 kHz. What is its physical height, expressed in wavelengths? Assume that one meter is equal to 3.28 feet.

ANSWER: We must first change the feet into meters. This is done by dividing the feet by 3.28:

$$\frac{500}{3.28} = 152 \text{ meters.}$$

Then we must change the frequency into wavelength, using the formula given above.

$$1 \text{ wavelength (in meters)} = \frac{300,000}{F} = \frac{300,000}{1,000} = 300 \text{ meters.}$$

Now that we have the physical height in meters, and we know the wavelength, we simply divide the physical height by the wavelength to find the physical height expressed in wavelengths.

$$\frac{152 \text{ meters}}{300 \text{ meters}} = .492 \text{ wavelength or almost } 1/2 \text{ wavelength.}$$

THE MARCONI ANTENNA. If one half of a half-wave Hertz antenna is replaced by a conducting plane, as illustrated in Fig. 17-9, the remaining quarter-wave will continue to radiate properly. This assumes that the conducting plane is large and acts as a good ground. The ground actually makes up for the other half of the antenna's electrical length. In other words, the antenna proper provides one-quarter wavelength and the ground supplies the additional one-quarter wavelength. The Marconi antenna is a practical example of this type of vertical antenna. The current and voltage distributions along the antenna length are as shown in Fig. 17-10. Notice that the generator feed point is still a high current, low impedance point, as in the case of the ungrounded Hertz antenna. Since the Marconi antenna is only 1/4 wavelength, it is 1/2 the physical length of a Hertz antenna and, therefore, is more practical for mobile operation. In the case of a mobile transmitting or receiving antenna, the metal mass of the car acts as the ground plane. For instance, if the quarter-wave whip antenna were mounted on the center of the auto roof, the automobile roof would act as an excellent ground plane, especially if the size of the roof were large compared to the wavelength being transmitted. In the case of a bumper mount antenna, the bumper, part of the auto body near the bumper and possibly the earth near the bumper, would constitute the ground plane.

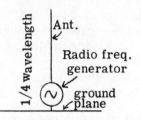

FIG. 17-9. MARCONI ANTENNA.

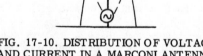

FIG. 17-10. DISTRIBUTION OF VOLTAGE AND CURRENT IN A MARCONI ANTENNA.

4 GROUND RADIALS. It was mentioned above that the ground behaves as one half of the quarter wave vertical antenna. This is accurate if the ground is a perfect conductor. However, we cannot depend upon the natural earth to be a perfect conductor. The moisture and mineral content may vary from time to time. A dependable, stable ground system must therefore be installed.

A stable ground system consists of wires (called RADIALS) of about one-half wavelength long, stretched radially outward from the ground connection. The radials are buried 6″ to 12″ below the surface of the earth and are soldered or welded to one another. With this system, we don't have to be concerned about ground changes due to temperature, moisture, etc.

If the radials are broken or corroded, the ground system ceases to be as reliable as it was. The efficiency will be reduced due to losses and the radiation pattern will probably be altered.

3 FEEDING A MARCONI ANTENNA. There are many ways in which a quarter-wave Marconi antenna can be fed. Fig. 17-11 indicates the series method of feeding a quarter-wave antenna.

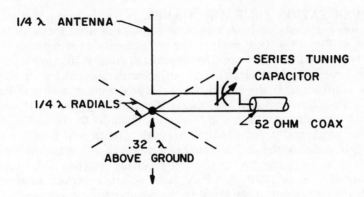

FIG. 17-11. A SERIES TUNED QUARTER WAVE ANTENNA.

In series feeding, the antenna is insulated from ground. It is placed at the proper height for its radiation resistance to approximately equal the impedance of the transmission line. A capacitor or inductance is used to resonate the antenna to the frequency being transmitted. This will cause the antenna to present a resistive load to the transmission cable.

Fig. 17-12 shows the shunt method of feeding an antenna. In the shunt method, the antenna base is grounded. The antenna can actually be a tower, provided its height is correct. The transmission line is run to a certain point close to the antenna. From this point, the inner conductor of the transmission line rises at a 45° angle to the antenna or tower. The point at which the line meets the antenna is the point where the impedance of the antenna is equal to the impedance of the line. In other words, the base of the antenna is grounded and therefore, is zero ohms. The top of the antenna has some high impedance. Somewhere in between we can find the match for the transmission line.

The shunt-fed antenna has advantages over the series-fed antenna in that it does not require a base insulator and does not require any lightning protection. The feeding is rather simple and because of this, it is not necessary to have a separate building to house the parts that couple the transmission line to the antenna.

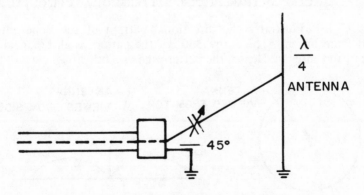

FIG. 17-12. SHUNT FEEDING AN ANTENNA.

345

POLARIZATION OF RADIO WAVES. It has been pointed out that a radio wave consists of both an electric field and a magnetic field. This is shown in Fig. 17-4. One part of the wave cannot exist without the other. They both constitute the wave that is radiated from an antenna.

The direction of the electric lines of force determines the "polarization" of the radio wave. If the electric lines of force are vertical (as in Fig. 17-4), we say that this particular radio wave is vertically polarized. If the electric lines of force are in a horizontal direction (parallel to the earth), the radio wave is horizontally polarized. A vertical antenna will produce vertically polarized radio waves and a horizontal antenna will produce horizontally polarized radio waves. A horizontal receiving antenna will receive both horizontally and vertically polarized radio waves. However, a much stronger signal will be present at the input to the receiver for a horizontally polarized wave than for a vertically polarized wave. By the same token, a vertical receiving antenna will favor a vertically polarized wave over a horizontally polarized one.

DIRECTIONAL CHARACTERISTICS OF ANTENNAS. A horizontal transmitting antenna radiates well in the two directions broadside (at right angles) to the length of the antenna. It radiates poorly in the direction along the length of the antenna. This is shown in Fig. 17-13. Fig. 17-13A shows the "figure 8" directional transmitting pattern of a horizontal antenna as viewed from the top. A receiver at point A would receive very little compared to one at point B.

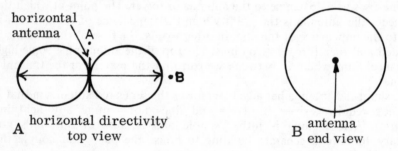

FIG. 17-13. DIRECTIONAL TRANSMITTING PATTERNS OF A HORIZONTAL ANTENNA.

Fig. 17-13B illustrates the directional pattern of the same antenna as viewed from an end. The entire 360° of the pattern is all broadside to the length of the antenna. Hence, the pattern shows a full circle.

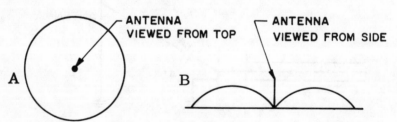

FIG. 17-14. DIRECTIONAL TRANSMITTING PATTERNS OF A VERTICAL ANTENNA.

Fig. 17-14A shows the directional pattern of a vertical antenna as viewed from the top. It radiates well in all horizontal directions. We refer to this pattern as omnidirectional or non-directional.

Fig. 17-14B shows the pattern of a vertical antenna as viewed from its side. It radiates well at low angles to the earth, but radiates very poorly directly above itself.

The radiation patterns discussed above are for transmitting antennas. However, they hold true for receiving antennas as well.

FIELD INTENSITY. Field strength or field intensity can be defined as "the amount of electric field due to a transmitting antenna at a specific point in space". Field strength is measured in millivolts or microvolts per meter. If 3 millivolts are induced in an antenna that is 1 meter long, we say that the field intensity is 3 millivolts per meter. If 6 microvolts are induced in an antenna 3 meters long, the field intensity is 2 microvolts per meter. (6 microvolts ÷ 3 meters = 2 microvolts per meter).

EXAMPLE: What is the effective height of a vertical antenna if a field intensity of 20 millivolts per meter develops 3 volts into an antenna.

ANSWER: We divide the field intensity into the total induced voltage to find the effective length of the antenna. 3 volts ÷ .020 millivolts per meter = 150 meters.

The field intensity is directly proportional to the antenna current or voltage. If we double the antenna current, we double the field intensity; if we triple the antenna current, we triple the field intensity, etc. The field intensity is also directly proportional to the square root of the output power of a transmitter. This is true because the current is proportional to the square root of the power. Since the field intensity is directly proportional to the current, it is directly proportional to the square root of the power.

The field strength of a standard broadcast station varies inversely with the distance from the transmitter. In other words, as the distance between the transmitter and receiver increases, the signal strength becomes weaker.

ANTENNA DESIGNS. There are many different types of antennas and antenna combinations. Each one is meant for a different purpose and has different characteristics. For instance, a loop antenna is used in conjuction with direction finding equipment; a multi-element beam antenna is used to concentrate the output of an antenna into a single direction, etc.

The terrain, the available space, the frequency, the reception area, the cost, etc. are all factors that determine the type of antenna to be used. In addition to the half-wave dipole that has been previously covered, we will discuss a few of the basic antennas that are being used.

DIRECTIVE ANTENNAS USING PARASITIC ELEMENTS. Fig. 17-15 illustrates a two-element antenna. Element A is an ordinary horizontal half-wave dipole. It operates in the manner previously described. Power is fed to its center from a transmitter. Element B is approximately the same size as A. However, it is not electrically connected to anything. We refer to it as a parasitic element. As current from the transmitter flows in dipole element A, an electromagnetic field is radiated from it. The field induces a

347

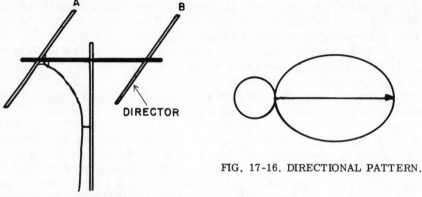

FIG. 17-16. DIRECTIONAL PATTERN.

DIRECTOR

FIG. 17-15. A 2-ELEMENT ANTENNA.

voltage in the new element and it, too, radiates an electromagnetic field.

If element B is made approximately 5% shorter than element A and is spaced approximately .2 of a wavelength away from A, the radiation pattern of the half-wave dipole is altered considerably. Most of the energy is radiated in one direction, the direction of the new element. We now refer to the directional pattern as unidirectional (one direction). See Fig. 17-16. The original dipole element (A) is called the driven element. The new element (element B) is called a "director" because most of the energy is radiated in its direction.

The 2-element antenna does not draw more power from the transmitter than the single element antenna. It merely concentrates the energy in one direction. However, from the receiving standpoint, the addition of the director is as though the power to the antenna were increased. A useful term that is used to compare the performance of antennas is POWER GAIN. The power gain of a particular antenna compares it to a standard reference antenna. The standard reference antenna is usually a half wave dipole antenna at the same height and having the same polarization and other conditions as the antenna being considered. The definition of power gain is the ratio of the power required to produce a given field strength using a reference antenna, to the power required to produce the same field strength with a particular antenna. This gain is expressed in decibels. For example, let us assume that a 2-element antenna produced a certain field strength with 5 watts being fed to the antenna. In order to get the same field strength with a single element half-wave reference dipole, we find it necessary to increase the antenna power to 50 watts. This means that the 2-element antenna has a power gain of 10 (50÷ 5 = 10) or, in terms of db, a power gain of 10 db.

Since the 2-element beam, with 5 watts applied to it, has the same effect at the receiver as the single element half wave dipole with 50 watts applied to it, we can say that the 2 element beam has an EFFECTIVE RADIATED POWER of 50 watts. The EFFECTIVE RADIATED POWER is the power that actually enters the antenna, multiplied by the antenna power gain.

EXAMPLE: What is the effective radiated power of a broadcast station if the output of a transmitter is 5,000 watts, the antenna transmission line loss is 200 watts and the antenna power gain is 5.

348

ANSWER: The power going to the antenna is the output power of the transmitter, minus the transmission line loss. Therefore, 4800 watts (5000 − 200 = 4800) is the power present at the antenna. We multiply this by the power gain to obtain the effective radiated power. 4800 x 5 = 24,000.

Another term used in antenna design is the "Antenna Field Gain". The "antenna field gain" of an antenna is the ratio of the free space field intensity produced at one mile in the horizontal plane, in millivolts per meter, to the field intensity produced at the same point when a simple dipole antenna is used. In other words, it is a comparison of the antenna under discussion to a standard reference antenna (a simple half wave dipole antenna).

PROBLEM: What is the effective radiated power when 500 watts is fed to an antenna having an antenna field gain of 2.4.

ANSWER: We multiply the power by the square of the antenna field gain:

$$500 \text{ watts} \times (2.4)^2 = 500 \times 5.76 = 2,880 \text{ watts.}$$

We square the 2.4 because antenna field gain is a function of voltage and we are looking for power. From the basic power formulas, we know that power is proportional to the square of the voltage.

3 Fig. 17-17 illustrates a 3-element antenna. Element A is the driven element; element B, which is 5% shorter than element A, is the director and element C, which is 5% longer than element A, acts as a REFLECTOR. The directional pattern is shown in Fig. 17-18.

The gain of the 3-element beam is more than that of the 2-element beam. The pattern is also sharper, hence, more directive. To increase the directivity and power gain further, we can add more elements. An antenna with many elements is referred to as a yagi-type antenna.

In order to obtain additional gain, we can take driven elements, with their associated reflectors and/or directors, and stack them one on top of the

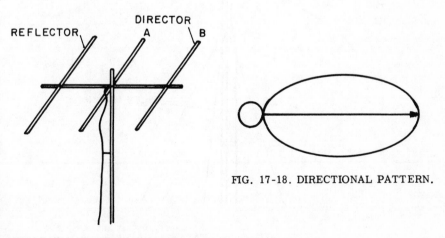

FIG. 17-18. DIRECTIONAL PATTERN.

FIG. 17-17. A 3-ELEMENT ANTENNA.

349

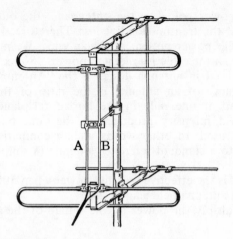

FIG. 17-19. A STACKED ANTENNA.

other or broadside to each other. We connect the antennas together and they are fed in phase. This will also result in a sharper directional pattern and better band pass characteristics. This type of antenna system is known as a STACKED ARRAY.

Fig. 17-19 illustrates a simple STACKED ANTENNA ARRAY. The driven elements are folded dipoles rather than simple dipoles. The lead-in wire is attached to one of the folded dipoles and two metal rods A and B attach it to the other.

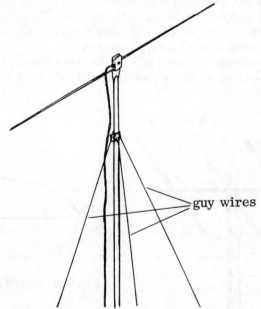

guy wires

FIG. 17-20. GUY WIRES PREVENT ANTENNA FROM SWINGING IN THE WIND.

The mast of an antenna has a bracket to which three wires are attached. These wires are called GUY WIRES. They are mechanical supports that are used to prevent the wind from bending and snapping the mast. The guy wires should lead away from the antenna in at least three different directions. See Fig. 17-20.

If the guy wires are of a certain length, they may act as absorbers or radiators of RF energy. This can destroy the directional pattern of the antenna system and also waste RF energy. Insulators are sometimes placed in the guy wires to prevent this. The insulators break up the guy wires so that they do not form resonant lines and therefore, will not affect the antenna system.

3 THE CORNER REFLECTOR ANTENNA.

Fig. 17-21 illustrates a simple corner reflector type of antenna. This antenna is really a form of the parasitic antenna previously discussed. The driven element is an ordinary dipole antenna. The reflector consists of two metal sheets formed in the shape of a "V". The reflector may be a solid sheet, a screen or it may be formed from parallel tubing. The apex angle between the two sheets is usually between 45 and 90°. The dipole antenna is on a line that bisects the apex angle and it is placed approximately a half wavelength from the corner of the apex angle. This gives the antenna maximum gain. The antenna is unidirectional in the direction of the dipole and it has high gain and a broad frequency response.

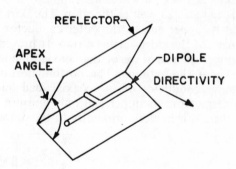

FIG. 17-21. A CORNER REFLECTOR.

3 V-BEAM ANTENNA.

The "V" antenna is actually a form of a long wire antenna. It is made by positioning two long wires in the form of a V. This is shown in Fig. 17-22. The gain of the V antennna is determined by the length of the radiators and the apex angle. For a given apex angle, the gain and sharpness of directivity increases as the length of the antenna increases. The gain can be made very high if the legs of the antenna are several wavelengths long.

Fig. 17-22 illustrates an unterminated V-beam antenna. Its pattern is bi-direcitonal. It transmits and receives well along the line bisecting the apex angle.

Fig. 17-23 illustrates the same beam with its ends terminated by the correct resistance. The terminated V-beam is unidirecitonal. It receives and transmits well in only one direction.

351

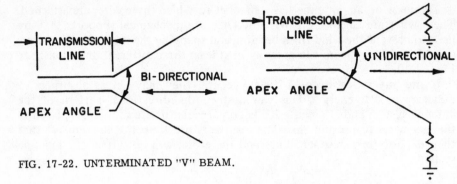

FIG. 17-22. UNTERMINATED "V" BEAM.

FIG. 17-23. TERMINATED "V" BEAM.

3 A COAXIAL WHIP ANTENNA. A coaxial whip antenna is a high performance antenna that has a low radiation angle. It is especially useful at very high frequencies. It is essentially a half wave antenna.

Fig. 17-24 shows a sketch of a simplified coaxial whip antenna. The whip is the upper half of the vertically polarized antenna. Its length is 1/4 of a wavelength. The bottom of the whip is connected to the center conductor of the coaxial line that connects the antenna to the transmitter or receiver. The insulator serves as support for the whip and insulates it from the skirt. The skirt is 1/4 of a wavelength long. It is the other half of the half wave dipole. It radiates as well as the whip. The skirt is a metal cylinder that is connected at its upper end to the outer conductor of the transmission line. The lower part of the skirt acts as a trap. It prevents currents from circulating on the upper quarter wave of the coaxial line and impairing the radiation capabilities of the antenna. The bottom portion of the skirt is isolated from the outer conductor of the coaxial feed line. We want the skirt to receive its energy from its upper end only and not from any other portion of the skirt where it is in close proximity to the outer conductor of the coaxial cable.

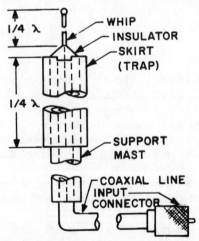

FIG. 17-24. A COAXIAL WHIP ANTENNA.

352

The support mast is the mount for the antenna. The function of the coaxial line is to connect the antenna to the receiver or transmitter. It is a 72 ohm line and since it feeds the center of a half-wave antenna, we have a perfect impedance match between the transmission line and the antenna. The input connector is a coaxial type connector that facilitates the electrical connection between the antenna and the coaxial cable.

3 **THE LOOP ANTENNA.** Fig. 17-25A represents a loop antenna. It is actually a coil whose shape may be circular, square or rectangular. The size of the loop is large compared to its length; however, its overall circumference is not more than a small fraction of its wavelength.

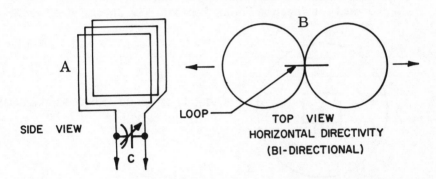

FIG. 17-25. A LOOP ANTENNA WITH ITS HORIZONTAL PATTERN.

When such a loop is used for reception and it is rotated so that its plane faces an oncoming signal, the strength of the signal will be minimum at the receiver. To explain this, we can consider the sides of the loop as two separate vertical antennas. If the loop faces the signal, both of these sides are equidistant from the signal and the e.m.f.'s in them are equal in amplitude, but oppose each other in the loop circuit. This is shown in Fig. 17-26. The two e.m.f.'s will then cancel and no signal is heard. This is referred to as a "NULL" position.

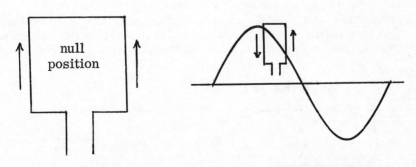

FIG. 17-26. NULL POSITION OF
LOOP ANTENNA.

FIG. 17-27. MAXIMUM POSITION
OF LOOP ANTENNA.

Fig. 17-27 shows what occurs when the loop is rotated so that its plane is parallel to the plane of signal propagation. Since the loop is a small part of the wavelength, it is indicated as being relatively small with respect to the size of the wave shown. From Fig. 17-27, it can be seen that the magnitude of the induced e.m.f. will be different in the two vertical sides of the loop. Therefore, a resultant e.m.f. will appear in the receiver.

Fig. 17-25B shows the top view radiation pattern of a vertical loop antenna. It is a figure eight pattern. Reception is low at right angles to the plane of the loop and high in a line with the plane of the loop.

If we took the loop and placed it in a horizontal position, it would receive well in all horizontal directions. This is shown in Fig. 17-28. However, it would have minimum reception in a vertical direction.

A loop is used for direction-finding because of its directional characteristics.

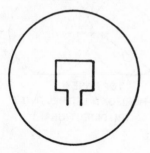

FIG. 17-28. DIRECTIONAL PATTERN OF HORIZONTAL LOOP ANTENNA.

4 **VERTICAL ANTENNA ARRAY.** The antennas discussed thus far consist of one driven element; that is, the transmission line feeds power to one element. The other elements receive their power from the driven element, through electromagnetic coupling and not from the transmission line.

Some broadcast stations use an antenna array consisting of more than one driven element. One of the simplest arrays of this type consists of two vertical antennas that are spaced one half wavelength apart. Each antenna is fed by a separate transmission line and each antenna receives equal currents that are in phase with each other. The radiation pattern from such an array is shown in Fig. 17-29. Notice that the pattern is a figure eight pattern. Maximum radiation is along a line perpendicular to the line joining the two antennas. The reason for this is as follows:

Normally, the pattern from each vertical antenna is a circle. This means that they radiate well in all horizontal directions. However, when the signal from antenna #1 reaches antenna #2, it is 180 degrees out of phase with the

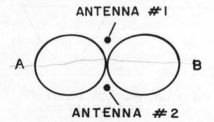

ANTENNA #1

ANTENNA #2

A   B

FIG. 17-29. RADIATION PATTERN OF A VERTICAL ARRAY.

354

signal from antenna #2. It therefore cancels out in this direction. When the signal from antenna #2 travels to antenna #1, it reaches there 180 degrees out of phase with the signal coming from antenna #1. It also cancels out. There is no radiation in this direction. However, when the signals from the two antennas reach points A or B, they reach these points at the same time and they reinforce each other. Therefore, there will be maximum radiation in the direction of A and B.

The directional characteristics of this array depend upon the antennas being fed signals that are in phase and of equal amplitude. If the amplitude is different or the phase is off, the entire directional pattern will be altered. It is, therefore necessary to sample the phase and amplitude of the currents entering both antennas. Loops are used to pick up energy and feed them back to a point where they can be observed and where adjustments can be made. The devices that pick up signals and monitor their phase are known as PHASE MONITORS. In addition to correcting the phase and amplitude of the signals, the phase monitors are also used when it is necessary to change the phase and amplitude of the signals in order to change the directional pattern of the antenna. There are times when a different directional pattern is required for day and a different pattern for night.

The distance between the vertical antennas can be expressed in electrical degrees, as well as in physical length. The following problem will illustrate the conversion of one into the other.

PROBLEM: If two towers of a 1260 kHz directional antenna are separated by 180 electrical degrees, what is the tower separation in feet?

SOLUTION: First we convert frequency into wavelength:

$$\lambda = \frac{300,000}{1260} = 238 \text{ meters}$$

Since 360 degrees is a complete wavelength, 180 degrees is one-half of a wavelength. The separation of the two towers is, therefore, $238 \div 2 = 119$ meters. We multiply meters by 3.28 to obtain feet. The distance in feet is therefore 119 x 3.28 = 390 feet.

ANTENNA LOADING. Since an antenna acts like a resonant circuit, it is resistive at its resonant frequency, and reactive at non-resonant frequencies. The antenna operates efficiently when it presents a resistive load to the generator.

If the physical length of the antenna is too long at the wavelength which it is to radiate, it will act as an inductive load on the generator. In this case, the electrical length of the antenna can be decreased by means of loading the antenna with a lumped capacitive reactance. This will counterbalance the effective inductive reactance of the antenna. The result is that the antenna is made to present a resistive load to the generator. Similarly, if the electrical length of the antenna is too short, it will present a capacitive load to the generator, resulting in inefficient radiation. Loading the antenna with an inductance or "Loading Coil" of the right value will resonate the antenna.

For reasons of economy and aircraft safety, it is often necessary to reduce the height of a vertical broadcast antenna to less than that which is

355

ordinarily required for optimum electrical operation. We do this by placing a network of conductors at the top of, and usually insulated from, the antenna. A coil is used to connect the conductors to the antenna. The network of conductors, which constitute a lumped capacity, together with the inductance, form a tuned circuit that effectively (from an electrical point of view) lengthens the antenna. This system of loading an antenna is referred to as TOP LOADING and is used in a number of large broadcast stations.

RADIATION RESISTANCE. The action of the antenna as a resistance and as a power dissipator has resulted in a term called the RADIATION RESISTANCE. It is defined as that value of resistance which, if substituted for the antenna and connected in its place, would dissipate the same amount of power in heat as the antenna dissipates in radiation. The term is somewhat fictitious, since the antenna is not a resistance, but is simply acting like one. The radiation resistance at the center of a half-wave Hertz antenna is 73 ohms. For a Marconi antenna, the radiation resistance is roughly 37 ohms. The radiation resistance can be used to determine the power input into an antenna by using the formula

$$P = I^2R \quad \text{where: I is the antenna current at the antenna}$$

input, R is the radiation resistance and P is the power input to the antenna in watts.

A few examples will illustrate the use of this formula or its variations.

EXAMPLE: What is the antenna current when a station is delivering 450 watts into an antenna having a resistance of 50 ohms?
ANSWER: We use the above power formula and algebraically solve for I.

$$P = I^2R, \quad \frac{P}{R} = I^2 \quad \sqrt{\frac{P}{R}} = I$$

We then substitute and solve:

$$I = \sqrt{\frac{450}{50}} = \sqrt{9} = 3 \text{ amps.}$$

EXAMPLE: If the day input power to a station having an antenna resistance of 50 ohms is 800 watts, what would the night power be if the antenna current were cut in half?

ANSWER: We first use the formula derived above to find out what the day current is.

$$I = \sqrt{\frac{P}{R}} = \sqrt{\frac{800}{50}} = \sqrt{16} = 4 \text{ amps.}$$

We then use the power formula to find the night power when the current is cut in half.

$$P = I^2R = (2)^2 50 = 4 \times 50 = 200 \text{ watts.}$$

DUMMY ANTENNA. When a transmitter is being tuned up for optimum operation, the antenna should be coupled to the final stage. However, coupling an antenna during the adjustment period is forbidden by law because radiation will result, which may cause interference. This difficulty is overcome by utilizing a dummy antenna which is nothing more than a resistive load of the correct power dissipation, coupled to the transmitter in the same manner as the antenna.

FADING. A signal, being received, may sometimes fade in and out. This variation is due to the interaction between two signals (that originally came from the same transmitter) at the receiving antenna that vary in and out of phase with each other. In other words, if two signals arrive at the receiving antenna that are opposite or almost opposite to one another in phase, they will cancel or tend to cancel each other out. The signals are continuously varying; they do not always have the same phase relationship to each other. Sometimes they oppose each other, sometimes they reinforce each other. This is why the signal at the output of a receiver is strong one instant and weak the next.

The two signals that we speak about were originally one and the same signal that came from a single transmitter. However, one may have taken a direct path from the transmitting antenna to the receiving antenna, while the other took a different path and was reflected from some object to the receiving antenna. Another possibility is that one signal was the sky wave, while the "second" signal was the ground wave.

3 One way to overcome fading is to use a "Diversity Antenna Receiving System". In this system, two or more receiving antennas are used. They are spaced several wavelengths apart so that they do not interact with one another. The signals induce voltages at different phases in each of the antennas. All the antennas are connected to an automatic switching device that automatically connects the antenna with the strongest signal to the receiver. In this way the strongest signal is always being received and the fading effects are reduced.

TRANSMISSION LINES. In practically all transmitter installations, the antenna is located some distance from the transmitter. It may be 10 feet or it may be 200 feet. In all cases, some means must be used to carry the RF energy from the output of the transmitter to the antenna. The lines that are used to carry this energy are called transmission lines. There are two common types of transmission lines. One is called parallel line or twin-lead; the other is called coaxial cable. These are shown in Fig. 17-30. The twin-lead consists of two parallel conductors, separated by flexible insulation or spacers. The coaxial cable consists of a conductor surrounded by a round flexible polyethelyne insulator. There is a concentric metallic covering made of flexible wire braid around this insulator. A weatherproof vinylite sheath surrounds the wirebraid.

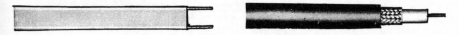

FIG. 17-30. TRANSMISSION LINES.

There is a type of coaxial cable which makes use of an inert gas instead of the flexible insulator between the center conductor and the outer conductor. The gas is installed under pressure and the cable is sealed. This prevents moisture from getting into the cable. The possibility of arcing is greatly reduced. This type of coaxial cable has less losses than the flexible insulator type. However, it is very expensive and is cumbersome to install.

The transmission line should carry the RF energy from the transmitter to the antenna with minimum losses. In order for this to occur, the impedance of the transmission line must be equal to the impedance of the transmitter's output and to the impedance of the antenna. If the three impedances are all equal, there will be a maximum transfer of power from the transmitter to the antenna. This will also result in minimum harmonic distortion.

When we speak about the impedance of a transmission line, we mean the ratio of the voltage to the current of a wave traveling along an infinite transmission line. The impedance is determined by the capacitance per unit length and the inductance per unit length of the transmission line.

The "characteristic" or surge impedance of a parallel wire air insulated transmission line can be found with the aid of the following formula:

$$Z_0 = 276 \log \frac{b}{a}$$

where: Z_0 is the characteristic impedance of the line, b is the center to center spacing between conductors and a is the radius of the conductors.

The characteristic impedance of a coaxial transmission line is given by the following formula:

$$Z_0 = 138 \log \frac{b}{a}$$

where: b is the inside diameter of the outer conductor and
a is the outside diameter of the inner conductor.

There is a certain amount of power loss in a transmission line. With the use of the simple power formulas, we can calculate this loss, as well as the existing power, voltage and current relationships in the line. A few examples will illustrate this.

EXAMPLE: How much power is being fed to a 600 ohm transmission line if the current in the line, at the input end, is 2 amperes?
ANSWER: We use a basic power formula and substitute:

$$P = I^2 R = 2^2 \times 600 = 4 \times 600 = 2400 \text{ watts}$$

EXAMPLE: The power input to a 50 ohm concentric transmission line is 3,000 watts. What is the r.m.s. voltage between the inner conductor and sheath?
ANSWER: We use a power formula that involves voltage and resistance and solve for voltage.

$$P = \frac{E^2}{R}, \quad PR = E^2, \quad \sqrt{PR} = E$$

$$E = \sqrt{PR}, = \sqrt{3000 \times 50} = \sqrt{150,000} = 387 \text{ V}.$$

EXAMPLE: A long transmission line delivers 5,000 watts to an antenna. The line current at the transmitter end is 4 amperes and at the antenna end (coupling house), it is 3.8 amperes. Assuming the line to be properly terminated and losses in the coupling system negligible, what is the power lost in the line?

ANSWER: We first find the impedance at the antenna end. This is also the line impedance since the transmission line is properly terminated. We take a basic power formula and solve for R.

$$P = I^2R, \quad \frac{P}{I^2} = R. \quad R = \frac{P}{I^2} = \frac{5000}{3.8^2} = \frac{5000}{14.4} = 347 \text{ ohms}.$$

We can now find the power that enters the transmission line at the transmitter end.

$$P = I^2R = 4^2 \times 347 = 16 \times 347 = 5552.$$

The line loss is the power entering the line minus the power leaving the line and entering the antenna. It is 5552-5000 or 552 watts.

STANDING WAVE RATIO. Fig. 17-31 illustrates the voltage and current graphs of a full-wave antenna. If the antenna were made longer, the graph would simply repeat itself along the full length of the antenna. The voltage maximums and minimums repeat themselves at half-wave intervals. The graph does not change with time and because of this, we refer to the waves as "STANDING WAVES". These standing waves result in maximum radia-

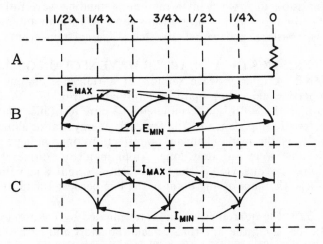

FIG. 17-31. I AND E GRAPHS OF STANDING WAVES ON A TRANSMISSION LINE.

tion of the signal and they are desirable in an antenna. However, standing waves are undesirable on a transmission line.

Standing waves will occur on a transmission line if the transmission line is not terminated properly. They will occur in the same manner as they occur on an antenna. This is shown in Fig. 17-31. Fig. 17-31B shows a standing wave graph of the voltages taken at points along the transmission line. The current graph is shown in Fig. 17-31C. Note that the maximums and minimums repeat themselves at half-wave intervals. If the transmission line is terminated properly in its characteristic impedance, then the voltage and current will both be constant values all along the line and no standing waves will exist.

We do not want the transmission line to radiate; we only want it to transfer energy. We therefore do not want standing waves on a transmission line. Standing waves on a transmission line result in the following:

(1) Loss of signal fed to the antenna.

(2) Inability to tune transmitter properly.

(3) Overheating and possible arcing on the line.

The standing waves on an antenna or transmission line give us maximum and minimum voltage and current points along the antenna or line. The ratio of the maximum current to minimum current or maximum voltage to minimum voltage is called the STANDING WAVE RATIO. Expressed as a formula, it is:

$$SWR = \frac{I_{max.}}{I_{min.}} \text{ or } \frac{E_{max.}}{E_{min.}}$$

where: SWR is the Standing Wave Ratio, $I_{max.}$ and $E_{max.}$ are the maximum current and voltage points on the line, $I_{min.}$ and $E_{min.}$ are the minimum current and voltage points on the line.

In a transmission line, we want a minimum standing wave ratio. This is done by properly terminating the transmission line with an antenna whose impedance is resistive and equal to that of the transmission line.

4 CHARACTERISTICS OF A QUARTER WAVE SECTION OF A TRANSMISSION LINE. A quarter-wave section of a transmission line exhibits different properties, depending upon its termination. Fig. 17-32A illustrates a quarter-wave section of a line terminated in a pure resistance that is equal to the characteristic impedance of the line. RF energy travels along the line and is absorbed by the load. There are no reflections or standing waves. It is as though the line were infinitely long. An ammeter or voltmeter inserted anywhere along the line would show the same current and voltage. The impedance is also the same at any point in the line because the ratio of E to I is the same.

In Fig. 17-32B, the quarter-wave line is terminated by a short circuit. The RF energy travels along the line till it meets the short and is then reflected back to the input. Standing waves will appear. At the short circuit, the current is high, the voltage is low and the impedance is low. The opposite is true at the input end. The current is low, the voltage is high and the impedance is infinite.

Fig. 17-32C shows a line whose termination is open. The RF energy travels to the end and is reflected back to form standing waves. Since the end is open, the current is zero and the voltage and impedance are high. At the input, the current is high and the voltage and impedance are low.

By examining the graph in Figs. 17-32B and 17-32C, we note that the impedance at one end is opposite to that at the other end. Thus we can use these quarter-wave sections as impedance inverters or as impedance matching devices.

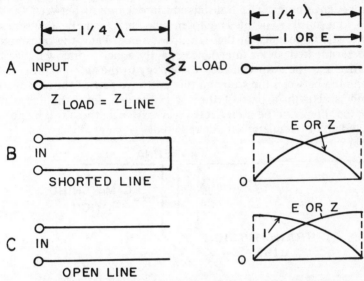

FIG. 17-32. QUARTER WAVE SECTIONS OF A TRANSMISSION LINE.

4 MATCHING THE TRANSMISSION LINE TO THE ANTENNA. The choice of the antenna and the choice of the transmission line and its length do not always lend themselves to a perfect impedance match. If the line is too long, or if the line is unbalanced and a balanced antenna is being used, there is bound to be a certain amount of mismatch. Also, the impedance of the transmission line that is available and economical may not necessarily be the same as the impedance at the center of the antenna that is being used. For these reasons, it may be necessary to use an aid in order to match the antenna to the transmission line.

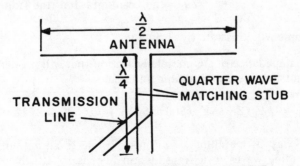

FIG. 17-33. QUARTER-WAVE MATCHING STUB.

361

One form of device that is used is a quarter-wave matching section or "stub". This is shown in Fig. 17-33. The antenna, in this case, is a half wavelength long. The matching stub is a quarter wavelength long. Both parts of the matching stub, together with the antenna, form a full wavelength. From what we have learned, the top of the matching stub is a high current, low impedance point. The bottom of the matching stub is a low current, high impedance point. The transmission line is moved between the top and the bottom until a point is chosen which is exactly the same as the characteristic impedance of the transmission line. Thus, the transmission line will be terminated at an impedance exactly equal to its own characteristic impedance and the stub will feed the energy to the antenna proper. There is no mismatch between the stub and the half-wave part of the antenna because the stub is actually a part of the total antenna. Since the line is properly terminated, there will be no reflected waves. Hence, there will be no standing waves and all of the energy will be radiated.

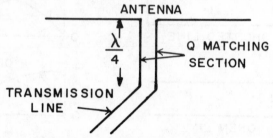

FIG. 17-34. Q-MATCHING SECTION.

Fig. 17-34 illustrates another method of matching a transmission line to an antenna where the impedances of the line and the antenna are not equal. The matching section, sometimes called a Q MATCHING SECTION, is a quarter wavelength long. If the matching section has the proper impedance, the unequal impedances of the antenna and transmission line can be compensated for. The following formula is used to determine the impedance of the matching section:

$$Z = \sqrt{Z_A \times Z_T}$$ where: Z = the impedance of the matching section, Z_A = the antenna's impedance, Z_T = the transmission line impedance.

An example will illustrate this principle:

Find the impedance of a Q matching section that will properly match a 50 ohm transmission line to a 300 ohm antenna.

$$Z = \sqrt{Z_A Z_T} = \sqrt{300 \times 50} = \sqrt{15000} = 122 \text{ ohms.}$$

Another way of matching a transmission line to an antenna and thereby reduce standing waves in a transmission line, is to attach a short stub of transmission line to a point on the main transmission line less than

362

one-quarter of a wavelength from the antenna. There are times when it should be attached to the junction of the antenna and the transmission line. See Fig. 17-35. The short stub acts as a reactance, and, if it is attached to a point of equal and opposite reactance, it will cancel the reactance at that point and reduce the standing waves in the line to a minimum.

In the above examples of impedance matching, the proper procedure is a "cut and try" method. We temporarily attach lines to points and observe the

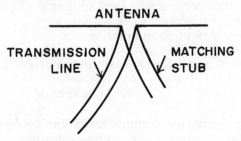

FIG. 17-35. CANCELLING REACTANCE WITH A SHORT STUB.

results on an SWR meter. When the standing wave reflections are at a minimum, we know we have the best impedance matching and we make permanent connections.

4 PROTECTING STATION EQUIPMENT FROM STATIC CHARGE AND LIGHTNING DISCHARGE ON AN ANTENNA.

During an electric storm, an antenna may be hit by lightning which can damage the station equipment. A means must be provided to safely bypass the lightning discharge to ground. What is usually done is to connect spark gaps of large current carrying capacity between the antenna and ground. The spark gap will provide an effective bypass for the lightning surge.

If an antenna is capacity coupled to the output of the transmitter, static charges of high potential may build up on the antenna because there is no direct leakage path to ground. In this case, static drain coils having a high resistance at the radiating frequency are connected from the base of the antenna to ground. They serve as the discharge path for any static charge on the antenna. An antenna grounding switch can also be used to discharge the atmospheric electricity that accumulates on the antenna system. During transmission or reception, the switch should be open.

The ammeter that reads antenna current is also subject to damage due to lightning. The way to protect this ammeter is to place a shorting switch across it and to short it out during electrical storms.

PRACTICE QUESTIONS - LESSON 17

1. What is the effective radiated power of a broadcast station if the transmitter output is 10,000 watts, the transmission line loss is 300 watts and the antenna power gain is 7?
a. 70,000 watts
b. 2,100 watts
c. 67,900 watts
d. 69,700 watts

2. If the voltage and current are the same on all points of a transmission line, the SWR is:
a. 1　　　　b. 2　　　　c. $\sqrt{2}$　　　　d. .636

3. The directional characteristics of an array consisting of two vertical driven antennas does not depend on: (4)
a. the amount of current in each antenna
b. the phases of the currents in each antenna
c. the ground terrain around each antenna
d. the phase monitors of each antenna

4. An advantage of gas-filled transmission cable is not:
a. easy to install　　　　c. low loss
b. efficient　　　　d. less arcing

5. The purpose of gas in a transmission line cable is not to:
a. prevent arcing　　　　c. reduce losses
b. reduce moisture　　　　d. match impedance

6. If the field strength of a transmitter's fundamental signal is 100 millivolts and its 3rd harmonic is 100 microvolts, what is the attenuation of the 3rd harmonic in db?
a. 20 db　　　b. 40 db　　　c. 60 db　　　d. 30 db

7. The maximum usable frequency does not depend on the: (3)
a. type of emission used　　　　c. time of year
b. time of day　　　　d. sun-spot activity

8. The power input to a 50 ohm transmission line is 2,000 watts. What is the voltage at the input point?
a. 100,000 V　　　b. 40 V　　　c. 316 V　　　d. 250 V

9. The field intensity of a broadcast station is:
a. inversely proportional to the distance from the transmitter
b. directly proportional to the output power
c. directly proportional to the antenna current
d. a and c

10. In a 2-element beam antenna:
a. the element connected to the transmission line is called the driven element
b. the other element is called the director
c. the other element is called the reflector
d. the other element does not receive any power

11. An antenna is 400 feet high and is operated at 1200 kHz. What is its physical height, expressed in wavelengths? Assume that one meter is equal to 3.28 feet.
a. .122λ　　　b. .488λ　　　c. .300λ　　　d. .480 λ

12. A vertical loop antenna has maximum radiation: (3)
   a. off the ends of the loop
   b. in a direction perpendicular to the plane of the antenna
   c. in a vertical direction only
   d. in a horizontal direction only

13. Which of the following does not constitute part of the ground plane of a quarter wave whip antenna mounted on a bumper?
   a. the bumper   c. the earth near the bumper
   b. the rear wheels   d. the auto body near the bumper

14. The usual means for protecting station equipment from damage by charges of atmospheric electricity (static) on the antenna system, is to: (4)
   a. connect a large size capacitor from top of antenna to ground
   b. use a static drain coil and/or an antenna grounding switch
   c. shunt the antenna with a low value resistance
   d. disconnect the coupling system from antenna when not in use

15. Insulators are placed in antenna guy wires: (3)
   a. to increase the inherent strength of the wires
   b. to prevent transmitter overloading
   c. to reduce the efficiency of the wires to act as radiators
   d. to increase RF losses in the guy wires

16. How much power is fed to a 300 ohm transmission line if the input line current is 3 amperes?
   a. 900 watts   b. 2700 watts   c. 100 watts   d. 9000 watts

17. Which one of the following antennas uses parasitic elements? (3)
   a. Marconi   b. whip   c. V beam   d. corner reflector

18. A broadcast transmitter delivers 5 amperes to a transmission line. At the antenna end of the transmission line, 4,000 watts at 4.5 amperes are delivered to the antenna. Assuming that the impedances are properly matched, what is the power lost in the line?
   a. 100 W   b. 50 W   c. 950 W   d. 400 W

19. In order to obtain optimum power output from an RF power amplifier:
   a. the antenna system should be matched to the rated tube load impedance
   b. a directional array antenna should be used
   c. link coupling is required
   d. Class B push-pull operation should be employed

20. A stable ground system uses: (4)
   a. hard earth   c. ground radials
   b. metallic earth deposits d. 1/4 wave copper rods

365

21. The top view directional pattern of two vertical driven antennas, spaced one-half wavelength apart, is a: **(4)**
    a. circle
    b. unidirectional pattern
    c. figure 8
    d. null in all horizontal directions

22. What is the field intensity of an 80 meter antenna that has 2 volts induced in it?
    a. 25 MV/meter
    b. 160 MV/meter
    c. 40 MV/meter
    d. 1.6 MV/meter

23. What is the wavelength of a 4250 kHz signal?
    a. 710 meters   b. 71 meters   c. 14 meters   d. 140 meters

24. A vertical Marconi antenna is:
    a. one-half wavelength long
    b. a full wavelength long
    c. one-quarter wavelength long
    d. an odd multiple of a half-wavelength long

25. An unterminated "V"-type antenna is: **(3)**
    a. unidirectional   b. bidirectional   c. tridirectional
    d. directional characteristics are determined by the length of the elements

26. Stub-tuning does not: **(4)**
    a. eliminate undesirable radiation
    b. eliminate standing waves
    c. match impedances
    d. filter out harmonics

27. Ionization of the upper atmosphere is primarily dependent upon radiation from the: **(3)**
    a. outer space   b. sun   c. moon   d. earth

28. What is the wavelength of a 100 MHz signal?
    a. .0033 meters   b. .33 meters   c. 3 meters   d. 300 meters

29. Find the frequency of a signal whose wavelength is 24 meters.
    a. 80,000 kHz   b. 8,000 kHz   c. 72,000 kHz   d. 12,500 kHz

30. What is the height of a vertical radiator 1/2 wavelength high if the operating frequency is 2,000 kHz?
    a. 75 meters   b. 150 meters   c. 37.5 meters   d. 300 meters

31. If a transmission line is properly matched to an antenna:
    a. there will be standing waves along the line
    b. there will be a sine wave pattern along the line
    c. the current will be the same at all points on the line
    d. the current will be the same at all points on the antenna

LESSON 18
FREQUENCY MEASUREMENTS

MEASUREMENT AND DETERMINATION OF FREQUENCY. The FCC requires all stations to maintain their exact operating frequency so that they do not interfere with each other. Therefore, one of the most important duties of the radio operator is to keep his station exactly on frequency. In order to do this, he must be able to measure the frequency of the transmitter. The instrument which is used to measure frequency is called a FREQUENCY METER or FREQUENCY MONITOR.

In addition to a frequency meter that monitors the transmitter's frequency, a broadcast station is required to have an independent frequency standard or service that can check the transmitter's frequency, as well as the accuracy of the station's frequency monitor.

Before we cover the more elaborate frequency meters, we will discuss some basic RF meter movements as well as a simple type of wavemeter.

4 **THE THERMO-COUPLE TYPE OF METER.** A thermo-couple type of ammeter is an ideal meter for use in measuring radio frequency currents. This meter depends on the principle of two dissimilar metals generating an e.m.f. when heated. The two dissimilar metals are placed at a point where

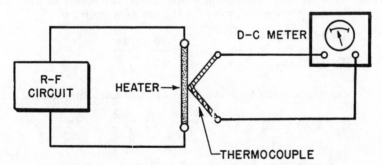

FIG. 18-1. A THERMOCOUPLE TYPE OF AMMETER.

the RF passes through and develops heat. The two dissimilar metals are connected to a DC millivoltmeter to measure the e.m.f. See Fig. 18-1. The more the RF current, the greater will be the heat and the greater will be the e.m.f. developed across the two dissimilar metals.

The heat that develops at the thermo-couple junction is proportional to the square of the current going through the junction. The e.m.f. that develops across the two dissimilar metals is proportional to the heat. Therefore, the meter reading will be proportional to the square of the current. In other words, if we were to double the RF current being read by the meter, the heat would go up four times as much, the developed e.m.f. would go up four times as much and the meter would read four times as high. This type of meter is known as a CURRENT SQUARE METER.

Fig. 18-2 indicates two scales that can be used with a meter of this type. Notice that the top scale is not linear, that is, the numbers are not proportional to the distances along the scale. This scale reads the RF current directly. The bottom scale is a linear scale.

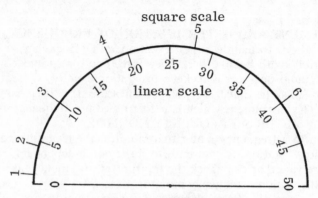

FIG. 18-2. LINEAR AND NON-LINEAR SCALES.

An example will show the relationship of the two scales.

QUESTION: When 6 milliamperes flow through the meter whose scale is shown in Fig. 18-2, the deflection on the lower scale is 40. What is the current flowing through the meter when the lower scale reads 10?

ANSWER: Since the deflection is proportional to the square of the current, we can set up a proportion and solve for the unknown current.

$$\frac{\text{Deflection}_1}{\text{Deflection}_2} = \frac{I_1^2}{I_2^2} \qquad \frac{40}{10} = \frac{6^2}{I_2^2}$$

We can algebraically solve for I_2 in the following manner:

$$I_2^2 \times 40 = 10 \times 6^2. \quad I_2^2 = \frac{10 \times 6^2}{40} = \frac{360}{40} = 9$$

$$I_2^2 = 9. \quad I_2 = \sqrt{9} = 3.$$

We can check the answer by looking at the scale. 3 ma lines up with a scale division of 10. In going from 3 ma to 6 ma, we are doubling current. The linear scale quadruples in going from 10 to 40.

A HOT WIRE type of meter may also be used to measure radio frequency currents. The hot wire meter depends upon the RF heating an element which expands and pulls a meter needle across a scale. The hot wire type of ammeter is not rugged and is not used as much as the thermocouple type meter.

368

ABSORPTION TYPE WAVEMETER. If a high "Q" tank circuit is placed in the vicinity of an RF field, it will absorb energy from this field and start to oscillate if the resonant frequency of the tank circuit is equal to the frequency of the radiation. This is the principle of the absorption type wavemeter. Its circuit is illustrated in Fig. 18-3.

The absorption type wavemeter consists of a rigidly constructed, accurately calibrated coil and a variable capacitor. The coil is usually interchangeable with other coils to permit measurements to be taken over a large portion of the radio frequency spectrum. The resonance indicator may be a flashlight bulb. A thermocouple ammeter, which is more sensitive, can be used in place of the bulb.

FIG. 18-3. ABSORPTION TYPE WAVEMETER.

In order to read an unknown frequency output from a circuit, the coil of the wavemeter is brought near the circuit and the capacitor is tuned for maximum indication on the indicator. As the capacitor is rotated, a pointer moves across a pre-calibrated scale. When the indicator reads maximum, the scale gives the unknown frequency.

A precaution to be followed in using the wavemeter is to place the instrument as far away as possible from the radiating source, consistent with a readable indication. The reason for this is that we do not want the wavemeter to affect the radiating source by a mutual coupling reaction.

3 THE GRID-DIP METER. A GRID-DIP METER is similar to a wavemeter in that it measures frequency. The grid-dip meter is an oscillator with a milliammeter in its grid circuit. The inductance of the oscillator's tuned

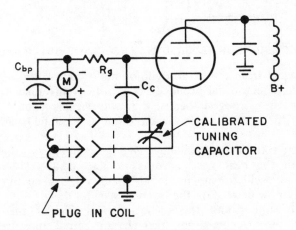

FIG. 18-4. A GRID-DIP METER.

369

circuit consists of plug-in coils. Each plug-in coil makes the oscillator resonant to a different band of frequencies. Fig. 18-4 illustrates a common form of grid-dip meter.

The purpose of the grid-dip meter is to measure the frequency of tuned circuits. In order to do this we must know the approximate range of the frequency to be measured. We then plug the correct coil into the meter. The coil with the meter is brought close to the tuned circuit being measured. The variable capacitor is rotated until the meter dips. This indicates that the grid dip oscillator is tuned to the same frequency as the tuned circuit being measured. The meter dips because the tuned circuit being measured draws energy from the meter. This reduces the amplitude of the oscillations and causes the grid current to drop. The calibrated dial, fastened to the tuning capacitor shield, indicates the frequency to which the oscillator is tuned.

The grid-dip meter can also be used as an absorption wave meter and it can be used to locate parasitic oscillations in transmitters.

THE HETERODYNE FREQUENCY METER. The Heterodyne Frequency Meter is a rigidly constructed, accurately calibrated oscillator and detector. For stability, the oscillator is usually of the electron-coupled type. An additional crystal oscillator can be incorporated in the frequency meter to check and calibrate the heterodyne oscillator at various check points. Fig. 18-5 illustrates a simple combination heterodyne frequency meter and monitor.

The frequency meter incorporates a detector circuit, into which two RF signals are fed. They are: (1) the transmitter signal picked up by an antenna

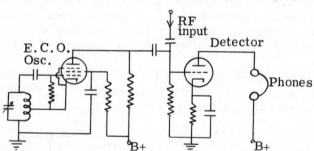

FIG. 18-5. COMBINATION HETERODYNE FREQUENCY METER AND MONITOR.

and (2) the signal from the heterodyne oscillator. These two signals mix in the grid of the detector and produce a beat note or difference frequency. In order to get the strongest beats, the two signals should have equal amplitudes. If the beat note is in the audio range, it will be heard in the head sets.

To check the transmitter frequency, vary the frequency of the heterodyne oscillator until the beat note becomes a zero beat. At zero beat, the transmitter and oscillator are producing exactly the same frequency. The frequency may now be read on the frequency meter dial.

In order to understand the operation and use of the Heterodyne Frequency meter, we will go through an actual measurement of a transmitter's frequency.

Assume that the oscillator portion of the meter has a range of 20 to 30 MHz and is capable of producing harmonics up to 300 MHz. Let us further assume that the heterodyne frequency meter has a built-in 1 MHz crystal-controlled oscillator that can produce harmonics up to 50 MHz. The transmitter we wish to check has an output frequency of 82.2 MHz. A step-by-step procedure in checking this frequency would be as follows:

(1) Set the oscillator (signal generator) section of the frequency meter to 20 MHz.

(2) Turn on the crystal-controlled oscillator and allow its 20th harmonic to beat with the oscillator signal.

(3) Adjust the oscillator so that there is a "zero beat" between the two signals when the dial reads 20 MHz.

(4) Do the same for 21 MHz.

These first four steps check the accuracy of meter's dial reading.

(5) Loosely couple the output of the transmitter to the frequency meter.

(6) Slowly rotate the dial of the meter between 20 and 21 MHz until a "zero-beat" is heard. If the transmitter's freqency is correct, the dial will read 20.55 MHz. The dial reading is multiplied by four since it is obvious that it is the fourth harmonic that is beating with the transmitter's output frequency.

A receiver, in conjuction with the frequency meter, can also be used to check the frequency of a transmitter. This is done by tuning in the unmodulated transmitter carrier. The proper harmonic of the correctly calibrated signal generator portion of the frequency meter is then coupled to the receiver. We zero beat the two signals in the receiver and read the frequency on the frequency meter's dial. The dial reading, multiplied by the harmonic used, gives the frequency of the transmitter.

A number of precautions to be observed in the use of the heterodyne type of frequency meters are as follows:

1. The heterodyne oscillator must be calibrated against the crystal oscillator check points for frequency accuracy.

2. When battery operated, check A and B battery voltages regularly because a change in battery voltage will affect the oscillator frequency.

3. Allow at least one half-hour warm-up period before using.

4. In the event that it is necessary to replace a tube in the meter, the entire calibration of the meter should be checked with a standard frequency generator to make sure it is accurate. This is especially true if the tube to be changed is an oscillator tube.

5. Wherever possible, unmodulated RF energy should be used for measuring purposes. A modulated signal has numerous sideband and harmonic frequencies that will give extraneous readings in the frequency meter.

A SECONDARY FREQUENCY STANDARD. A Secondary Frequency Standard is an instrument that is used to calibrate and check frequency measuring meters and signal generators. It does this by generating a highly accurate and very stable signal, which is then compared with the signal from the frequency meter or signal generator being checked.

Fig. 18-6 illustrates a basic Secondary Frequency Standard. The crystal-controlled oscillator generates a stable signal of 100 kHz or 1.0 MHz. This signal is used to synchronize a harmonic generator. The harmonic generator can be a multivibrator that generates a fundamental signal at 100 kHz, 10 kHz or 1 kHz, together with many harmonics up to as high as 60-70 MHz. The multivibrator is used because it generates signals that are rich in harmonics.

Following the harmonic generator is an amplifier with switchable tuned circuits. The tank circuit that is chosen is closest to the frequency that we wish to have in the output of the secondary standard. This gives the desired frequency more gain.

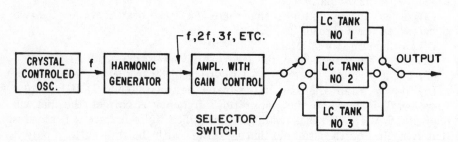

FIG. 18-6. BLOCK DIAGRAM OF A SECONDARY FREQUENCY STANDARD.

In order to calibrate a frequency meter, the output of the frequency meter is mixed with the output of the secondary frequency standard in a receiver or other suitable detector. When a "zero-beat" is obtained, the frequencies of the two signals are identical. The frequency meter can then be adjusted so that its dial reads the exact frequency.

Since the secondary frequency standard puts out signals at intervals of 1 MHz or 100 kHz, we can only check the frequency meter's oscillator at these points. These points are known as "calibration check points." and it must be assumed that if the oscillator is correct at the calibration check points, it is sufficiently accurate at the frequencies in between the check points. The frequency meter should be checked with the secondary frequency standard each time the frequency meter is used.

Fig. 18-6 is referred to as a "secondary" frequency standard. The "primary" frequency standards are maintained by the National Bureau of Standards in Washington, D.C. The Central Radio Propagation Laboratory of the National Bureau of Standards maintains two radio transmitting stations for broadcasting standard radio frequencies of very high accuracy. One of these stations is WWV, which broadcasts radio signals at 2.5, 5, 10, 15, 20 and 25 MHz. These signals are guaranteed accurate to within one part in 100,000,000.

The secondary frequency standard can be made accurate by comparing its output to Station WWV. This is done by mixing the two signals in a receiver or other detector. If a receiver is used, the BFO should be off. A trimmer on the secondary frequency standard's oscillator is adjusted until a "zero-beat" is heard.

A COMPLETE HETERODYNE FREQUENCY METER. Fig. 18-7 illustrates a block diagram of an elaborate Heteroydne Frequency Meter. It contains its own secondary frequency standard. This is indicated by the blocks labeled "crystal oscillator" and "crystal osc. harmonic amplifier."

The unknown signal frequency is measured by feeding it into the "RF input" terminal. The switch is turned to position #2. The unknown signal and the output of the variable frequency oscillator go to the mixer and detector. The audio difference between the two signals is amplified in the AF amplifier and passed on to a speaker or headsets. The VFO is then adjusted for "zero-beat." The dial reading on the VFO tells us what the unknown frequency is.

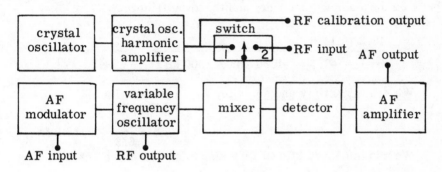

FIG. 18-7. A HETERODYNE-FREQUENCY METER.

In order to calibrate the VFO, the switch is turned to position #1. The output of the secondary frequency standard is mixed with the output of the VFO, and the difference frequency is fed to the detector and AF amplifier. The VFO is then adjusted and calibrated to "zero-beat" with the output of the secondary frequency standard.

The variable frequency oscillator can be used as a signal generator. Its output is taken from the terminal marked "RF output."

The RF signal can be modulated in the event a modulated RF signal is required. A modulated VFO signal can be used for greater accuracy in "zero-beating."

4 INTERPOLATION. There are many times when a frequency meter's dial is not calibrated in frequency but in a common numerical sequence, such as 0 to 100. In order to find the frequency, we must look up a chart which correlates the numbers with the frequencies. But, suppose the dial reads between two numbers. What is the frequency? We must observe the distance of the dial pointer between two known points, and then use the same percentage in the frequency chart. For instance, if 15 on a linear scale corresponds to 800 kHz and 16 on the scale corresponds to 900 kHz, what would be the frequency if the pointer is halfway between 15 and 16? Obviously, it is 850 kHz. If the pointer lands three quarters of the way up, the frequency would be 875 kHz. This is called INTERPOLATION.

The examples of interpolation given above are rather simple and can be done mentally. The following example will illustrate one of the methods to be used when the numbers are not simple.

EXAMPLE: If a heterodyne frequency meter, having a straight line relation between frequency and dial reading, has a dial reading of 42.5 for a frequency of 1500 kHz and a dial reading of 48.8 for a frequency of 1600 kHz, what is the frequency corresponding to a scale reading of 45.2?

ANSWER: The way to solve this problem is to set up a proportion and solve for the unknown. The difference between the scale reading corresponding to the unknown frequency and the lower scale reading, over the difference between the upper and lower scale readings, is equal to the difference between the unknown frequency and the lower frequency, over the difference between the upper and lower frequencies. We will call the difference between the unknown frequency and the lower frequency X.

$$\frac{45.2 - 42.5}{48.8 - 42.5} = \frac{X}{1600 \text{ kHz} - 1500 \text{ kHz}} \qquad \frac{2.7}{6.3} = \frac{X}{100}$$

We cross multiply and solve for X: $6.3X = 2.7 \times 100$
$$6.3X = 270$$
$$X = \frac{270}{6.3} = 42.86 \text{ kHz}$$

We add the 42.86 kHz to 1500 kHz to arrive at the unknown frequency. $1500 \text{ kHz} + 42.86 \text{ kHz} = 1542.86 \text{ kHz}$

FREQUENCY TOLERANCE OF A TRANSMITTER. Most transmitters are assigned specific frequencies on which to operate. Since a transmitter cannot be expected to maintain an exact frequency, a certain amount of tolerance is permitted. For instance, a transmitter may be assigned a specific frequency with a specific tolerance percentage. This means that the actual transmitter's output frequency may be slightly higher or lower than the assigned frequency, but not by more than the allowable tolerance. An example will make this clear:

Let us assume that a transmitter is assigned a frequency of 156.30 MHz with a tolerance of plus or minus 0.005 percent. What would be the maximum and minimum frequencies that the transmitter could actually transmit at and still be within the tolerance specifications?

First we convert the percentage of tolerance into an actual frequency:

$$156.30 \text{ MHz} \times .00005 = .007815 \text{ MHz or } 7.815 \text{ kHz}$$

The maximum frequency that the transmitter could transmit at would be 156.30 MHz + .007815 MHz = 156.307815 MHz.

The minimum frequency that the transmitter could transmit at would be 156.30 MHz - .007815 MHz = 156.292185 MHz.

The transmitter's output frequency is measured by a frequency meter. The accuracy of the measuring instrument should therefore be taken into account in determining whether the transmitter is within its tolerance limits.

For instance, if the meter in the above problem is guaranteed accurate to within .001 percent, we must reduce our frequency tolerance by this amount. Instead of using .005 percent in the calculations, we should use .004 percent. The maximum frequency limit, as read by the frequency meter, would then be 156.306252 MHz and the minimum frequency limit would be 156.293748 MHz.

4 It is important to know how accurate the station's frequency meter is. This accuracy can be given in percentage or it can be given in actual Hz or kHz. One way of determining the actual accuracy of the meter is to combine the transmitter's frequency error as reported by a known accurate frequency meter, and the transmitter's error in frequency as reported by the frequency meter under question. For instance, let us assume that a broadcast station received an accurate frequency measurement report indicating that the station frequency is 75 Hz lower than it should be. At the same time, the station frequency monitor indicates that the transmitter is 40 Hz lower than it should be. The error in the station frequency meter is obviously the difference, or 35 Hz. If the station frequency meter read 35 Hz lower, it would have been perfectly accurate.

On the other hand, if, at the same time, the station frequency monitor indicates that the transmitter is 20 Hz HIGHER than it should be, then the error in the station frequency meter would be 95 Hz. The difference between the two meters is 95 Hz. (75 + 20 = 95).

PRACTICE QUESTIONS - LESSON 18

1. A Heterodyne Frequency Meter does not contain a:
a. crystal oscillator and harmonic amplifier
b. variable frequency oscillator
c. mixer
d. ratio detector

2. The heart of the Heterodyne Frequency Meter is a/an:
a. crystal oscillator   c. Colpitts oscillator
b. grid-leak detector   d. electron-coupled oscillator

3. A frequency meter with a straight line relationship between frequency and the dial reading reads 34.2. The chart shows that 33.1 indicates 4475 kHz and 35.3 indicates 4500 kHz. What is the frequency being read? (4)
a. 4501.1 kHz   c. 4487.5 kHz
b. 4476.1 kHz   d. 4486.1 kHz

4. In frequency measurements using the heterodyne "zero-beat" method, what is the best ratio of the signal e.m.f. to the heterodyne oscillator e.m.f.?
a. 1 to 2   b. 1 to 1   c. 2 to 1   d. 4 to 1

5. An example of a primary frequency standard is:
a. WWV   b. FCC   c. a BFO   d. an ECO

6. A precaution to be observed in the use of the battery operated heterodyne frequency meter is to:
   a. check the crystal frequency
   b. check the oscillator with a standard frequency
   c. check the A and B battery voltages
   d. check the tube filaments

7. A current-square meter has a scale divided into 40 equal divisions. When 30 ma flows through the meter, the deflection is 34 divisions. What is the current flowing through the meter when the scale deflection is 20 divisions? (4)
   a. 20 ma   b. 15 ma   c. 17 ma   d. 23 ma

8. If a broadcast station receives an accurate frequency measurement report indicating that the station frequency is 35 Hz high and the transmitter's monitor indicates that the station frecy is 20 Hz low, what is the error in the station's monitor ? (4)
   a. 35 Hz   b. 20 Hz   c. 15 Hz   d. 55 Hz

9. A meter that depends on the principle of two dissimilar metals generating an e.m.f. when the heat is applied, is called: (4)
   a. current square meter   c. thermo-couple meter
   b. grid-dip meter   d. hot-wire meter

10. An instrument that checks frequency measuring meters is a:
    a. signal generator   c. secondary frequency standard
    b. checking oscillator   d. synchronizing standard

LESSON 19*
ULTRA HIGH FREQUENCY
CIRCUITS AND COMPONENTS

3*UHF CONSIDERATION. Circuits and components operating in the Very High Frequency (VHF) range (30 MHz − 300 MHz) and above behave quite differently than those operating in the lower frequencies. An RF amplifier that operates well at 4 MHz could not operate at 900 MHz by simply changing the values of the tuned circuit components. The wiring, the tubes, the types of capacitors and inductors would all have to be changed. Stray capacitances, which have little effect at low frequencies, are very important at high frequencies. This is shown in Fig. 19-1, which illustrates a wire having a stray capacity to ground of 2 pf. In A, the wire carries a 4 MHz signal and the capacitive reactance is approximately 40,000 ohms. This is sufficient to prevent the signal from being shunted to ground. However, in B, the wire carries an 800 MHz signal and the reactance to ground is only 100 ohms. This means that a considerable amount of the signal will be shunted to ground and lost.

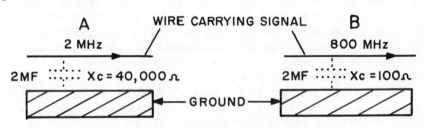

FIG. 19-1. STRAY CAPACITY.

The effects of stray inductances at high frequencies are similar to those of stray capacitances. A bend in a wiring lead develops sufficient inductance at high frequencies to cause a high inductive reactance and thereby impede a high frequency signal.

The following factors require special attention at VHF and UHF frequencies: (The term, UHF, implies frequencies from 300 MHz to 3,000 MHz)

NEUTRALIZATION: A tetrode RF amplifier does not require neutralization at low frequencies. However, at high frequencies, it probably would require neutralization.

The grounded grid amplifier is used extensively at high frequencies. It does not require neutralization.

LEADS: In order to reduce the inductance of leads, they should be as short as possible. There should be no sharp bends. The diameter of the wire should be as large as possible because high frequency currents tend to flow

*This entire lesson is exclusive to Element 3.

on the surface of the wire (skin effect). Silver plated wire will help reduce the reactance of the wire at high frequencies. Since the current flows on the surface of the wire, the wire can be hollow for purposes of economy.

The leads should be placed as far as possible away from each other and from ground. This will prevent undesired coupling and losses.

CAPACITORS: Components should be used that are designed for high frequencies. The ordinary capacitor is a typical component that behaves one way at low frequencies and another way at very high frequencies. At low frequencies, the inductance of the capacitor is unimportant; at high frequencies it becomes a critical factor. At very high frequencies, the inductance and capacitance of a capacitor form a parallel resonant circuit. Instead of the capacitor by-passing a signal, it will block the signal.

Special capacitors are made for use at high frequencies. They are physically small and have low internal inductance. They use low-loss high frequency dielectric material. Some of the more common types of high frequency capacitors are the button mica and the feed-thru coaxial. A variable high frequency capacitor is the "butterfly-type". It incorporates a single turn of inductance to form a complete resonant circuit.

COAXIAL CABLE AND TRANSMISSION LINES. There are two types of transmission line losses that become quite significant at high frequencies. They are RADIATION LOSSES and DIELECTRIC LOSSES. The radiation losses occur primarily in parallel transmission lines; coaxial cable has very little radiation loss because its outer conductor acts as an electromagnetic shield. The radiation loss of parallel transmission lines can be minimized by designing it with minimum spacing between conductors.

In order to reduce dielectric losses occurring at high frequencies, the insulating material (dielectric) that separates the two conductors should be made of special low loss material such as polyethylene and teflon. Still better, if air could be used as the dielectric, the losses would be cut to the barest minimum. "Open wire line" comes closest to using air as its insulator. It consists of two conductors separated by air, using polyethylene spacers at intervals along the line.

A special low loss coaxial cable uses an inert gas as the dielectric insulator. This type of cable is discussed in Lesson 17.

SPECIAL UHF TUBES. There are three main factors that limit the operation of a vacuum tube at high frequencies. They are: transit time, lead inductance and interelectrode capacitance. The transit time is the time it takes electrons to move from the cathode to the plate. At very high frequencies, the transit time approaches the time it takes for one cycle of the signal. This causes undesirable phase shifts and a reduction of the tube's operating efficiency.

As the operating frequency is increased, the capacitive reactances of the interelectrode capacitances decrease and cause the signal to be by-passed instead of amplified. At high frequencies, the lead lengths of the tube's elements become significant. Their inductive reactance will limit the tube's use.

The amount of interelectrode capacitance, lead inductance and the effect of transit time are minimized in the construction of tubes that are used at ultra-high frequencies. These tubes have very small electrodes that are placed close together. Thus, the transit time and the interelectrode capacitance are reduced without affecting the amplification factor of the tube. The tube elements' lead lengths are reduced by removing the tube base and socket and by bringing out the tube's connections with wire pins at points in the glass

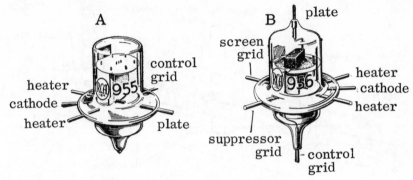

FIG. 19-2. ACORN TUBES.

envelope close to the elements that they connect to.

The Acorn tubes of Fig. 19-2 are excellent high frequency tubes. They resemble an acorn in appearance and size. Their electrodes are very small and close together. The element leads are short and brought directly out through the glass. There is no tube base. In some cases, several leads coming out of a tube are connected to a single element. This allows the external component to be connected to the lead that it is closest to. Also, the leads may be connected to each other externally, thereby paralleling and reducing the lead inductance.

Note that the plate lead of Fig. 19-2B comes out on top, while the grid lead comes out on bottom. This isolates the two elements and prevents feedback from the plate to the grid.

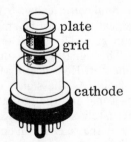

FIG. 19-3. A LIGHTHOUSE TUBE.

Another tube that is commonly used for ultra high frequencies is the Lighthouse tube (Fig. 19-3), also known as a disc seal tube. Its elements, which are very small and close together, are assembled in a parallel plane instead of the usual coaxial method. Wherever possible, rods and tubing are used as elements. The elements either extend out of the glass seal to be connected to the external components, or they are connected to parallel disks which extend out through the seal. This system eliminates tube lead inductance almost completely.

Lighthouse tubes are used as oscillators and amplifiers.

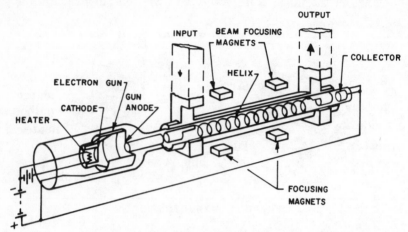

FIG. 19-4. A TYPICAL TRAVELING WAVE TUBE.

THE TRAVELING-WAVE TUBE. A traveling-wave tube is used primarily as a UHF amplifier. It can amplify signals above 10,000 MHz. It also has excellent bandwidth response; it can handle bandwidths that are 10% of the frequency being amplified. Fig. 19-4 illustrates a Traveling-Wave tube. It contains an electron gun similar to that of a cathode ray tube. The electron gun shoots a finely focused beam of electrons down the center of the tube towards the collector at the other end. The collector is about 2,000 volts positive with respect to the cathode. As the beam travels down the tube, it is kept in focus by means of electromagnetic coils or magnets that surround the tube.

There is a tightly wound wire, called a HELIX, along the body of the tube. The microwave signal that is to be amplified is fed into the helix at its end nearest the electron gun. The signal enters the helix via a small stub attached to the helix. The signal travels along the helix to the end of the helix closest to the collector. Here it exits from the tube via another short stub attached to the helix. As the signal travels along the helix, there is interaction between the signal and the beam. The magnetic field of the signal causes the beam to alternately slow up and speed up. This, in turn, develops regions of both dense and sparse electron concentrations, known as "bunching". This "bunching" induces additional energy into the helix, which increases the amplitude or gain of the microwave signal. Thus we have amplification. Generally speaking, the longer the helix, the greater is the amplification.

An attenuator device is placed near the center of the helix to prevent feedback and self-oscillation. By removing or overcoming the effect of the attenuator, the traveling wave tube can be made into an oscillator.

WAVE GUIDES. A waveguide is a transmission line that conducts high frequency energy from one point to another in much the same manner as a transmission line. A waveguide consists of a rectangular or circular conducting tube through which the energy is transmitted in the form of electromagnetic waves. See Fig. 19-5. These waves are both electric and magnetic, and they are propagated through the waveguide tubes by reflections against the inner walls. Skin effect prevents the electromagnetic energy from escaping through the metal walls.

The primary reason for using waveguides at high frequencies is that they have low losses. At high frequencies, coaxial cable exhibits very high dielectric losses. Waveguides use air as the dielectric, making the dielectric

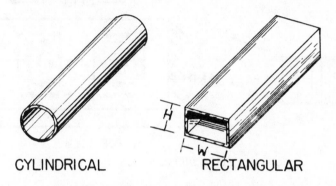

CYLINDRICAL   RECTANGULAR

FIG. 19-5. BASIC SHAPE OF WAVEGUIDES.

losses almost negligible.

The cross-sectional size of a waveguide is directly proportional to the wavelength of the energy that it is to conduct. The higher the frequency, the lower is the wavelength and the smaller is the cross-sectional size of the waveguide. The width of a rectangular waveguide ("W" in Fig. 19-5), must be more than 1/2 of the wavelength of the lowest frequency to be conducted. In practice, it is between .7 and .8 of the wavelength of the lowest frequency to be conducted. The height of the rectangular waveguide ("H" in Fig. 19-5), is usually about 1/2 of the width. In a circular waveguide, the radius must be more than 1/3 of the wavelength of the lowest frequency to be transmitted. The reason that waveguides cannot be used at lower frequencies (higher wavelengths) is obvious. The size would be prohibitive.

ELECTROMAGNETIC FIELDS IN A WAVEGUIDE. It has been pointed out that the energy travels through a waveguide in a form of electric and magnetic fields. These fields can arrange themselves in many different configurations. Each of these configurations is called a "mode" of operation. All "modes" fall into two general groups. One group is known as the Transverse Magnetic group, abbreviated TM. In this group, the planes of the magnetic fields are TRANSVERSE or perpendicular to the direction of propagation of the high frequency energy and a component of the electric field is in the direction of propagation. The other group is called the Transverse Electric group, abbreviated TE. In this group, the electric field is

381

transverse to the direction of propagation, but a component of the magnetic field is in the direction of propagation.

Fig. 19-6 shows a rectangular waveguide with a TE mode. The solid lines of Fig. 19-6A show the electric field from an end view. The arrows show the direction of the electric field. The electric field is perpendicular or transverse to the direction of propagation. A top view of a waveguide is shown in Fig. 19-6B. The dotted lines indicate the magnetic field. The lines of magnetic flux appear as magnetic whirlpools, spaced 1/2 wavelength apart, each group reversed in direction. Their plane is in line with the direction of propagation, further satisfying the definition of a TE mode.

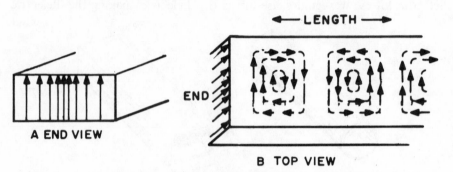

FIG. 19-6. FIELD DISTRIBUTION OF A TE MODE.

COUPLING ENERGY TO A WAVEGUIDE. There are three different ways in which energy can be inserted or removed from a waveguide. The first is by placing a small loop of wire into the waveguide in such a way that it is parallel to or couples to the magnetic field. This is known as inductive coupling and it is shown in Fig. 19-7A. The loop can be made from an extension of the inner conductor of the coaxial cable. By turning the loop through 90°, we can vary the amount of coupling.

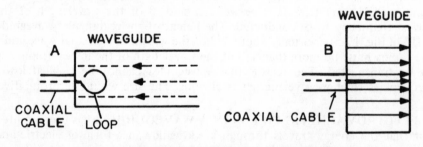

FIG. 19-7. COUPLING ENERGY TO A WAVEGUIDE.

Fig. 19-7B illustrates the second method of coupling energy to or from a waveguide. A straight extension of the inner conductor of a coaxial cable is placed into and parallel to the electric field of the waveguide. We can adjust the coupling by varying the angle of the "probe" or by placing it in the waveguide at different electric intensity points.

The third method of coupling energy to or from a waveguide is through the use of slots or windows in the wall of the waveguide. This method is generally used when only a small amount of coupling is desired. In this method, a beam of radio waves is directed toward a hole in the wall or by shooting a beam of electrons through the hole.

ADVANTAGES AND DISADVANTAGES OF WAVEGUIDES. The advantages of waveguides are obvious: At microwave frequencies, they exhibit the lowest losses of any type of transmission line. They are simpler and more rugged than coaxial cable. They provide complete shielding of the signal. There is no radiation loss. Since there is no center conductor and no dielectric, there is no copper loss and very little dielectric loss. Waveguides can handle high power at the high frequencies.

The disadvantages of waveguides are: They have to be used at very high frequencies because the cross-sectional size is directly proportional to the wavelength. The installation of waveguides is difficult because they are not flexible and the bends must not be too sharp.

Since the efficiency of a waveguide depends on the reflections from the walls, the insides must be smooth, clean and dry. There must be no dents in the walls. When assembling waveguides, the installer must be careful not to allow solder to run over to the inside of the waveguide. For higher efficiency, the inside of the waveguide should be silver plated.

The use of long horizontal waveguides should be avoided because condensed moisture can collect on the inside and cause increased losses and possible arcing.

CAVITY RESONATORS. A cavity resonator is formed by taking a section of a waveguide and closing it off at both ends so that it becomes a hollow metal chamber. This hollow metal chamber is actually a tuned circuit at an extremely high frequency. Fig. 19-8 shows some common shapes of cavity resonators. They can be rectangular, cylindrical or spherical. The resonant frequency of the rectangular and cylindrical cavities are independent of their heights if their heights are less than 1/2 wavelength. The frequency of the cavity resonator can be varied by a sliding shorting disc or by an adjustable tuning "slug" inside the cavity.

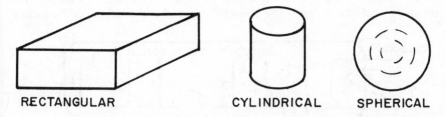

RECTANGULAR   CYLINDRICAL   SPHERICAL

FIG. 19-8. COMMON SHAPES OF CAVITY RESONATORS.

Q values of several thousand can be obtained in a cavity resonator. If the inside wall is plated with gold or silver, the Q can be as high as 30,000.

The cavity resonator behaves in a manner similar to that of a conventional tuned LC circuit. In the LC circuit, we have internal circulating currents; in the cavity resonator, it is a circulating electromagnetic field. In the conventional tank circuit, the energy is shifting between the electrostatic field across the capacitor and the magnetic field surrounding the coil. In the resonant cavity, the energy is continuously being exchanged between the electric field and the magnetic field.

The most common uses for resonant cavities are: (1) tuned circuits for ultra-high frequency oscillators (2) impedance matching devices to transfer energy between waveguides of different impedances. (3) measuring devices for ultra high frequencies.

In joining a cavity resonator to a waveguide, or in joining two waveguide sections, the flanges of the two adjoining surfaces should be clean and tightly sealed. "Choke" joints should be used where possible. A "choke" joint is a well-designed mechanical coupling that maintains good electrical continuity. Special moisture-proof gaskets are used at the choke joints to keep out moisture and dirt. Moisture can also be kept out by filling the waveguide with pressurized air or inert gas.

UHF OSCILLATORS. The conventional oscillator has an upper frequency limit above which it cannot be used. The three main factors that limit the output and efficiency of a conventional oscillator are the interelectrode inductances and capacitances, the increased RF losses and the electron transit time.

An ultra high frequency oscillator must use principles that circumvent the above factors. In order to understand UHF oscillators, we will describe two of the more common types, namely, the KLYSTRON and the MAGNETRON.

THE KLYSTRON OSCILLATOR. The klystron is a velocity modulated tube. A velocity modulated tube is one whose operation depends upon the modulation or change in the speed of the electron stream. By changing the electron speed, "bunches" or large masses of electrons are formed that are separated by spaces where there are very few electrons. This principle of electron "bunching" is used to produce amplification in a tube.

Fig. 19-9 represents a klystron tube. Its operation is as follows: The heater, cathode and acceleration grid form an electron gun that shoots a stream of electrons towards the collector. Grids 2 and 3 are called "buncher"

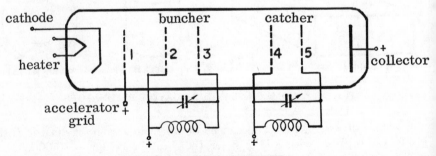

FIG. 19-9. A KLYSTRON TUBE.

384

grids. They have the same DC potential as the accelerator grid. However, there is also an AC potential across grids 2 and 3. This is because the two grids are across a tuned circuit. As the electrons shoot through the "buncher" grids, they are either slowed down or accelerated, depending upon the instantaneous potential across the grids. This slowing-down and acceleration causes the electrons to bunch up when they leave the vicinity of the buncher grids.

Grids 4 and 5 are called "catcher" grids. The "catcher" grids are across an oscillating tank circuit. The potential on grid 4 is such that it is negative when a mass of electrons hits it. It therefore slows down the electrons and in doing so, absorbs energy from them. By the time this bunch of electrons reaches grid 5, grid 5 also becomes negative and slows down the electrons. In so doing, it absorbs more energy from the electrons. After passing through grid 5, the electrons go to the collector plate which removes them from the circuit.

Since very little energy is required to cause "bunching" and since a large amount of energy is absorbed by the tuned circuit from the "catcher" grids, we can see that small amounts of energy injected into the bunching area will be amplified in the catcher area.

If the output from the catcher is fed back to the buncher, and if the proper phase and energy relations are maintained, the tube operates as an oscillator.

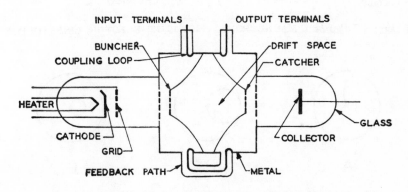

FIG. 19-10. A KLYSTRON TUBE WITH A CAVITY RESONATOR.

LC tuned circuits do not operate properly at high frequencies. In order for the klystron to operate at the very high frequencies, the tuned circuits of Fig. 19-9 are replaced by cavity resonators. See Fig. 19-10. The buncher and catcher grids are connected to each side of the cavity. These resonant cavities are very efficient and their high Q's suppress unwanted harmonics. The feedback path between the catcher section and buncher section permits the tube to operate as an oscillator. Energy is fed in and taken out of the tube by means of one-turn coupling loops.

THE MAGNETRON. The basic magnetron, shown in Fig. 19-11, consists of a diode and a pair of magnets. The diode part of the magnetron contains a

385

cathode surrounded by a cylindrical plate. The magnetic field is perpendicular to the electric field existing between the cathode and the plate.

With no magnetic field and with the proper electrical potentials applied to the elements, electrons will flow from the cathode to the plate in straight lines. They will flow parallel to the electric lines of force shown in Fig. 19-12. When a small magnetic field is applied, the reaction of the magnetic field and the electrons causes the electrons to move to the plate in a curved manner. See Fig. 19-13A. As we increase the magnetic field strength, we reach a certain critical value where the electrons curve sufficiently to miss the plate and return to the cathode (Fig. 19-13B). A further increase in magnetic strength causes the radius of the circular path of the electrons to decrease (Fig. 19-13C).

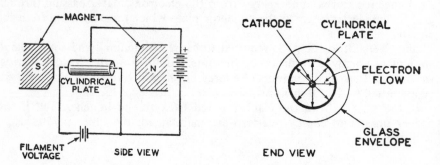

FIG. 19-11. THE BASIC MAGNETRON.   FIG. 19-12. ELECTRIC LINES OF FORCE.

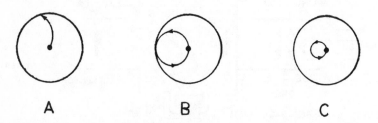

FIG. 19-13. ELECTRON FLOW WHEN MAGNETIC FIELD IS APPLIED.

For proper oscillation, the magnetic field is set at the critical value. As the electrons move close to the plate, they electrostatically induce energy into the plate. A tuned circuit is placed between the plate and the cathode. The energy that the circular stream of electrons induces in the plate is sufficient to sustain the oscillations of the tuned circuit. The frequency of this basic magnetron is determined by the tuned circuit values and also by the time it takes the electrons to travel from the cathode toward the plate and back again.

MULTI-ANODE MAGNETRON. In the multi-anode magnetron, shown in Fig. 19-14, there is no tuned circuit. The anode is a large cylindrical mass containing many resonant cavities. The size of the resonant cavities is the primary factor in determining the frequency of the magnetron.

The multi-anode magnetron operates in a manner similar to the basic magnetron. The magnetic field causes the electrons to move away from the

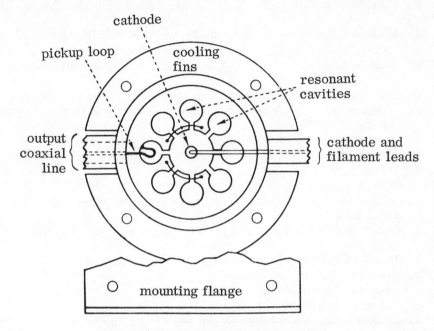

FIG. 19-14. A MULTI-ANODE MAGNETRON.

cathode in circular paths. As the electrons pass the slots of the cavities, they induce energy into the cavities, thereby shock-exciting them into oscillation. The various cavities are connected together so that a probe inserted into one of them will serve as the RF output device for the magnetron.

The multi-anode magnetron oscillator has considerably more efficiency than the basic magnetron. It is therefore used for the higher frequencies.

PRACTICE QUESTIONS - LESSON 19

1. Which of the following would be used to transmit extremely high frequencies?
a. magnetron
b. klystron
c. traveling wave tube
d. waveguide

2. In a Travelling Wave tube, how does the signal to be amplified enter and exit from the tube?
a. enters via the grid and leaves via the collector
b. enters via the grid and leaves via an output stub at collector end
c. enters via a stub at the cathode end and leaves via the collector
d. enters via a stub at the electron gun end and leaves via a stub at the collector end

387

3. Which of the following precautions need not be observed in handling wire leads in UHF circuits?
a. as short as possible   c. silver plating of leads
b. no sharp bends   d. use small diameter leads

4. Which of the following can not be used as a UHF tube?
a. Acorn tube   c. waveguide tube
b. Lighthouse tube   d. Travelling Wave tube

5. In a waveguide, a transverse magnetic group indicates that:
a. a component of the electric field is in the direction of propagation
b. the magnetic field is in the direction of propagation
c. the electron field is transverse to the direction of propagation
d. b and c

6. Which of the following is used as a velocity modulated oscillator tube?
a. klystron   b. magnetron   c. Acorn   d. Lighthouse

7. In a Travelling Wave tube, the bunching of electrons:
a. prevents secondary emission
b. prevents feedback and self-oscillation
c. induces energy into the helix
d. causes interaction between the signal and the beam

8. Which of the following is a transmission line for UHF energy?
a. Travelling Wave tube   c. magnetron
b. klystron   d. waveguide

9. Energy travels through waveguides by:
a. reflections against the walls   c. skin effect
b. electrostatic waves   d. coaxial guides

10. In which tubes are the elements assembled in a parallel plane?
a. Acorn tube   c. waveguide tube
b. Lighthouse tube   d. Travelling Wave tube

11. A Travelling Wave tube is primarily used as a:
a. UHF amplifier   c. UHF detector
b. UHF oscillator   d. UHF mixer

12. Once the cavities of a magnetron receive their energy, they:
a. amplify and feed the energy back to the input
b. impart additional energy to the beams
c. force the electron beams into bunches
d. are shock-excited into oscillation

13. The cross-sectional size of a waveguide is:

a. inversely proportional to the wavelength of the energy to be conducted
b. directly proportional to the wavelength of the energy to be conducted
c. 1/4 of the wavelength of the lowest frequency to be conducted
d. directly proportional to the square of the wavelength of the lowest frequency to be conducted

14. A well-designed mechanical coupling that maintains good electrical continuity at UHF frequencies is called a:
  a. UHF gasket   b. choke joint   c. slug   d. transfer joint

15. The multi-anode magnetron contains:
  a. two resonant cavities   c. several bunching magnets
  b. many resonant cavities   d. several catching magnets

16. An advantage of waveguides is not:
  a. low copper losses   c. simple installation
  b. complete shielding   d. low dielectric losses

17. In a magnetron, electrons move in:
  a. circular paths   c. bunches
  b. straight paths   d. sheets

18. In which element of a Travelling Wave tube does the signal and beam interact?
  a. collector   b. cathode   c. helix   d. gun anode

19. In a Klystron oscillator, the:
  a. output at the buncher area is fed back to the catcher area
  b. output at the catcher area is fed back to the buncher area
  c. tuned circuit absorbs considerable energy from buncher grids
  d. catcher grids speed up the electron flow

20. A cavity resonator behaves like a/an:
  a. high frequency amplifier   c. long vertical waveguide
  b. LC tuned circuit   d. long horizontal waveguide

21. UHF energy is generally not coupled to a waveguide by:
  a. means of a straight wire probe   c. inductive coupling
  b. means of a slot in the waveguide   d. dielectric coupling

LESSON 20*
TELEVISION

TELEVISION RECEPTION AND TRANSMISSION. A complete text-book would be required in order to cover this subject adequately. The material presented on the following pages will give the reader a bird's-eye view of the subject and will prepare him for any questions that will be asked on the FCC exams. Detailed information on television receivers is not given because the FCC tests do not contain receiver questions.

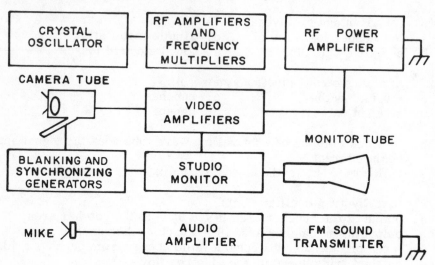

FIG. 20-1. BLOCK DIAGRAM OF A BASIC BLACK AND WHITE TELEVISION TRANSMITTER.

Fig. 20-1 illustrates a block diagram of a basic black and white television transmitter. Its operation is as follows:

The scene to be televised is focused on to a photo-sensitive plate in the camera tube. The camera tube changes the picture information into electronic or video information. From the camera tube, the video signal is fed into video amplifiers where the video information is amplified. From the output of video amplifiers a small portion of the signal is fed to a studio monitor, which, in turn, feeds the signal to one or more monitor tubes. The monitor tubes change the video information back into picture information. The purpose of the monitor tubes is to permit the television operators to view the picture and to see if there are any faults in it. The monitor picture tube shows the actual picture that is being broadcast.

*This entire lesson is exclusive to Element 4.

The crystal oscillator develops the basic carrier frequency. As in any transmitter, the output of the crystal oscillator is amplified by frequency multipliers up to the proper output frequency. It is then fed into a power amplifier where it is modulated by the video signal. Amplitude modulation is used for the video portion of all TV transmitters. The signal is then fed to an antenna where it is radiated.

The box labeled "blanking and synchronizing generators" consists of oscillators and synchronizing circuits that develop signals that control the beam in the camera tube as it moves back and forth and up and down scanning the picture. (The actual scanning process will be discussed in a later section). The oscillators that develop these timing signals are multivibrators. They develop a sawtooth wave that causes the beam to move properly.

The sound at the TV studio is fed into a microphone. The microphone output is then fed to the audio amplifier. From here, the audio signal is sent to an FM transmitter and then to the antenna. All TV sound transmitters use FM as the method of modulation for the audio signal.

We will now discuss the major parts of the television transmitter in more detail.

THE TV CAMERA TUBE. The TV camera tube is used to convert a scene or picture information into an electrical signal. Fig. 20-2 illustrates a basic camera tube, called the ICONOSCOPE. In the iconoscope, the scene to be televised is focused by an optical lens system on to a mosaic plate. The mosaic plate is made up of a thin sheet of mica approximately .001″ thick. On the side of the sheet facing the lens system, there is a layer of microscopic globules of cesium silver. The globules are placed on the mica plate in such a way that they do not touch each other. Each one is insulated from the other. On the other side of the mica plate, there is a coating of colloidal graphite. This coating acts as the signal electrode and conducts the

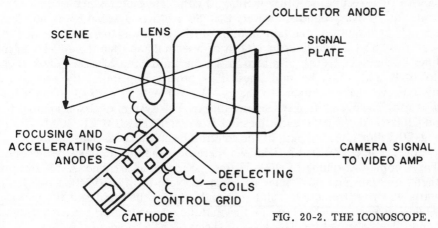

FIG. 20-2. THE ICONOSCOPE.

video signal current to the external circuit for amplification.

The cesium silver globules are photo-sensitive and each globule will emit electrons in proportion to the light intensity striking it. The scene is focused on the cesium silver globules and the cesium silver globules emit electrons in proportion to the particular image that is being televised. Thus each globule takes on a different positive charge because of the loss of electrons. Each globule, together with the colloidal graphite directly behind the globule, forms a capacitor, with the mica acting as the dielectric. We now have a group of charged capacitors. The charge on each globule depends on the amount of light that fell on it. The camera has thus succeeded in converting the scene into a series of electrical charges.

ELECTRON BEAM SCANNING. Scanning is the process of sub-dividing a picture into tiny areas so that information can be transmitted in an orderly manner. Each bit of picture information is sent out, one bit at a time. The bits of information are then re-assembled in the correct manner at the receiver to form a complete picture.

Let us return to the picture tube of Fig. 20-2. The electron gun in the neck of the tube develops a fine beam of electrons that flows to the mosaic. By allowing the beam to pass over each globule, we replace the electrons that were originally lost due to the light. By means of capacitor action, this change in the charge of the globule is transferred to the colloidal graphite plate and a small pulse of current flows in the external circuit. This small pulse of current is the video signal. As we pass over the various globules, pulses of current are developed which conform in amplitude to the original light intensities of the various elements of the picture. How can we have the beam pass over each globule? The way it is done in actual practice is to break up the mosaic into 525 horizontal lines. The beam then passes over each of these 525 lines from left to right. When the beam completes its tracing of all the lines, the beam is brought up to the top of the picture and starts all over again.

In the initial development of television, the 525 lines were scanned in 1/30th of a second. In other words, 30 complete pictures per second were sent out. It was found, however, that 30 pictures a second was not fast enough. It produced a certain amount of flicker. It was therefore decided to scan the 262-1/2 odd lines in 1/60th of a second and then the 262-1/2 even lines in the next 1/60th of a second. In the third 60th of a second we then go back and scan the odd lines. This process continues. By using this method, we make it appear to the eye that 60 pictures per second are being sent out. The eye no longer sees any flicker. This system of first scanning the odd lines and then the even lines is known as INTERLACED SCANNING. Fig. 20-3 illustrates the path of the electron beam in interlaced scanning.

262-1/2 lines is called a field. We therefore send out 60 fields per second. The complete scanning of the 525 lines is known as a frame. A TV station therefore transmits 30 frames per second. Note in Fig. 20-3 that one field starts at the extreme left hand side and ends in the middle of the picture while the second field starts in the middle and ends at the extreme right hand side of the picture. This gives us the extra half line per field.

The reason that the field frequency is 60 per second is because the commercial power available to us is 60 cycles per second. If the field frequency were different from the commercial frequency, the slight AC ripple that is normally present in the video section would cause dark areas to move up and down. This would be annoying to the eye. In current TV sets, the slightly dark areas may be present, but since they don't move, they are not noticeable to the eye.

If the picture tube at the receiver is changed from a small one to a large one, the number of horizontal lines does not change. The number still remains 525 horizontal lines to the picture. However, the thickness of each line will change.

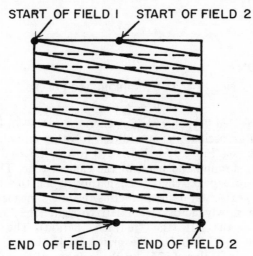

START OF FIELD I   START OF FIELD 2

END OF FIELD I   END OF FIELD 2

FIG. 20-3. INTERLACED SCANNING.

BLANKING AND SYNCHRONIZING SIGNALS. In order to receive a correct picture at the TV receiver, the electron beam in the receiver picture tube must be perfectly synchronized with the electron beam in the camera tube. When the beam at the camera tube is starting to sweep line 3, the beam at the receiving tube must be at line 3. In this way, the information sent out for line 3 will be reproduced in the receiver picture tube at line 3. In order to accomplish this synchronization, the TV signal contains various pulses in addition to video information.

When the beam reaches the end of a line, a pulse is inserted in the signal at the transmitter (and it is sent out to the receiver at the same instant). This pulse is known as a horizontal pulse. It triggers an oscillator that causes the beam to be shot back to the left hand side of the picture to start the next line. These horizontal pulses are shown in Fig. 20-4.

While the beam is moving from left to right and back, it is gradually being brought down to the bottom of the picture. After completing the last line at the bottom, a complex vertical pulse (see Fig. 20-4) triggers an oscillator that brings the beam back up to the top of the picture. These horizontal and vertical pulses that trigger the oscillators to start a new line or a new field at the transmitter, also trigger oscillators in the receivers to do exactly the same thing. Therefore, when the video transmitter is sending a piece of information in a particular part of the picture, the receiver's picture tube is reproducing that information in the exact same spot on the picture.

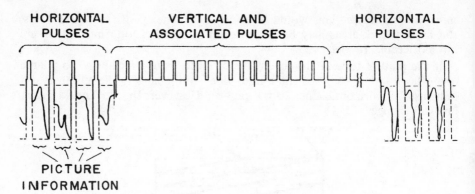

HORIZONTAL PULSES	VERTICAL AND ASSOCIATED PULSES	HORIZONTAL PULSES

PICTURE
INFORMATION

FIG. 20-4. TV SYNCHRONIZING PULSES.

The block labeled "synchronizing generators, etc." in Fig. 20-1, contains two multivibrator oscillators, in addition to other circuits. One generates a saw-tooth wave (see Fig. 20-5) that is fed to the horizontal deflection coils that are present around the neck of the camera tube. The saw-tooth wave rises gradually to a peak, then falls sharply. When this type of current is applied to the horizontal deflection coils, the coil's magnetic field causes the beam to move slowly across from left to right (the "trace" period) and rapidly back to the left (the "re-trace" period). The frequency of the saw-tooth wave is 15,750 Hz. We arrive at this by multiplying the total number of horizontal lines (525) by the number of frames per second (30). 525 x 30 = 15,750.

SLOW TRACE PERIOD   FAST TRACE PERIOD

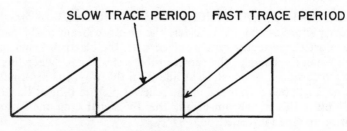

FIG. 20-5. A SAWTOOTH WAVE.

A second oscillator in the block generates a saw-tooth wave that is applied to the vertical deflection coils that are present at the neck of the camera tube. This saw-tooth wave causes the beam to move gradually from top to bottom (while it is scanning the horizontal lines), and then rapidly back up to the top. The frequency of this wave is 60 Hertz. This is because there are 60 fields per second.

The purpose of the horizontal and vertical pulses is to trigger the transmitter's horizontal and vertical oscillators at the correct time and, at the very same time, to trigger the horizontal and vertical oscillators in the receiver.

The horizontal pulses rest on a wider pulse called the BLANKING PULSE (See Fig. 20-6). The purpose of the blanking pulse is to blank out the beam

394

while it is being brought from the right side to the left side (during the re-trace period). If we did not blank out the beam during the retrace periods, we would see 525 horizontal lines superimposed on the picture.

The blanking pulse is actually a large negative voltage that is applied to the control grid of the picture cathode ray tube. It cuts off the beam and there is no light at the screen of the picture tube. The vertical pulse also rests on a broad blanking pulse. This cuts off the beam while it is being returned to the top of the screen during the vertical retrace period.

In Fig. 20-6, the synchronizing and blanking pulses are at the top of the figure while the picture information is at the bottom. The top of the figure is negative with respect to the bottom. It would have to be in order to blank out the picture during retrace periods and let the beam through when picture information is being sent out.

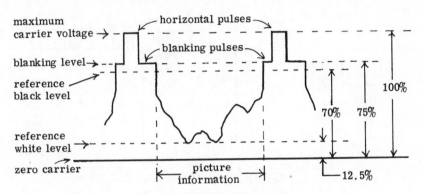

FIG. 20-6. A LINE OF PICTURE INFORMATION,
TOGETHER WITH BLANKING AND HORIZONTAL PULSES.

THE COMPLETE TELEVISION BROADCAST SIGNAL. We can sum up the information learned thus far by reviewing the components of a complete television signal. It consists of the following:

(1) The video information. Fig. 20-6 shows a complete horizontal line of video information, together with the horizontal and blanking pulses. The whiter parts of the picture are at the bottom of the graph.

(2) Horizontal pulses. Their functions have been described. Note from Fig. 20-6 that they are rectangular in shape and occupy 25% of the total signal.

(3) Vertical pulse. The vertical pulse is very wide. See Fig. 20-4. It is broken up into six parts and is therefore called a serrated vertical pulse. It is broken up so that every other serrated segment can continue to trigger the horizontal oscillator and keep it synchronized during the vertical retrace.

(4) Equalizing pulses. See Fig. 20-4. The six narrow pulses in front of the vertical pulse and the six narrow pulses after the vertical pulse are called EQUALIZING PULSES. Their purpose is to insure the correct starting time for the vertical oscillator when the beam reaches the bottom of the scene. Since one field ends in the middle of a line and the other field ends at the end of the line, the timing of the vertical pulse would be slightly off without the equalizing pulses.

395

(5) Blanking pulses. Their function is to blank out the beam during retrace times.

(6) FM sound signal. A complete FM transmitter, similar to those described in lesson 16 transmits the audio.

The scanning process used in color TV is similar to that used in black and white. It has to be since black and white receivers can receive color programs and color receivers can receive black and white programs. The only real difference between the two scanning systems is that there is a "color burst" synchronizing signal on the blanking pulse immediately following the horizontal pulse in the color system. See Fig. 20-7. The "color burst" frequency is approximately 3.58 MHz. It is actually a sub-carrier whose purpose is to synchronize the reproduction of colors at the receiver with those being sent out at the transmitter.

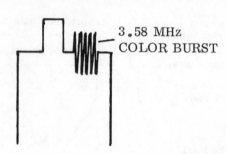

3.58 MHz
COLOR BURST

FIG. 20-7. THE "COLOR BURST" SYNCHRONIZING SIGNAL.

PRACTICE QUESTIONS - LESSON 20

1. The vertical and horizontal oscillators in a TV system generate:
a. a square wave
b. a sawtooth wave
c. a sine wave
d. a pulsed wave

2. With respect to the video information, the blanking and synchronizing pulses apply:
a. a high positive voltage to the grid of the CRT
b. a slight positive voltage to the grid of the CRT
c. a negative voltage to the grid of the CRT
d. a negative voltage to the cathode of the CRT

3. What percentage of the peak carrier level is the blanking level?
a. 75%   b. 70%   c. 12.5%   d. 50%

4. The synchronizing pulses in a television receiver are fed to the:
a. high voltage stage
b. vertical and horizontal oscillator stages
c. damping stage
d. AVC circuit

5. The photo sensitive material on the mosaic plate of a camera tube is:
a. colloidal graphite
b. mercury oxide
c. cesium silver
d. mica

6. For what fraction of a second does a field last?
a. 1/30th   b. 1/20th   c. 1/60th   d. 1/120th

7. The horizontal pulse triggers an oscillator that sends the beam:
a. from right to left   c. from top to bottom
b. from left to right   d. from bottom to top

8. An iconoscope is a basic:
a. TV camera tube   c. TV monitor tube
b. TV receiver tube   d. TV blanking tube

9. What percentage of the peak carrier level is the black reference level?
a. 75%   b. 70%   c. 12.5%   d. 50%

10. In order to prevent hum bars from moving across the screen, the basic design of the television system calls for:
a. the television transmitter using very large filter capacitors
b. the use of a pre-emphasis circuit in the transmitter and a de-emphasis circuit in the receiver
c. interlaced scanning
d. the field frequency being equal to the commercial power supply frequency

11. In the complete television signal, the video:
a. is AM and the sound is FM   c. and sound are both FM
b. is FM and the sound is AM   d. and sound are both AM

12. How many frames are there per second in a TV picture?
a. 30   b. 60   c. 262.5   d. 525

13. If we increase the diameter of a picture tube from 10 inches to 20 inches, the number of horizontal lines:
a. doubles   b. quadruples   c. halves   d. remains the same

14. How many fields per second are there in a TV picture?
a. 30   b. 60   c. 120   d. 240

15. The vertical oscillator of a TV system produces a frequency of:
a. 30 Hz   b. 60 Hz   c. 120 Hz   d. 262-1/2 Hz

16. In addition to horizontal and blanking pulses, a TV field contains:
a. a vertical pulse and 6 equalizing pulses
b. a serrated vertical pulse and 6 equalizing pulses
c. a vertical pulse and 12 equalizing pulses
d. a serrated vertical pulse and 12 equalizing pulses

17. In order to eliminate flicker, the modern TV system uses:
a. synchronized scanning   c. interlaced scanning
b. AC screening   d. 60 Hz power

LESSON 21
RULES AND REGULATIONS

There are various rules and regulations which govern the operation of commercial radio transmissions. It is important that the prospective commercial radio operator be familiar with them. The examinations for Elements 3 and 4 of the Commercial Radio Operator examinations contain questions based on various sections of the FCC rules and regulations. These questions are based primarily on the extracts given below.

PART 2. FREQUENCY ALLOCATIONS AND TREATY MATTERS; GENERAL RULES AND REGULATIONS.

3

SEC. 2.1 DEFINITIONS.

The following definitions are issued:

AUTHORIZED FREQUENCY. The frequency assigned to a station by the FCC and specified in the instrument of authorization.

CARRIER. In a frequency stabilized system, the sinusoidal component of a modulated wave whose frequency is independent of the modulating wave; or

The output of a transmitter when the modulating wave is made zero; or

A wave generated at a point in the transmitting system and subsequently modulated by the signal.

BASE STATION. A land station in the land mobile service carrying on a service with land mobile stations.

COAST STATION. A land station in the maritime mobile service.

EARTH STATION. A station in the earth-space service located either on the earth's surface or on an object which is limited to flight between points on the earth's surface.

FIXED STATION. A station in the fixed service.

SPACE STATION. A station in the earth-space service or the space service located on an object which is beyond or intended to go beyond the major portion of the earth's atmosphere and which is not intended for flight between points on the earth's surface.

HARMFUL INTERFERENCE. Any emission, radiation or induction which endangers the functioning of a radio-navigation service or of other safety services or seriously degrades, obstructs, or repeatedly interrupts a radiocommunication service.

LAND MOBILE SERVICE. A mobile station in the land mobile service capable of surface movement within the geographical limits of a country or continent.

LAND STATION (FL). A station in the mobile service not intended for operation while in motion.

MOBILE SERVICE. A service of radio communication between mobile and land stations, or between mobile stations.

PRIMARY STANDARD OF FREQUENCY. The primary standard of frequency for radio frequency measurements shall be the national standard of frequency maintained by the National Bureau of Standards, Department of Commerce, Washington, D. C. The operating frequency of all radio stations will be determined by comparison with this standard or the standard signals of station WWV of the National Bureau of Standards.

3

SEC. 2.101. NOMENCLATURE OF FREQUENCIES.

Frequency subdivision	Frequency range
VLF (very low frequency)	Below 30 kHz
LF (low frequency)	30 to 300 kHz
MF (medium frequency)	300 to 3,000 kHz
HF (high frequency)	3,000 to 30,000 kHz
VHF (very high frequency)	30,000 kHz to 300 MHz
UHF (ultra high frequency)	300 MHz to 3,000 MHz
SHF (super high frequency)	3,000 MHz to 30,000 MHz
EHF (extreme high frequency)	30,000 MHz to 300,000 MHz

SEC. 2.201. A few types of transmissions and their symbols are given in the following table:

Type of modulation or emission	Type of transmission	Supplementary characteristics	Symbol
Continuous wave	absence of any modulation.		A∅
Continuous wave	telegraphy without the use of modulating AF.		A1
Amplitude	telephony	double sideband, full carrier.	A3
Amplitude	telephony	single sideband, reduced carrier.	A3A
Amplitude	television		A5
Amplitude	television	vestigial sideband.	A5C
Frequency	telephony		F3
Frequency	television		F5
Pulse	telephony	amplitude modulated pulse.	P3D

3

SEC. 2.551 PROGRAM DEFINED.

To promote the improvement of equipment and to promote the efficient use of the radio spectrum, the Commission has designated 2 specific procedures for securing advance approval of equipment. These procedures are designated as type approval and type acceptance. Ordinarily, type approval contemplates tests conducted by Commission personnel, while type acceptance is based on data concerning the equipment submitted by the manufacturer or the individual prospective licensee.

STANDARD BROADCAST STATIONS

DEFINITIONS

73.1 STANDARD BROADCAST STATION.

The term "standard broadcast station" means a broadcasting station licensed for the transmission of radiotelephone emissions primarily intended to be received by the general public, and operated on a channel in the band 535-1605 kHz.

73.2 STANDARD BROADCAST BAND.

The term "standard broadcast band" means the band of frequencies extending from 535 to 1605 kHz.

73.6 DAYTIME.

The term "daytime" means that period of time between local sunrise and local sunset.

73.7 NIGHTTIME.

The term "nighttime" means that period of time between local sunset and local sunrise.

73.9 BROADCAST DAY.

The term "broadcast day" means that period of time between local sunrise and 12 midnight local time.

4
73.10 EXPERIMENTAL PERIOD.

The term "experimental period" means that time between 12 midnight local time and local sunrise. This period may be used for experimental purposes in testing and maintaining apparatus by the licensee of any standard broadcast station on its assigned frequency and with its authorized power, provided no interference is caused to other stations maintaining a regular operating schedule within such period. No station licensed for "daytime" or "specified hours" of operation may broadcast any regular or scheduled program during this period.

73.11 SERVICE AREAS.

(a) The term "primary service area" of a broadcast station means the area in which the groundwave is not subject to objectionable interference or objectionable fading.

(b) The term "secondary service area" of a broadcast station means the area served by the skywave and not subject to objectionable interference. The signal is subject to intermittent variations in intensity.

(c) The term "intermittent service area" of a broadcast station means the area receiving service from the groundwave, but beyond the primary service area and subject to some interference and fading.

4 73.14 TECHNICAL DEFINITIONS.

(d) MAXIMUM RATED CARRIER POWER. "Maximum rated carrier power" is the maximum power at which the transmitter can be operated satisfactorily and is determined by the design of the transmitter and the type and number of vacuum tubes used in the last radio stage.

(e) PLATE INPUT POWER. "Plate input power" means the product of the DC plate voltage and the total DC plate current in the tubes of the last RF stage, measured without modulation.

(g) ANTENNA CURRENT. "Antenna current" means the RF current in the antenna with no modulation.

(h) ANTENNA RESISTANCE. "Antenna resistance" means the total resistance of the transmitting antenna system at the operating frequency and at the point at which the antenna current is measured.

(i) MODULATOR STAGE. "Modulator stage" means the last amplifier stage of the modulating wave which modulates a radio-frequency stage.

(n) HIGH LEVEL MODULATION. "High level modulation" is modulation produced in the plate circuit of the last radio stage of the system.

(o) LOW LEVEL MODULATION. "Low level modulation" is modulation produced in an earlier stage than the final.

EQUIPMENT

4
73.39 INDICATING INSTRUMENTS - SPECIFICATIONS.

(a) Instruments indicating the plate current or plate voltage of the last radio stage (linear scale instruments) shall meet the following specifications:

(2) Accuracy shall be at least 2 percent of the full scale reading.

(b) Instruments indicating antenna current, common point current, and base currents shall meet the following specifications:

(1) For instruments having logarithmic or square law scales:

(iii) No scale division above one-third full scale reading (in amperes) shall be greater than one-thirtieth of the full scale reading. (Example: An ammeter having a full scale reading of 6 amperes is acceptable for reading currents from 2 to 6 amperes, provided no scale division between 2 and 6 amperes is greater than one-thirtieth of 6 amperes, or 0.2 ampere.)

(5) Calibration of a remote reading ammeter shall be checked against the regular meter at least once a week.

4
73.40 TRANSMITTER; DESIGN, CONSTRUCTION AND SAFETY OF LIFE REQUIREMENTS.

(a) DESIGN. The equipment shall be so designed that:

(2) The equipment is capable of satisfactory operation at the authorized operating power or the proposed operating power with modulation of at least 85 to 95 percent, with no more distortion than given in paragraph (3).

(3) The total audio frequency distortion does not exceed 5 percent harmonics when modulated from 0 to 84 percent, and not over 7.5 percent harmonics when modulating 85 percent to 95 percent.

(9) The transmitter is equipped with automatic frequency control equipment capable of maintaining the operating frequency within the limit specified by 73.59.

(i) The maximum temperature variation at the crystal from the normal operating temperature shall not be greater than:

Plus or minus 0.1° C. when an X or Y cut crystal is employed, or Plus or minus 1.0° C. when a low temperature coefficient crystal is employed.

TECHNICAL OPERATION

73.51 OPERATING POWER; HOW DETERMINED.

(a) Except as provided in paragraph (b) below, the operating power shall be determined by the direct method, i.e., as the product of the antenna resistance at the operating frequency and the square of the antenna current at this frequency, measured at the point where the antenna resistance has been determined.

(b) The operating power shall be determined on a temporary basis by the indirect method described in paragraph (c) below, in the following circumstances: (1) In an emergency, where the authorized antenna system has been damaged, or (2) pending completion of authorized changes in the antenna system, or (3) if changes occur in the antenna system or its environment which affect or appear likely to affect the value of antenna resistance or (4) if the antenna current meter becomes defective. Prior authorization for determination of power by the indirect method is not required.

(c) Operating power is determined by the indirect method of applying an appropriate factor to the plate input power, in accordance with the following formula:

$$\text{Operating power} = E_p \times I_p \times F$$

where: E_p = plate voltage of the final radio stage, I_p = total plate current of the final radio stage and F = efficiency factor.

4

73.52 OPERATING POWER; MAINTENANCE OF.

(a) The operating power of each station shall be maintained as near as practicable to the licensed power and shall not exceed the limits of 5 percent above and 10 percent below the licensed power, except that in an emergency, when due to causes beyond the control of the licensee, it becomes impossible to operate with full licensed power, the station may be operated with reduced power for a period not to exceed 10 days: *Provided,* That the Commission and the Engineer-in-Charge of the radio district in which the station is located shall be notified immediately after the emergency develops and also upon the resumption of licensed power.

(b) In addition to maintaining the operating power within the above limitations, stations employing directional antenna systems shall maintain the ratio of the antenna currents in the elements of the system within 5 percent of that specified by the terms of the license or other instrument of authorization.

4

73.58 INDICATING INSTRUMENTS.

(b) In the event that any one of the indicating instruments becomes

402

defective when no substitute which conforms with the required specifications is available, the station may be operated without the defective instrument pending its repair or replacement for a period not in excess of 60 days without further authority of the Commission: *Provided,* That:

(1) Appropriate entries shall be made in the maintenance log of the station showing the date and time the meter was removed from and restored to service.

(2) The Engineer-in-Charge of the radio district in which the station is located shall be notified both immediately after the instrument is found to be defective and immediately after the repaired or replacement instrument has been installed and is functioning properly.

(c) If conditions beyond the control of the licensee prevent the restoration of the meter to service within the above allowed period, informal request may be filed with the Engineer-in-Charge of the radio district in which the station is located for such additional time as may be required to complete repairs of the defective instrument.
4

73.59 FREQUENCY TOLERANCE.

The operating frequency of each station shall be maintained within 20 Hertz of the assigned frequency.
4

73.63 AUXILIARY TRANSMITTER.

(c) The auxiliary transmitter shall be maintained so that it may be placed in operation at any time for any one of the following purposes:

(1) The transmission of the regular programs upon the failure of the main transmitter.

(2) The transmission of the regular programs during maintenance or modification work on the main transmitter necessitating discontinuance of its operation.

(3) Emergency Broadcast System operation, provided the auxiliary transmitter is used in connection with a National Defense Emergency Authorization.

(d) The auxiliary transmitter shall be tested at least once each week to determine that it is in proper operating condition and that it is adjusted to the licensed frequency.
4

73.67 REMOTE CONTROL OPERATION.

(a) Operation by remote control shall be subject to the following conditions:

(1) The equipment at the operating and transmitting positions shall be so installed and protected that it is not accessible to or capable of operation by persons other than those duly authorized by the licensee.

(2) The control circuits from the operating positions to the transmitter shall provide positive on and off control and shall be such that open circuits, short circuits, grounds or other line faults will not actuate the transmitter and any fault causing loss of such control will automatically place the transmitter in an inoperative position.

(4) Control and monitoring equipment shall be installed so as to allow the licensed operator at the remote control point to perform all the functions in a manner required by the Commission's rules.

4
73.72 OPERATION DURING EXPERIMENTAL PERIOD.

The licensee of each standard broadcast station shall operate or refrain from operating its station during the experimental period as directed by the Commission in order to facilitate frequency measurement or for the determination of interference.

4
73.93 OPERATOR REQUIREMENTS.

(a) One or more radio operators holding a valid radiotelephone first-class operator license, shall be in actual charge of the transmitting apparatus and shall be on duty either at the transmitter location or remote control point.

4
73.95 EQUIPMENT TESTS.

(a) During the process of construction of a standard broadcast station, the permittee, after notifying the Commission and Engineer-in-Charge of the radio district in which the station is located, may, without further authority of the Commission, conduct equipment tests during the experimental period for the purpose of such adjustments and measurements as may be necessary to assure compliance with the terms of the construction permit, the technical provisions of the application therefore, the rules and regulations, and the applicable engineering standards.

4
73.96 PROGRAM AND SERVICE TESTS.

(a) Upon completion of construction of a standard broadcast station in accordance with the terms of the construction permit, the technical provisions of the application therefor, and the rules and regulations and applicable engineering standards, and when an application for station license has been filed showing the station to be in satisfactory operating condition, the permittee may request authority to conduct program tests: PROVIDED, That such request shall be filed with the Commission at least 10 days prior to the date on which it is desired to begin such operation and that the Engineer-in-Charge of the radio district in which the station is located is notified.

FM BROADCAST STATIONS

EQUIPMENT

4
73.254 REQUIRED TRANSMITTER PERFORMANCE.

(a) The construction, installation, operation and performance of the FM broadcast transmitting system shall be in accordance with 73.317.

(b) The measurement program shall yield the following information:

(1) Audio frequency response from 50 to 15,000 Hertz for approximately 25, 50 and 100 percent modulation. Measurements shall be made on at least the following audio frequencies: 50, 100, 400, 1000, 5000, 10,000 and 15,000 Hz.

4
73.258 INDICATING INSTRUMENTS.

(a) Each FM broadcast station shall be equipped with indicating instruments for measuring the direct plate voltage and current of the last radio stage and the transmission line radio frequency current, voltage or power.

4
73.265 OPERATOR REQUIREMENTS - FM BROADCAST STATION.

(a) One or more radio operators holding a valid radiotelephone first-class operator license, shall be in actual charge of the transmitting apparatus and shall be on duty either at the transmitter location or remote control point.

4
73.267 OPERATING POWER; DETERMINATION AND MAINTENANCE OF.

(a) Determination. The operating power of each station shall be determined by either the direct or indirect method.

(1) Using the direct method (as given in 73.51), the power shall be measured at the output terminals of the transmitter while operating into a dummy load of substantially zero reactance and a resistance equal to the transmission line characteristic impedance. The transmitter shall be unmodulated during this measurement.

(2) Using the indirect method, the operating power is the product of the plate voltage and the plate current of the last radio stage, and an efficiency factor, F.

(3) The efficiency factor, F, shall be established by the transmitter manufacturer for each type of transmitter for which he submits data to the Commission.

(b) Maintenance. (1) The operating power shall be maintained as near as practicable to the authorized power and shall not be less than 90 percent nor greater than 105 percent of authorized power.

4
73.269 FREQUENCY TOLERANCE.

The center frequency of each FM broadcast station shall be maintained within 2000 Hertz of the assigned center frequency.

FM TECHNICAL STANDARDS

4
73.310 DEFINITIONS:

CENTER FREQUENCY. The term "center frequency" means:

(1) The average frequency of the emitted wave when modulated by a sinusoidal signal or,

(2) The frequency of the emitted wave without modulation.

FM BROADCAST CHANNEL. A band of frequencies 200 kHz wide and designated by its center frequency. Channels for FM broadcast stations begin at 88.1 MHz and continue in successive steps of 200 kHz to and including 107.9 MHz.

FREQUENCY SWING. The instantaneous departure of the frequency of the emitted wave from the center frequency resulting from modulation.

PERCENTAGE MODULATION. The ratio of the actual frequency swing to the frequency swing defined as 100 percent modulation, expressed in percentage. For FM broadcast stations, a frequency swing of ± 75 kHz is defined as 100 percent modulation.

4 73.317 TRANSMITTERS AND ASSOCIATED EQUIPMENT.

(a) ELECTRICAL PERFORMANCE STANDARDS. The general design of the FM broadcast transmitting system shall be in accordance with the following principles and specifications:

(2) The transmitting system shall be capable of transmitting a band of audio frequencies from 50 to 15,000 Hz.

73.320 INDICATING INSTRUMENTS - SPECIFICATIONS.

The following requirements and specifications shall apply to indicating instruments used by FM broadcast stations:

(a) Instruments indicating the plate current or plate voltage of the last radio stage or the transmission line current or voltage (linear scale instruments) shall meet the following specifications:

(2) Accuracy shall be at least 2 percent of the full scale reading.

4

73.331 REQUIREMENTS FOR TYPE APPROVAL OF FREQUENCY MONITORS.

(2) The range of the indicating device shall be at least from 2000 Hz below to 2000 Hz above the assigned center frequency.

4

73.569 FREQUENCY TOLERANCE.

(a) The center frequency of each noncommercial educational FM broadcast station licensed for transmitter power output of 10 watts or less shall be maintained within 3,000 Hz of the assigned center frequency.

(b) The center frequency of each noncommercial educational FM broadcast station licensed for transmitter power output above 10 watts shall be maintained within 2,000 Hz of the assigned center frequency.

4

73.661 OPERATOR REQUIREMENTS.

One or more operators holding a valid radiotelephone first-class operator license shall be on duty at the place where the transmitting apparatus is located or at a remote control point and in actual charge thereof whenever the transmitter is delivering power to the transmitting antenna.

TV TECHNICAL STANDARDS

4

73.681 DEFINITIONS.

ASPECT RATIO. The ratio of picture width to picture height as transmitted.

VESTIGIAL SIDEBAND TRANSMISSION. A system of transmission wherein one of the generated sidebands is partially attenuated at the transmitter and radiated only in part.

4

73.682 TRANSMISSION STANDARDS AND CHANGES.

(a) TRANSMISSION STANDARDS. (1) The width of the television broadcast channel shall be 6 MHz.

(5) The chrominance subcarrier frequency shall be 3.579545 MHz ±10 Hz with a maximum rate of change not to exceed one-tenth Hz.

(7) The aspect ratio of the transmitted television picture shall be 4 units horizontally to 3 units vertically.

(12) The blanking level shall be transmitted at 75±2.5 percent of the peak carrier level.

73.687 TRANSMITTERS AND ASSOCIATED EQUIPMENT.

(b) Aural transmitter. The transmitter shall operate satisfactorily with a frequency swing of ±25 kHz, which is considered 100 percent modulation.

(2) The entire transmitting system shall be capable of transmitting a band of audio frequencies from 50 to 15,000 Hz.

(c) REQUIREMENTS APPLICABLE TO BOTH VISUAL AND AURAL TRANSMITTERS. (1) Automatic means shall be provided in the visual transmitter to maintain the carrier frequency within ± one kHz of the authorized frequency; automatic means shall be provided in the aural transmitter to maintain the carrier frequency 4.5 MHz above the actual visual carrier frequency within ± one kHz.

73.689 OPERATING POWER.

(a) DETERMINATION - (1) VISUAL TRANSMITTER. The operating power of the visual transmitter shall be determined at the output terminals of the transmitter, which includes any vestigial sideband and harmonic filters which may be used during normal operation. For this determination, the average power output shall be measured while operating into a dummy load of substantially zero reactance and a resistance equal to the transmission line characteristic impedance. During this measurement, the transmitter shall be modulated only by a standard synchronizing signal with blanking level set at 75 percent of peak amplitude as observed in an output monitor.

(2) AURAL TRANSMITTER. The operating power of the aural transmitter shall be determined by either the direct or indirect method, as shown in 73.51 above.

(b) MAINTENANCE – (1) VISUAL TRANSMITTER. The operating power shall be maintained as near as is practicable to the authorized power and shall not be less than 80 percent nor more than 110 percent of the authorized power, except in emergencies.

(2) AURAL TRANSMITTER. (i) The operating power shall be maintained as near as practicable to the authorized power and shall not be less than 80 percent nor greater than 110 percent of authorized power, except in emergencies.

INTERNATIONAL BROADCAST STATIONS

EQUIPMENT

4
73.752 FREQUENCY CONTROL.

The transmitter of each international broadcast station shall be equipped with automatic frequency control apparatus so designed and constructed that it is capable of maintaining the operating frequency within 0.003 percent of the assigned frequency.

4 73.767 FREQUENCY TOLERANCE.

The operating frequencies of international broadcast station transmitters shall, at all times, be maintained within the frequency tolerances specified in 73.752.

EXPERIMENTAL TELEVISION BROADCAST STATIONS

4
74.166 OPERATOR REQUIREMENTS.

One or more radio operators holding radiotelephone first-class or radiotelephone second-class operator licenses shall be on duty at the place where the transmitting apparatus of any experimental television broadcast station is located and in actual charge of its operation. The licensed operator on duty and in charge of a broadcast transmitter may, at the discretion of the licensee, be employed for other duties or for the operation of another station or stations in accordance with the class of operator's license which he holds and the rules and regulations governing such stations.

AURAL BROADCAST STL & INTERCITY RELAY STATIONS

4
74.536 DIRECTIONAL ANTENNA REQUIRED.

Each aural broadcast STL and intercity relay station is required to employ a directional antenna. Considering one kilowatt of radiated power as a standard for comparative purposes, such antenna shall provide a free space field intensity at one mile of not less than 435 mv/m in the main lobe of radiation toward the receiver and not more than 20 percent of the maximum value in any azimuth 30 degrees or more off the line to the receiver.

4
74.561 FREQUENCY TOLERANCE.

The licensee of each aural broadcast STL and intercity relay station shall maintain the operating frequency of the station within plus or minus 0.005 percent of the assigned frequency.

EXTRACTS FROM STANDARDS OF GOOD ENGINEERING PRACTICE CONCERNING STANDARD BROADCAST STATIONS.

4 SPARE TUBES. A spare tube of every type employed in the AM or FM transmitter and frequency and modulation monitors shall be kept on hand. When more than one tube of any type is employed, the following table determines the number of spares of that type required:

Number of each type employed	Spares required
1 or 2	1
3 to 5	2
6 to 8	3
9 or more	4

4 AUTHORIZED POWER. The "authorized power" or "licensed power" is the power specified in the instrument of authorization for a standard broadcast station.

3
89.3 DEFINITIONS.

AUTHORIZED BANDWIDTH. The maximum width of the band of frequencies, as specified in the authorizations, to be occupied by an emission.

BANDWIDTH OCCUPIED BY AN EMISSION. The width of the frequency band (normally specified in kilohertz) containing those frequencies upon which a total of 99 percent of the radiated power appears, extended to include any discrete frequency upon which the power is at least 0.25 percent of the total radiated power.

STATION AUTHORIZATION. Any construction permit, license, or special temporary authorization issued by the Commission.

3
89.51 STATION AUTHORIZATION REQUIRED.

No radio transmitter shall be operated in the Public Safety Radio Services except under and in accordance with a proper station authorization granted by the Federal Communications Commission.

3
89.53 PROCEDURE FOR OBTAINING A RADIO STATION AUTHORIZATION AND FOR COMMENCEMENT OF OPERATION.

(a) Persons desiring to install and operate radio transmitting equipment should first submit an application for a radio station authorization.

(b) When a construction permit only has been issued for a base, fixed or mobile station and installation has been completed in accordance with the terms of the construction permit and the applicable rules of the Commission, the permittee shall proceed further as follows:

(1) Notify the Engineer-in-Charge of the local radio district of the date on which the transmitter will first be tested in such manner as to produce radiation, giving name of the permittee, station location, call sign, and frequencies on which tests are to be conducted. This notification shall be made in writing at least two days in advance of the test date. FCC Form 456 may be used for this purpose. No reply from the radio district office is necessary before the tests are begun.

3
89.55 FILING OF APPLICATIONS.

Standard numbered forms applicable to the Public Safety Radio Services may be obtained from the Washington, D. C. 20554, office of the Commission, or from any of its field engineering offices.

3
89.75 CHANGES IN AUTHORIZED STATIONS.

Authority for certain changes in authorized stations must be obtained from the Commission before these changes are made, while other changes do not require prior Commission approval. The following paragraphs describe the conditions under which prior Commission approval is or is not necessary.

(a) Proposed changes which will result in operation inconsistent with any of the terms of the current authorization require that an application for modification of construction permit and/or license be submitted to the

Commission and shall be submitted on FCC Form 400, or, in the case of microwave stations, on FCC Form 402, and shall be accompanied by exhibits and supplementary statements.

(c) Proposed changes which will not depart from any of the terms of the outstanding authorization for the station involved may be made without prior Commission approval. Included in such changes is the substitution of various makes of transmitting equipment at any station provided the particular equipment to be installed is included in the Commission's "List of Equipment Acceptable for Licensing" and designated for use in the Public Safety, Industrial and Land Transportation Radio Services and provided the substitute equipment employs the same type of emission and does not exceed the power limitations as set forth in the station authorization.

3
89.103 FREQUENCY STABILITY.

(a) A permittee or licensee in these services shall maintain the carrier frequency of each authorized transmitter within the following percentage of the assigned frequency:

Frequency range in MHz	All fixed and base stations in percent	All mobile stations	
		Over 3 watts in percent	3 watts or less in percent
below 25	0.01	0.01	0.02
25 to 50	0.002	0.002	0.005
50 to 1000	0.0005*	0.0005	0.0005

*Stations authorized for operation on or before Dec. 1, 1961, in the frequency band 73.0-74.6 MHz may operate with a frequency tolerance of 0.005 percent.

3
89.107 EMISSION LIMITATIONS.

(a) Each authorization issued to a station operating in these services will show, as the prefix to the emission classification, a figure specifying the maximum authorized bandwidth in kilohertz to be occupied by the emission. The specified band shall contain those frequencies upon which a total of 99 percent of the radiated power appears.

(b) The maximum authorized bandwidth of emission and the maximum authorized frequency deviation in the case of frequency or phase modulated emission, shall be as follows:

Frequency band (MHz)	Authorized bandwidth (kHz)	Frequency deviation (kHz)
25 to 50	20	5
50 to 150	20*	5*
150 to 450	20	5

*Stations authorized for operation on or before Dec. 1, 1961, in the frequency band 73.0-74.6 MHz may continue to operate with a bandwidth of 40 kHz and a deviation of ± 15 kHz.

3
89.109 MODULATION REQUIREMENTS.

(b) When amplitude modulation is used for telephony, the modulation

410

percentage shall be sufficient to provide efficient communication and normally shall be maintained above 70 percent on peaks, but shall not exceed 100 percent on negative peaks.

3

89.113 TRANSMITTER CONTROL REQUIREMENTS.

(b) A control point is an operating position which meets all of the following conditions:

(1) The position must be under the control and supervision of the licensee;

(2) It is a position at which the monitoring facilities required by this section are installed; and

(3) It is a position at which a person immediately responsible for the operation of the transmitter is stationed.

3

89.115 TRANSMITTER MEASUREMENTS.

(a) The licensee of each station shall employ a suitable procedure to determine that the carrier frequency of each transmitter, authorized to operate with a plate input power to the final radio frequency stage in excess of 3 watts, is maintained within the tolerance prescribed in this part. This determination shall be made, and the results thereof entered in the station records, in accordance with the following:

(1) When the transmitter is initially installed;

(2) When any change is made in the transmitter which may affect the carrier frequency or the stability thereof;

(3) At intervals not to exceed one year, for transmitters employing crystal-controlled oscillators;

(4) At intervals not to exceed one month, for transmitters not employing crystal-controlled oscillators.

(b) The licensee of each station shall employ a suitable procedure to determine that the plate power input to the final radio frequency stage of each base station or fixed station transmitter, authorized to operate with a plate input power to the final radio frequency stage in excess of 3 watts, does not exceed the maximum figure specified on the current station authorization. Where the transmitter is so constructed that a direct measurement of plate current in the final radio frequency stage is not practicable, the plate input power may be determined from a measurement of the cathode current in the final radio frequency stage. When the plate input to the final radio frequency stage is determined from a measurement of the cathode current, the required entry shall indicate clearly the quantities that were measured, the measured values thereof, and the method of determining the plate power input from the measured values. This determination shall be made, and the results thereof entered in the station records, in accordance with the following:

(1) When the transmitter is initially installed;

(2) When any change is made in the transmitter which may increase the transmitter power input;

(3) At intervals not to exceed one year.

(c) The licensee of each station shall employ a suitable procedure to determine that the modulation of each transmitter, authorized to operate with a plate input power to the final radio frequency stage in excess of 3 watts, does not exceed the limits specified in this part. This determination shall be made and the results thereof entered in the station records, in accordance with the following:

(1) When the transmitter is initially installed;

(2) When any change is made in the transmitter which may affect the modulation characteristics;

(3) At intervals not to exceed one year.

3

89.153 STATION IDENTIFICATION.

(a) The required identification for stations in these services shall be the assigned call signal.

(d) Each station in these services shall transmit the required identification at the end of each transmission or exchange of transmissions, or once each 30 minutes of the operating period, as the licensee may prefer.

(e) A mobile station authorized to the licensee of the associated base station and which transmits only on the transmitting frequency of the associated base station is not required to transmit any identification.

3

89.175 CONTENT OF STATION RECORDS.

Each licensee of a station in these services shall maintain records in accordance with the following:

(a) For all stations, the results and dates of the transmitter measurements required by these rules and the name of the person or persons making the measurements.

3

89.177 FORM OF STATION RECORDS.

(a) The records shall be kept in an orderly manner and in such detail that the data required are readily available.

(b) Each entry in the records shall be signed by a person qualified to do so, having actual knowledge of the facts to be recorded.

(c) No record or portion thereof shall be erased, obliterated, or willfully destroyed within the required retention period. Any necessary correction may be made only by the persons originating the entry who shall strike out the erroneous portion, initial the correction made and indicate the date of the correction.

PRACTICE QUESTIONS - LESSON 21

1. Frequencies of 3,000 to 30,000 kHz are known as: (3)
a. VHF   b. LF   c. HF   d. MF

2. Within what limits must the operating power of the aural transmitter of a TV station be maintained? (4)
a. 10% above and 10% below the authorized power
b. 10% above and 20% below the authorized power
c. 5% above and 10% below the authorized power
d. 5% above and 5% below the authorized power

3. A land station in the land mobile service carrying on a service with land mobile stations, is known as a: (3)
a. coast station   c. earth station
b. base station   d. fixed station

4. A carrier is defined as: (3)
a. the output of an AM transmitter without modulation
b. the output of an FM transmitter with modulation
c. the output of a transmitter without modulation
d. the sine wave output of a crystal-controlled transmitter

5. The indirect method of measuring the operating power of a transmitter: (4)
a. makes use of the antenna current and the antenna resistance
b. equals product of plate voltage and plate current of last stage
c. uses a factor, F, that depends on the type of modulation used
d. can always be used to measure the power of a transmitter

6. If a broadcast transmitter uses five tubes of a particular type, it must keep: (4)
a. one spare on hand   c. three spares on hand
b. two spares on hand   d. four spares on hand

7. The percentage of modulation capability required of a standard broadcast station is: (4)
a. 75–80%   b. 80–85%   c. 85–95%   d. 90–105%

8. The frequency tolerance of the video carrier of a television broadcast transmitter is: (4)
a. $\pm.01$ kHz   b. $\pm.05$ kHz   c. $\pm.1$ kHz   d. ± 1 kHz

9. A licensee need not secure FCC approval in the event he: (3)
a. desires to make a change that may affect the frequency
b. desires to change the power of the station
c. desires to substitute equivalent equipment listed on the Commission's approved list
d. changes the hours of operation, provided the total number of hours per day remains the same

10. What is the authorized frequency deviation of Public Safety Radio stations operating at 430 MHz? (3)
a. ± 5 kHz   b. ± 20 kHz   c. ± 15 kHz   d. ± 40 kHz

11. The abbreviation for double sideband AM is:
a. A4   b. A2   c. A3A   d. A3

12. A land station in the maritime mobile service is known as a:(3)
a. base station   c. fixed station
b. space station   d. coast station

13. A remote-reading ammeter must be checked against a regular antenna ammeter at least: (4)
a. once a day   c. once a month
b. once a week   d. before and after each transmission

14. The maximum power at which a transmitter can be operated in accordance with its design, is referred to as: (4)
a. maximum technical power   c. plate input power
b. maximum rated carrier power   d. maximum output power

15. When AM is used in the Public Safety Radio Services, the modulation percentage shall: (3)
a. not exceed 100% on negative peaks
b. be between 85 and 100%
c. be between 75 and 95%   d. be between 90 and 105%

16. An auxiliary transmitter may not be used: (4)
a. when the main transmitter fails
b. during the experimental period
c. during modification of the main transmitter
d. during repair of the main transmitter

17. The term "daytime" indicates:
a. local sunrise to local sunset
b. local sunrise to 6:00 P.M.
c. local sunrise to 12:00 midnight
d. 6:00 A.M. to local sunset

18. What is the frequency tolerance of a non-commercial educational FM broadcast station whose output power is 7 watts ?(4)
a. 3 kHz   b. 2 kHz   c. 20 Hz   d. 200 Hz

19. Each station in the Public Safety Radio Services must transmit its assigned call signal: (3)
a. at the beginning and end of each transmission
b. every 15 minutes   c. every 30 minutes
d. at the end of each contact

20. What is the separation in frequency between the aural transmitter carrier and the visual transmitter carrier? (4)
a. 4.5 MHz   b. .25 MHz   c. 1.25 MHz   d. 1.5 MHz

21. How is the operating power determined by the direct method?
a. the final plate voltage, multiplied by the final plate current [4]
b. the antenna resistance, multiplied by the antenna current
c. the final plate voltage, multiplied by the final plate current, multiplied by the efficiency of the final stage
d. the antenna resistance, multiplied by the square of the antenna current

22. The term "broadcast day" indicates:
a. local sunrise and 8:00 P.M.
b. 6:00 A.M. to 12:00 midnight
c. local sunrise and 12:00 midnight
d. 6:00 A.M. to 6:00 P.M.

23. Which name is given to the procedure for securing advance approval of equipment by the FCC wherein tests are to be conducted by the FCC? (3)
a. type acceptance   c. FCC approval
b. type approval   d. advance approval

24. The operating frequency of all radio stations is determined by comparison with the signals of station: (3)
a. KWK of the National Frequency Control Authority
b. WWV of the National Bureau of Standards
c. WWW of the FCC   d. WKW of Washington, D.C.

25. When transmitter measurements at a Public Safety Radio Station are made, which of the following need not be entered in the station records? (3)
a. date of measurements   b. times of measurements
c. name of person making the measurements
d. results of the measurements

26. In stations employing a directional antenna system, what tolerance is permitted in the ratio of antenna currents in the elements of the system? (4)
a. .05%   b. 5.0%   c. 1.0%   d. 2.0%

27. What is the width of an FM broadcast channel? (4)
a. 10 kHz   b. 30 kHz   c. 150 kHz   d. 200 kHz

28. The ratio of picture width to picture height is called: (4)
a. vestigial ratio   c. maximum width-height ratio
b. aspect ratio   d. blanking ratio

29. When using a low temperature coefficient crystal in a standard broadcast transmitter, what is the maximum temperature variation permitted? (4)
a. 0.1^o C   b. 0.5^o C   c. 1.0^o C   d. 2.0^o C

30. The maximum authorized frequency deviation permitted to a transmitter in the Public Safety Radio Services operations, at a frequency of 42.63 MHz is: (3)
a. 3 kHz   b. 5 kHz   c. 6 kHz   d. 15 kHz

31. What method of determining power must be normally used by a standard broadcast station? (4)
a. direct method   c. efficiency method
b. indirect method   d. efficiency factor method

32. What is the frequency tolerance of an international broadcast station? (4)
   a. .001%   b. .002%   c. .003%   d. .01%

33. We apply modulation in measuring the input power to the last stage of a broadcast transmitter because: (4)
   a. it is more realistic   b. it is more accurate
   c. the modulator adds power to the stage
   d. we do not apply modulation when making these measurements

34. The frequency swing of the aural part of a TV transmitter is: (4)
   a. ±10 kHz   b. ±20 kHz   c. ±25 kHz   d. ±150 kHz

35. Instruments indicating plate current or plate voltage in the final stage of a standard broadcast transmitter shall be accurate to within at least what percentage of the full scale reading? (4)
   a. .005%   b. .5%   c. 1.0%   d. 2.0%

36. What is the frequency tolerance at an FM broadcast station? (4)
   a. ±1.0%   b. ±20 Hz   c. ±2 kHz   d. ±0.1%

37. How often shall the auxiliary transmitter be tested?
   a. once a day   c. once a month
   b. once a week   d. at the discretion of the operator

38. The term "experimental period" means the time from: (4)
   a. local sunset to 12:00 midnight
   b. 12:00 midnight to local sunrise
   c. local sunrise to 6:00 PM   d. 6:00 PM to 12:00 midnight

39. What is the frequency tolerance of a standard broadcast station?
   a. ±10 Hz   b. ±1%   c. ±20 Hz   d. ±.01%

40. For how long may a standard broadcast station be operated if an indicating instrument becomes defective, pending its repair or replacement? (4)
   a. 30 days   b. 60 days   c. 90 days
   d. it may not be operated without its indicating instruments

41. The symbol for telegraphy without modulation is:
   a. A5   b. A∅   c. P3   d. A1

42. UHF frequencies are from: (3)
   a. 30,000 MHz to 300,000 MHz   c. 30 MHz to 300 MHz
   b. 3,000 MHz to 30,000 MHz   d. 300 MHz to 3,000 MHz

43. The maximum authorized bandwidth of Public Safety stations operating between 25 and 50 MHz is: (3)
   a. 20 kHz   b. 10 kHz   c. 30 kHz   d. 150 kHz

44. The symbol for amplitude modulated television is:
   a. A5   b. F5   c. A3A   d. P3D

416

FINAL FCC-TYPE EXAMINATION
ELEMENT 3

1. The fully charged voltage of a lead-acid cell is:
a. 2.1 V.   b. 6.3 V.   c. 1.5 V.   d. 12.6 V.

2. The electrons that take part in a current flow come from the:
a. outer rings of an atom   c. molecules of a conductor
b. nucleus of an atom   d. atoms of a conductor

3. The unit of electromotive force or potential of difference, is:
a. ampere   b. volt   c. watt   d. coulomb

4. Permeability is:
a. another name for magnetomotive force
b. the ability of a coil to induce a voltage into another coil
c. the ability of a material to conduct magnetic lines of force
d. the ability of a magnet to retain its magnetism

5. Which of the following losses do not occur in the core of a transformer?
a. eddy currents   c. reluctance
b. hysteresis   d. copper losses

6. The impedance of a series resonant circuit, containing no resistance, is:
a. infinite   c. equal to that of a parallel resonant circuit
b. zero   d. one-half that of a parallel resonant circuit

7. The output voltage of a separately excited generator (keeping the frequency constant) is controlled by a:
a. phase control   c. voltage regulator
b. field rheostat   d. magnetic shoe

8. The speed of a synchronous motor is determined by the:
a. applied voltage   c. number of poles
b. frequency and number of poles   d. load

9. What is the efficiency of a stage whose output power is 300 watts if the plate voltage is 900 volts and its current is 600 ma?
a. 180%   b. 55%   c. 80%   d. 45%

10. A vibrator power supply:
a. steps up DC   c. is non-synchronous
b. steps down DC   d. is synchronous

11. In forward-biasing of a semiconductor:
a. the positive terminal of the battery connects to the N part and the negative terminal connects to the P part
b. the negative terminal of the battery connects to the N part
c. the positive terminal of the battery connects to the P part
d. B and C are correct

12. A voltage regulator tube:
a. does not contain gas   b. produces a fixed output voltage
c. uses a conventional cathode-filament structure
d. operates in the same manner as a transistor

13. The second harmonic of 500 Hz is:
a. 500 Hz   b. 1500 Hz   c. 1000 Hz   d. 250 Hz

14. Maximum plate dissipation refers to:
a. maximum safe heat radiation capability of the plate in watts
b. transconductance expressed in watts
c. power gain of an amplifier   d. power sensitivity of a tetrode

15. In a Class A amplifier, the output signal is:
a. similar to a sine wave
b. a faithful reproduction of the input signal
c. smaller than the input signal
d. twice the frequency of the input signal

16. Push-pull operation:
a. doubles the second harmonic in the grid circuit
b. improves the signal strength
c. cancels out the second harmonic in the plate circuit
d. cancels out the third harmonic in the plate circuit

17. A transistorized grounded emitter circuit is the equivalent of a tube's:
a. grounded cathode circuit   c. grounded plate circuit
b. grounded grid circuit   d. cathode follower circuit

18. A power reducing device accepts 50 watts at its input and puts out 5 watts. What is its power loss in db?
a. -2 db   b. -20 db   c. -100 db   d. -10 db

19. The electron-coupled oscillator does not have:
a. excellent frequency stability
b. large frequency variations with variations in supply voltage
c. coupling of energy from oscillator section to plate circuit by means of the electron stream
d. frequency independent of load variations

20. A carbon microphone has:
a. excellent frequency response   c. a low noise level
b. a high output   d. a high impedance

21. A VTVM is used to measure the grid-leak voltage of an oscillator because:
a. it has a high resistance   b. it has high sensitivity to RF
c. it draws very little power from the circuit
d. a and b are correct

22. Harmonic emissions are attenuated by:
a. a low-pass filter at the transmitter
b. a high-pass filter at the transmitter
c. a band-stop filter at the transmitter
d. a crystal lattice filter at the transmitter

23. What is used to cancel the upper or lower sideband in a single sideband transmitter?
a. a heterodyne circuit   c. a high-pass filter
b. a filter circuit   d. a linear amplifier

24. In a 100% sine wave amplitude modulated signal, the upper sideband contains:
a. 1/2 of the total power   c. 1/3 of the total power
b. 1/6 of the total power   d. 2/3 of the total power

25. A pentagrid converter is:
a. a mixer oscillator tube   c. an AF amplifier
b. an RF amplifier   d. an audio power amplifier

26. A pre-emphasis circuit is similar to a:
a. low-pass filter   c. band-pass filter
b. predistorter circuit   d. high-pass filter

27. A primary advantage of a ratio detector is that it:
a. can use solid state diodes   c. has high gain
b. does not require a limiter   d. has excellent selectivity

28. Shunt feeding a Marconi antenna:
a. requires lightning protection
b. requires a 90º angle between transmission line and antenna
c. requires a separate building to house the coupling between the transmission line and the antenna
d. does not require a base insulator

29. If a quarter wave section of a transmission line is terminated in a short circuit:
a. the impedances at opposite ends are opposite to one another
b. the impedance and current are in phase all along the line
c. the impedance is out of phase with the voltage at the ends
d. the current is low at the shorted end

30. A superheterodyne with an IF of 255 kHz and tuned to 700 kHz has what image frequency?
a. 1210 kHz   b. 955 kHz   c. 510 kHz   d. 445 kHz

31. Which of the following is not a precaution to be observed in the use of a Heterodyne Frequency meter?
   a. allow one-half hour warmup before using
   b. use modulated RF energy for measuring purposes
   c. heterodyne oscillator should be checked against crystal oscillator
   d. entire calibration should be checked after replacing an oscillator tube

32. "Type approval" when applied to equipment, indicates that:
   a. the manufacturer has submitted data concerning the equipment
   b. the FCC has conducted tests on the equipment
   c. the licensee has submitted data concerning the equipment
   d. none of the above

33. Given the following readings in a standard broadcast station: Plate voltage of a push-pull stage - 1200 V, Plate current in each tube - 400 ma, Antenna resistance - 70 ohms, Antenna current - 3 A, Efficiency factor, F, of last stage - .67. Find the operating power via the indirect method.
   a. 210 W   b. 643 W   c. 321.5 W   d. 630 W

34. Find the operating power in the above example, via the direct method.
   a. 643 W   b. 210 W   c. 630 W   d. 321.5 W

35. The positive terminal of a lead-acid cell is:
   a. pure lead   b. lead sulphate   c. nickel   d. lead peroxide

36. In a circuit containing some resistance and some capacitance:
   a. the current and voltage are in phase
   b. the current lags behind the voltage
   c. the current leads the voltage by 90°
   d. the voltage lags behind the current

37. A given length of resistance is 5 ohms. What is the resistance when its cross-sectional area is cut to 1/3 of its original value?
   a. 15 ohms   b. 45 ohms   c. 1-2/3 ohms   d. .55 ohms

38. The term used to describe the time it takes for a capacitor to charge up to 63.6% of the source voltage is called:
   a. voltage regulation   c. ripple time
   b. phase relationship   d. time constant

39. A field rheostat is not used to control the output voltage of:
   a. a generator   c. a dynamotor
   b. a motor-generator   d. none of the above

40. A VTVM is known for its:
   a. high input Z   c. high input C
   b. low input Z   d. use of a D'Arsonval movement

41. One reason that we increase the filament voltage of a tube 20% above its rating is to:
a. lengthen the life of the tube
b. obtain more power from the tube
c. even out the wear on the filament, thereby lengthening the life of the tube
d. the filament voltage should not be higher than its rating

42. The value of the bias voltage of Fig. 42 is:
a. 6.25 volts
b. 5 volts
c. 1.25 volts   Fig. 42
d. 50 volts

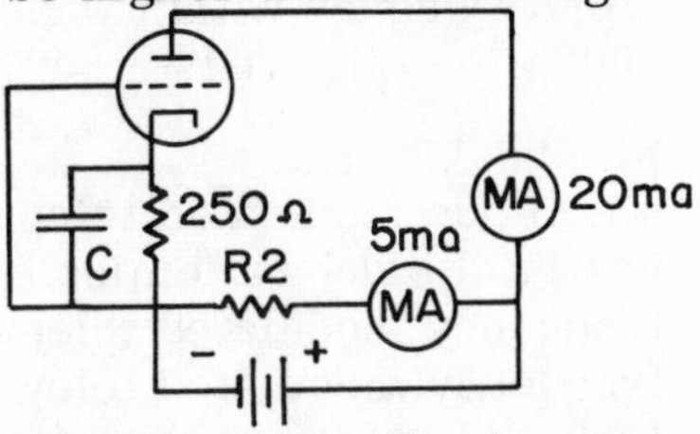

Fig. 42

43. What is the value of C, assuming the lowest audio frequency to be passed is 100 Hz?
a. 6 mf   b. 64 mf   c. 32 mf   d. 21 mf

44. The phase relationship between the input and output circuits in a transistor common emitter amplifier is:
a. 180° out of phase   c. 45° out of phase
b. in phase   d. 90° out of phase

45. Grid-leak bias in an oscillator develops by the action of the:
a. grid resistor and capacitor   c. plate voltage
b. feedback from the tank circuit   d. plate current

46. The modulation index is equal to:
a. twice the highest modulating frequency
b. carrier frequency deviation divided by modulating frequency
c. the carrier frequency deviation divided by the deviation ratio
d. the deviation ratio, divided by the carrier frequency deviation

47. What is the main advantage of a three-element horizontal beam antenna over a simple horizontal dipole?
a. radiates more total power
b. radiates more power in one direction
c. radiates more power in two directions
d. minimizes radiation of power in a vertical direction

48. A grid-dip meter is essentially:
a. an oscillator   c. a bridge circuit
b. an RF amplifier   d. a discriminator

49. The power dissipation in a 230 ohm resistor with 0.3 amps flowing through it is:
a. 69 W.   b. 20.7 W.   c. 766 W.   d. 255 W.

50. The opposite of conductance is:
a. resistance   b. current   c. voltage   d. quantity

421

51. The maximum authorized frequency deviation permitted to a transmitter in the Public Safety Radio Service, operating at a frequency of 172.14 MHz is:
a. 15 kHz   b. 3 kHz   c. 5 kHz   d. 30 kHz

52. A station in the Public Safety Radio Service, operating at 453 MHZ with a licensed power of 75 watts, must maintain its carrier frequency within what percentage of its licensed value?
a. .002%   b. .01%   c. .0005%   d. .005%

53. F3 stands for:
a. amplitude modulated telephony
b. vestigial sideband emission
c. frequency modulated telephony
d. frequency modulated television

54. Applications relative to the Public Safety Radio Service may not be obtained from:
a. the FCC in Washington, D. C.
b. the nearest Engineering Field Office
c. the Public Safety Commission
d. any Engineering Field Office

55. Stations in the Public Safety Radio Services may be operated without a station authorization for a period:
a. not to exceed 3 months   c. not to exceed 48 hours
b. not to exceed 30 days   d. none of the above

56. SHF (super high frequency) means the frequency range between:
a. 300,000 MHz and 300,000,000 MHz
b. 30,000 kHz and 3,000 MHz
c. 3,000 MHz and 30,000 MHz
d. 3,000 MHz and 30,000 kHz

57. How much would it cost to run a 120-volt, 192 ohm lamp for 24 hours? The cost of electricity is 5.3¢ per kilowatt-hour.
a. 4.1¢   b. 1.8¢   c. 9.5¢   d. 23¢

58. A relay whose contacts are normally open, is known as a/an:
a. break-contact relay   c. closed-circuit relay
b. open-contact relay   d. make-contact relay

59. The line current in a parallel circuit is equal to:
a. the sum of the branch currents, divided by two
b. the source voltage, divided by the smallest resistor
c. the sum of the individual branch currents
d. a very small value

60. What value of resistance must be connected in series with a 40 watt, 120 volt bulb in order to cause a 0.1 amp. current to flow through the bulb. The source voltage is 50 V.
a. 360 ohms   b. 400 ohms   c. 33.3 ohms   d. 140 ohms

61. Electrical energy is measured by a/an:
a. watt-hour meter b. wavemeter c. ammeter d. voltmeter

62. If an alternating current of 2 amperes flows in a series circuit consisting of 3 ohms of resistance, 14 ohms of inductive reactance and 10 ohms of capacitive reactance, what is the voltage across the circuit?
a. 6 V. b. 54 V. c. 10 V. d. 14 V.

63. What would happen if the field of a shunt-wound DC motor is opened while the motor is running under no load?
a. a high armature current would be drawn
b. a high counter-e.m.f. would develop in the armature
c. the armature speed would rise d. a and c are correct

64. Of the following formulas, pick out the incorrect one:
a. $I = \dfrac{E}{R}$ b. $E = RI$ c. $R = \dfrac{I}{E}$ d. $P = I^2 R$

65. Assume a 5 henry choke in series-aiding with a 4 henry choke and a mutual inductance of 2 henries. What is the total inductance of the circuit?
a. 13 henry b. 11 henry c. 5 henry d. 10 henry

66. In a Class A amplifier, the average plate current:
a. decreases with application of a signal
b. increases with application of a signal
c. remains constant with application of a signal
d. varies with application of a signal

67. Removing the load on a DC series motor would cause:
a. the motor to slow down c. no change in speed
b. the motor to speed up d. the counter-e.m.f. to decrease

68. Grid current does not flow in:
a. an oscillator c. a Class A amplifier
b. a Class C amplifier d. a Class B amplifier

69. An important advantage of a tetrode over a triode is:
a. reduced possibility of oscillation in a tetrode RF amplifier
b. repulsion of secondary emission electrons
c. increased cathode emission d. reduced rectification

70. An advantage of a mercury vapor rectifier over a high vacuum rectifier is NOT:
a. better voltage regulation b. low internal voltage drop
c. a critical inverse peak voltage rating
d. a relatively high current rating

71. The indirectly-heated cathode has:
a. low emission efficiency c. short warm-up time
b. high operating temperature d. freedom from hum

72. It is most important to use short leads in:
a. audio circuits   c. oscillator circuits
b. UHF circuits   d. transistor circuits

73. The cross-sectional size of a waveguide:
a. is proportional to the frequency of the signal
b. is proportional to the wavelength of the signal
c. has little to do with wavelength
d. determines the gain of the signal

74. Overmodulation will cause:
a. a lower signal-to-noise ratio   b. excessive bandwidth
c. a higher signal-to-noise ratio
d. partial attenuation of the lower sideband

75. What type of filament can be reactivated?
a. indirectly heated   c. silicon coated
b. directly heated   d. thoriated tungsten

76. The approximate bandwidth of an FM signal is equal to the:
a. frequency deviation multiplied by the audio frequency
b. modulation index multiplied by the deviation ratio
c. carrier deviation divided by the modulation index
d. significant sidebands multiplied by audio modulating frequency

77. In a transmission line, the maximum current, divided by the minimum current, is known as the:
a. average current   c. standing wave ratio
b. effective current   d. band-pass impedance

78. The principal disadvantage of crystal-controlled oscillators is:
a. frequency instability more pronounced
b. high voltage requirements
c. insufficient "drive" to the final
d. difficulty in changing operating frequencies

79. Which of the following does not improve oscillator stability?
a. using buffer stage between oscillator and power amplifier stage
b. tank circuit tuned to lowest possible plate current
c. a well-regulated power supply
d. a low value of grid-leak resistor

80. In a Foster-Seeley discriminator, an RF choke connects:
a. a tap on the secondary coil to the junction of two resistors
b. a tap on the secondary coil to ground
c. the top of the primary coil to ground
d. the bottom of the secondary coil to the junction of two resistors

81. A problem that can arise with long horizontal waveguides is:
a. moisture accumulation   c. increased inductance
b. reduction of Q   d. increased capacitance

82. A signal of 600 MHz has a wavelength of:
   a. .5 meters   b. 2 meters   c. 1800 meters   d. 20 cm

83. The speed of a DC series motor is determined mainly by its:
   a. load   b. field strength   c. voltage   d. line frequency

84. What is the total capacitance of the circuit shown?
   a. 45 mfd
   b. 30 mfd
   c. 6.6 mfd
   d. 3.3 mfd

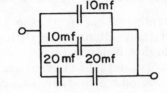

85. Assuming that the chokes in problem 65 are series opposing, what is the total inductance of the circuit?
   a. 13 H   b. 11 H   c. 5 H   d. 10 H

86. Terminating a transmission line in an impedance equal to the characteristic impedance of the line prevents:
   a. standing waves   c. overmodulation
   b. distortion   d. downward modulation

87. If a 500 kHz X-cut crystal is calibrated at 40° C. and it has a temperature coefficient of -15 Hz per MHz per degree C., at what frequency will it oscillate when its temperature is 50° C?
   a. 500.75 kHz   c. 499.925 kHz
   b. 500.150 kHz   d. 499.725 kHz

88. The principle disadvantage to using a grid-leak as the only source of bias in a Class C RF power amplifier is:
   a. poor efficiency   b. varying bias voltage   c. it distorts output
   d. loss of excitation will drop bias to zero, resulting in heavy plate current

89. The basic principle in the Heterodyne Frequency meter involves the use of:
   a. frequency modulation   c. amplitude modulation
   b. zero beating   d. interpolation

90. The alpha cutoff frequency is primarily dependent upon the:
   a. emitter current   b. collector-to-base voltage
   c. physical thickness of the base
   d. material makeup of the collector

91. In a klystron oscillator, LC tuned circuits are replaced by:
   a. waveguides   c. cavity resonators
   b. silver plated coils   d. buncher grids

92. What size bleeder resistor should be used in a 400 volt power supply? The resistance of the bleeder is 20,000 ohms.
   a. 5 watts   b. 6.5 watts   c. 15 watts   d. 4 watts

93. A precaution to be observed in the use of the absorption type frequency meter is to:
a. loosely couple the frequency meter to oscillator tank circuit
b. calibrate the frequency meter
c. check the B+ voltage of the frequency meter
d. zero-beat the output of the wavemeter

94. Which of the following is not a characteristic of a grounded cathode Class A amplifier stage?
a. high efficiency   b. input and output are out of phase
c. average plate current remains constant
d. tube operates over linear portion of Eg-Ip curve

95. Fig. 95 illustrates:
a. automatic volume control
b. single-sideband detection
c. a squelch circuit
d. a noise limiter

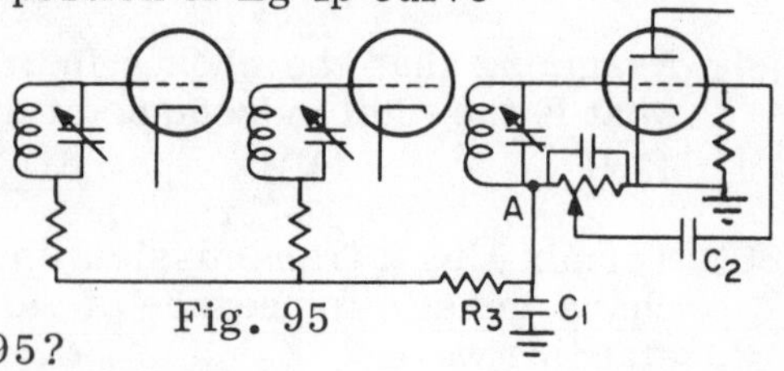

Fig. 95

96. What is wrong with Fig. 95?
a. C2 should be shunted with a resistor
b. C1 is on the wrong side of R3
c. there should be a resistor between C2 and the volume control
d. nothing is wrong with Fig. 95

97. Referring to Fig. 95, what would happen if C2 were open?
a. distortion would be introduced
b. regeneration would take place
c. there would be no audio
d. volume would be reduced, but fidelity would be improved

98. Parasitic oscillations are oscillations:
a. at frequencies other than the desired output frequency
b. occurring at exactly twice the desired frequency
c. occurring in the receiver only
d. which take place in the audio section of the transmitter

99. In Fig. 99 shown:
a. battery A circuit is reverse-biased and battery B section is forward-biased
b. battery A circuit is forward-biased and battery B circuit is reverse-biased
c. both circuits are forward-biased
d. both circuits are reverse-biased

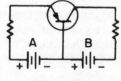

Fig. 99

100. The percentage regulation of a power supply with a no-load voltage output of 126.5 volts and a full-load voltage output of 115 volts is:
a. approximately 93%   b. 10%   c. 126.5%   d. 110%

101. The energy stored in a capacitor is in the form of:
  a. an electromagnetic field   c. positive charges
  b. an electrostatic field   d. negative charges

102. According to the molecular theory of magnetism:
  a. all magnetic molecules are perpendicular to the lines of force
  b. all magnetic molecules point to the North pole of the magnet
  c. all magnetic molecules point to the North pole of the earth
  d. none of the above

103. An increase in positive grid voltage causes the plate:
  a. current to decrease   c. resistance to increase
  b. resistance to decrease   d. voltage to increase

104. Feedback in a crystal-controlled oscillator is due to:
  a. capacity across crystal   c. grid-leak capacitor
  b. interelectrode tube capacity   d. none of the above

105. With reference to Fig. 14-13 on Page 274, what would happen
     if R7 opened up?
  a. the plate current of V4 and the antenna current would go down
  b. the plate current of V4 would go up and the antenna current
     would go down
  c. the plate current of V4 and V5 would go up
  d. the plate current of V4 and V6 would go down

106. With reference to Fig. 14-13 on Page 274, what would happen
     if the crystal became defective?
  a. the plate current of V1 and the antenna current would go up
  b. the plate current of V1 and the antenna current would go down
  c. the plate current of V1 and V2 would go up
  d. the plate current of V1 would go down and the antenna current
     would go up

107. With reference to Fig. 14-13 on Page 274, what would happen
     if the tank capacitor of the V1 stage opened up?
  a. the plate current of V1 drops and plate current of V2 rises
  b. the plate current of V1 rises and plate current of V2 rises
  c. the plate current of V1 drops and the antenna current drops
  d. the plate current of V2 drops and the antenna current drops

108. Which of the following situations doesn't require neutralization?
  a. a tetrode in an ultra high frequency circuit
  b. a triode in an ultra high frequency circuit
  c. a tetrode in a 1500 kHz circuit
  d. a triode in a 1500 kHz circuit

109. What is the DC power input to a tube having a plate voltage of
     750 V. and a plate current of 90 ma?
  a. 63.3 W.   b. 67.5 W.   c. 67,500 W.   d. 63,300 W.

110. What is the resistance between points A and B of the following circuit?

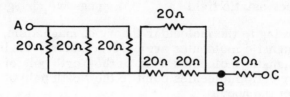

a. 20 ohms   b. 26.67 ohms   c. 40 ohms   d. 13.67 ohms

111. The use of decoupling networks will not:
a. reduce motorboating   c. alter the phase of the signal
b. reduce feedback   d. reduce oscillations

112. Adding an inductor in series with an antenna would:
a. reduce the resonant frequency of the antenna
b. increase the resonant frequency of the antenna
c. be similar to shortening the antenna
d. not affect the antenna's resonant frequency

113. A Class B amplifier:
a. is biased at the center of the Ip-Eg curve
b. has excellent fidelity
c. has its plate current flowing for approximately 1/3 of the cycle
d. has medium efficiency

114. A shorted filter capacitor:
a. causes the power supply current to drop
b. causes the plate of the rectifier tube to become red hot
c. causes the choke to short
d. reduces the ripple frequency

115. Which of the following can be used as an indication that an oscillator is working?
a. measure the plate voltage
b. measure the voltage across the grid-leak resistor
c. measure the plate current
d. measure the voltage across the tank circuit

116. Diversity reception is used to:
a. reduce distortion   c. reduce fading
b. reduce harmonic reception d. reduce interference

117. Which of the following is a difference between a full-wave rectifier and a bridge rectifier?
a. the transformer centertap   c. the filtering system
b. the ripple frequency   d. the type of rectifier used

FINAL FCC-TYPE EXAMINATION

ELEMENT 4

1. What is the total current in the circuit shown?
   a. .30 A
   b. .29 A
   c. .45 A
   d. 2.0 A

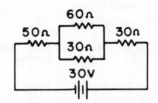

2. A certain device reduces power by 99%. What is the power reduction in decibels?
   a. -20 db   b. -10 db   c. -9.9 db   d. -1 db

3. A 2050 kHz low-drift crystal has a positive temperature coefficient of 3 Hz per MHz per degree C. If the temperature at the start of operation is 60°C, what will be the oscillating frequency at 30° C.?
   a. 2050.1845 kHz   c. 2050 kHz
   b. 2049.8155 kHz   d. 2031.55 kHz

4. The turns ratio in an iron-core transformer determines the:
   a. copper losses   c. voltages
   b. current capacity   d. current losses

5. What is the speed of a 3-phase, 120 V, 8-pole, 60 Hz induction motor?
   a. 3600 rpm   b. 900 rpm   c. 400 rpm   d. 2400 rpm

6. In a grounded grid amplifier:
   a. neutralization is not required
   b. the output capacity is twice that of a grounded cathode circuit
   c. 100% plate modulation is easily achieved
   d. none of the above are correct

7. A standard broadcast antenna ammeter is protected from lightning by using a/an:
   a. lightning arrestor across the ammeter
   b. spark gap across the ammeter
   c. shorting switch across the ammeter
   d. static drain coil across the ammeter

8. How much power is in the sidebands of a 5 kilowatt transmitter modulated 85%?
   a. 4250 W.   b. 1800 W.   c. 2125 W.   d. 3600 W.

9. We have available a 10:1 step-down transformer that is to be used to transfer power from a tube with a plate impedance of 12,000 ohms to a load of 100 ohms. What value of resistance should be placed across the plate to effect an impedance match?
a. 10,000 ohms b. 60,000 ohms c. 5,000 ohms d. 50,000 ohms

10. An ideal harmonic generator in a secondary frequency standard is a:
a. Hartley oscillator   c. multivibrator
b. Colpitts oscillator   d. Pierce generator

11. The width of the complete broadcast television channel is:
a. 1.25 MHz   b. 4.5 MHz   c. 4.75 MHz   d. 6 MHz

12. A Class C amplifier has:
a. high efficiency   c. excellent regulation
b. low efficiency   d. excellent fidelity

13. Within what limits must the operating power of a standard broadcast station be maintained?
a. 5% above and 5% below the licensed power
b. 10% above and 10% below the licensed power
c. 10% above and 5% below the licensed power
d. 5% above and 10% below the licensed power

14. If a frequency doubler stage has an input frequency of 2 MHz and the plate inductance is 40 microhenries, what value of plate capacitance is necessary for resonance, neglecting stray capacitances?
a. 420 mmfd   b. 62.3 mmfd   c. 39.5 mmfd   d. 23.4 mmfd

15. What meter should not be used to measure AVC?
a. a 20,000 ohm per volt meter   c. a VTVM
b. a 50,000 ohm per volt meter   d. a 1,000 ohm per volt meter

16. How is the operating power of an FM broadcast station determined?
a. direct method   b. indirect method   c. a and b   d. a or b

17. In a Foster-Seeley discriminator, there is/are:
a. two capacitors and two resistors in its output
b. the plate of one diode and the cathode of another diode connected to the ends of the secondary coil
c. a tapped secondary coil   d. a and c

18. For maximum transfer of power from a transmission line to an antenna:
a. the impedances should be equal
b. the antenna must be fed at its center
c. the antenna must be fed at one of its ends
d. a low-loss transmission line should be used

430

19. What is the current flowing in a 72 ohm concentric line if the power input to it is 2 kilowatts?
a. 1.44 amperes   c. 5.26 amperes
b. 3.6 amperes   d. 2.77 amperes

20. In a DC shunt-wound motor:
a. the speed is constant   b. the counter-emf is high
c. the speed varies according to the load
d. the counter-emf is low

21. What is the output power of an audio amplifier if the voltage across its 600 ohm load is 30 volts?
a. .05 W.   b. 20 W.   c. .67 W.   d. 1.5 W.

22. The ratio of the field intensity produced by a particular antenna to the field intensity produced by a simple dipole is called:
a. effective radiated power   c. power gain
b. antenna field gain   d. effective power gain

23. The aspect ratio of the picture that is transmitted by a television broadcast transmitter is:
a. 5 to 4   b. 4 to 5   c. 4 to 3   d. 3 to 2

24. A Q-matching section is used to match a 50 ohm transmission line to a 600 ohm antenna. What is the impedance of the Q-matching section?
a. 12 ohms   b. 173 ohms   c. 30,000 ohms   d. 72 ohms

25. A push-push amplifier has:
a. its grids in push-pull and plates in parallel
b. its grids in parallel and plates in push-pull
c. its grids in parallel and plates in series
d. its grids in series and plates in push-pull

26. A broadcast station receives an accurate frequency measurement report indicating that the station frequency is 30 Hz low. The transmitter's monitor indicates that the station's frequency is 10 Hz low. What is the error in the station frequency monitor?
a. 20 Hz   b. 40 Hz   c. 10 Hz   d. 30 Hz

27. Fig. 27 is a trapezoidal pattern indicating:
a. 50% modulation
b. 75% modulation
c. 100% modulation
d. overmodulation

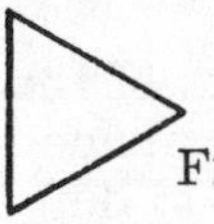

Fig. 27

28. The purpose of a pre-emphasis circuit in an FM transmitter is to boost the:
a. high frequency audio   c. high frequency RF
b. low frequency audio   d. low frequency RF

29. For maximum frequency stability, a crystal-controlled oscillator is tuned to:
a. a slightly lower frequency than the crystal frequency
b. the exact crystal frequency
c. a sub-harmonic of the crystal frequency
d. a slightly higher frequency than the crystal frequency

30. What is the total current flow in a parallel circuit containing 5 ohms of resistance, 8 ohms of inductive reactance and 10 ohms of capacitive reactance? The supply voltage is 20 volts.
a. 4.0 A   b. 4.5 A   c. 8.5 A.   d. 3.7 A

31. A mercury vapor rectifier has:
a. a constant internal voltage drop
b. a very high internal voltage drop
c. a higher internal voltage drop than a high vacuum rectifier
d. no internal voltage drop

32. A line equalizer is a:
a. high-pass filter   c. "T" pad
b. low-pass filter   d. peak amplitude limiter

33. Three single-phase transformers, with a step-up ratio of 1 to 5, are connected with their primaries in delta and their secondaries in Y. What is the secondary line voltage if 3-phase 100 volts is fed to the primaries?
a. 1500 V.   b. 866 V.   c. 707 V.   d. 500 V.

34. A blanking pulse is used to:
a. trigger the vertical oscillator
b. erase the beam while it is being brought back to the left side of the picture
c. blank out the vertical oscillator while the horizontal oscillator is operating, and vice versa
d. trigger the horizontal oscillator during re-trace periods

35. What is the capacitive reactance in a series circuit having a resistance of 5 ohms, an inductive reactance of 15 ohms and an impedance of 13 ohms?
a. 10 ohms   b. 8 ohms   c. 7 ohms   d. 3 ohms

36. What is the purpose of the monitor picture tube at a TV broadcast station?
a. to synchronize all parts of the TV system
b. to permit the studio audience to view the programs
c. to permit the operator to determine any fault in the picture
d. to synchronize the picture with the sound

37. What percentage of the peak carrier level is the white reference level?
a. 75%   b. 70%   c. 12.5%   d. 50%

38. A vacuum tube voltmeter gives an accurate voltage reading because it:
a. contains an accurate D'Arsonval meter movement
b. has a low internal resistance
c. has a high internal resistance   d. uses vacuum tubes

39. The peak negative voltage across a half-wave rectifier tube is:
a. the RMS secondary voltage   c. the full secondary x 1.414
b. 1/2 the secondary x 1.414   d. twice the secondary x 1.414

40. A tetrode is superior to a triode as a radio-frequency amplifier because of its:
a. suppressor grid   c. increased cathode emission
b. high plate resistance   d. reduced possibility of oscillations

41. If an 850 kHz AM carrier is modulated by audio frequencies from 40 Hz to 4,500 Hz, what are the highest and lowest frequencies transmitted?
a. 850.040 and 854.4 kHz   c. 845.5 and 850.040 kHz
b. 849.960 and 854.5 kHz   d. 845.5 and 854.5 kHz

42. The formula for determining the characteristic impedance of an air insulated parallel conductor transmission line is:
a. $27 \log.ab$ b. $\dfrac{276}{\log. ab}$ c. $276 \log. \dfrac{b}{a}$ d. $276 \dfrac{\log. a}{\log. b}$

43. The fundamental operating range of a multivibrator is primarily determined by the:
a. plate voltages   b. screen voltages
c. coils and capacitors in the plate circuit
d. resistors and capacitors in the grid circuit

44. If a power supply has an output voltage of 200 volts at no load and the regulation is 10%, what is the output voltage at full load?
a. 180 V.   b. 220 V.   c. 218 V.   d. 182 V.

45. $\Delta Ep/\Delta Eg$ is the formula for:
a. transconductance   c. plate resistance
b. amplification factor   d. mutual conductance

46. Which of the following is used to make certain that a load receives maximum power from its source?
a. observe polarity   c. match impedances
b. use a series resonant circuit   d. use bleeder resistors

47. A T or H pad attenuator provides, in addition to attenuation:
a. equalization   c. impedance matching
b. neutralization   d. none of the above

48. What is the sensitivity, in ohms per volt, of a voltmeter using a 0-5 ma movement?
a. 1000   b. 500   c. 200   d. .005

49. The term "secondary service area" of a broadcast station means:
a. the area where the ground wave is not subject to objectionable interference or objectionable fading
b. the area served by the skywave and not subject to objectionable interference
c. the area receiving service from the ground wave, but subject to some interference and fading
d. none of the above

50. The horizontal oscillator of a TV system produces a frequency of:
a. 525 Hz   b. 7875 Hz   c. 15,750 Hz   d. 31,500 Hz

51. What happens to the transmission line current of an FM transmitter when it is modulated 100%?
a. it increases 22.5%   c. it increases 50%
b. it remains the same   d. it increases 100%

52. Capacitive coupling in a transformer can be reduced by:
a. a permanent magnet   c. an inductive loop
b. an electrostatic shield   d. capacitive feedback

53. A frequency meter with a straight line relationship between frequency and the dial reading reads 24.3. The chart shows that 23.6 indicates 4250 kHz and 24.9 indicates 4300 kHz. What is the frequency being read?
a. 4273 kHz   b. 4277 kHz   c. 3252.7 kHz   d. 4270 kHz

54. The overall purpose of pre-emphasis and de-emphasis circuits is to:
a. improve selectivity   c. reduce noise
b. improve sensitivity   d. reduce distortion

55. An important step in neutralizing an RF amplifier is:
a. remove the plate voltage of the stage to be neutralized
b. remove the filament voltage of the oscillator
c. remove the plate coil   d. lower the plate voltage

56. In a CRT, the beam's movement to the right is called:
a. trace   b. retrace   c. persistance   d. sweep

57. Crystals are sometimes operated in temperature-controlled ovens in order to:
a. increase frequency drift   b. increase frequency stability
c. eliminate the need for neutralization
d. minimize parasitic oscillations

58. A full-wave bridge rectifier:
a. operates on both halves of the cycle
b. operates on one-half of the cycle
c. utilizes one-half of the transformer
d. has a 60-cycle output ripple frequency

ANSWERS TO ALL QUESTIONS

LESSON 1

1. b	2. c	3. c	4. c	5. d	6. c	7. a
8. d	9. d	10. a	11. d	12. c	13. c	14. c
15. b	16. a					

LESSON 2

1. c	2. b	3. c	4. c	5. b	6. b	7. d
8. a	9. b	10. b	11. b	12. a	13. d	14. a
15. a	16. c					

LESSON 3

1. d	2. b	3. b	4. a	5. c	6. d	7. d
8. b	9. d	10. c	11. c	12. d	13. b	14. b
15. d	16. a	17. a				

LESSON 4

1. a	2. c	3. a	4. c	5. b	6. c	7. d
8. a	9. c	10. a	11. c	12. c	13. a	14. c
15. c	16. d	17. b	18. c	19. d	20. c	21. a
22. d	23. c	24. b	25. a	26. b	27. a	28. d
29. d	30. b					

LESSON 5

1. d	2. b	3. c	4. d	5. a	6. c	7. c
8. d	9. d	10. a	11. d	12. c	13. a	

LESSON 6

1. a	2. a	3. c	4. b	5. c	6. d	7. b
8. a	9. a	10. b	11. b	12. b	13. d	14. a
15. a	16. d					

LESSON 7

1. b	2. a	3. b	4. a	5. b	6. a	7. b
8. d	9. a	10. d	11. b	12. c	13. d	14. c
15. c	16. d	17. d	18. a	19. c	20. c	21. b
22. a	23. b	24. c	25. c	26. b		

LESSON 8

1. d	2. a	3. c	4. c	5. d	6. c	7. b
8. b	9. a	10. c	11. b	12. b	13. c	14. a
15. b	16. a	17. a	18. d	19. a	20. d	

LESSON 9

1. d	2. c	3. a	4. a	5. d	6. a	7. c
8. c	9. d	10. b	11. a	12. d	13. c	14. c
15. b	16. d	17. c	18. a	19. b	20. d	21. d
22. d	23. c	24. a	25. b	26. d	27. c	28. a
29. c						

LESSON 10

1. d	2. c	3. d	4. b	5. c	6. b	7. d
8. a	9. d	10. d				

LESSON 11

1. c	2. d	3. d	4. d	5. d	6. c	7. a

8. b	9. b	10. b	11. c	12. c	13. d	14. d
15. a	16. b	17. b	18. b	19. d		

LESSON 12

1. d	2. b	3. c	4. a	5. b	6. c	7. a
8. d	9. b	10. a	11. d	12. c	13. c	14. c
15. b	16. b	17. a	18. d	19. b		

LESSON 13

1. c	2. a	3. c	4. c	5. b	6. d	7. a
8. d	9. b	10. d	11. b	12. a	13. c	14. c
15. d	16. d	17. a	18. d	19. a	20. b	21. c
22. c	23. b	24. c	25. c	26. a	27. a	28. b
29. d	30. d	31. d	32. c	33. b		

LESSON 14

1. c	2. d	3. c	4. d	5. d	6. a	7. c
8. a	9. c	10. d	11. c	12. c	13. c	14. b
15. d	16. d	17. c	18. c	19. a	20. a	21. a
22. b	23. b	24. d				

LESSON 15

1. b	2. d	3. d	4. c	5. c	6. c	7. b
8. d	9. a	10. b	11. b	12. d	13. d	14. b
15. c	16. a	17. d	18. c	19. c	20. d	

LESSON 16

1. b	2. b	3. d	4. c	5. c	6. a	7. b
8. c	9. c	10. b	11. a	12. a	13. c	14. c
15. c	16. c	17. c	18. a	19. d	20. b	21. a
22. d	23. a	24. c	25. b	26. c	27. d	28. d

LESSON 17

1. c	2. a	3. d	4. a	5. d	6. c	7. a
8. c	9. d	10. a	11. b	12. a	13. b	14. b
15. c	16. b	17. d	18. c	19. a	20. c	21. c
22. a	23. b	24. c	25. b	26. d	27. b	28. c
29. d	30. a	31. c				

LESSON 18

1. d	2. d	3. c	4. b	5. a	6. c	7. d
8. d	9. c	10. c				

LESSON 19

1. d	2. d	3. d	4. c	5. a	6. a	7. c
8. d	9. a	10. b	11. a	12. d	13. b	14. b
15. b	16. c	17. a	18. c	19. b	20. b	21. d

LESSON 20

1. b	2. c	3. a	4. b	5. c	6. c	7. a
8. a	9. b	10. d	11. a	12. a	13. d	14. b
15. b	16. d	17. c				

LESSON 21

1. c	2. b	3. b	4. c	5. c	6. b	7. c
8. d	9. c	10. a	11. d	12. d	13. b	14. b
15. a	16. b	17. a	18. a	19. c	20. a	21. d
22. c	23. b	24. b	25. b	26. b	27. d	28. b
29. c	30. b	31. a	32. c	33. d	34. c	35. d

36. c   37. b   38. b   39. c   40. b   41. d   42. d
43. a   44. a

ELEMENT 3 FINAL EXAM

1. a	2. a	3. b	4. c	5. d	6. b	7. b
8. b	9. b	10. a	11. d	12. b	13. c	14. a
15. b	16. c	17. a	18. d	19. b	20. b	21. c
22. a	23. b	24. b	25. a	26. d	27. b	28. d
29. a	30. a	31. b	32. b	33. b	34. c	35. d
36. d	37. a	38. d	39. c	40. a	41. d	42. b
43. b	44. a	45. a	46. b	47. b	48. a	49. b
50. a	51. c	52. c	53. c	54. c	55. d	56. c
57. c	58. d	59. c	60. d	61. a	62. c	63. d
64. c	65. a	66. c	67. b	68. c	69. a	70. c
71. d	72. b	73. b	74. b	75. d	76. d	77. c
78. d	79. d	80. a	81. a	82. a	83. a	84. b
85. c	86. a	87. c	88. d	89. b	90. c	91. c
92. c	93. a	94. a	95. a	96. b	97. c	98. a
99. b	100. b	101. b	102. b	103. b	104. b	105. a
106. c	107. b	108. c	109. b	110. a	111. c	112. a
113. d	114. b	115. b	116. c	117. a		

ELEMENT 4 FINAL EXAM

1. a	2. a	3. b	4. c	5. b	6. a	7. c
8. b	9. b	10. c	11. d	12. a	13. d	14. c
15. d	16. d	17. d	18. a	19. c	20. a	21. d
22. b	23. c	24. b	25. a	26. a	27. c	28. a
29. d	30. a	31. a	32. a	33. b	34. b	35. d
36. c	37. c	38. c	39. c	40. d	41. d	42. c
43. d	44. d	45. b	46. c	47. c	48. c	49. b
50. c	51. b	52. b	53. b	54. c	55. a	56. a
57. b	58. a					

INDEX

E

E.C.O., 225
Eddy currents, 84
Edison effect, 103
Effective radiated power, 348
Effective AC value, 52
Efficiency of a transformer, 85
   of a tube, 141
Electric charges, Law of, 7
Electrical pressure, 7
Electrolyte, 12
Electrolytic capacitor, 63
Electromagnetism, 35
Electromotive force, 11
Electron, 6, 8
Electron cloud, 107
Electron coupled oscillator, 225
Electron emission, 103
Element, 6
Emission, electron, 103
Emitter, transistor, 186
Energy, 26
Energy in an inductance, 54
Equalizer, 212
Equalizing pulses, 395
Equalizing resistors, 123

F

Fall of potential, 11
Family of curves, 135
Farad, 59
Faraday shield, 239, 251
Feedback, current, 173
   degenerative, 174
   increase, 174
   negative, 173
   oscillator, 220
   voltage, 173
Feeding antennas, 344
Field coils, 93
   frequency, 392
   generator, 93
   intensity, 347
   rheostat, 93
   strength, 347
Filament, 104
   cathode, 104
   thoriated tungsten, 105
Filtering system, 116

Filters, band-pass, 302
   band-stop, 255
   capacitor input, 117
   choke input, 118
   high-pass, 255
   low-pass, 255
Filter, pi, 117
First detector, 291
Fixed bias, 241
Fixed capacitor, 63
FM (see Frequency Modulation)
Foster-Seeley discriminator, 326
Forward biasing, 110
Frame frequency, 392
Frequency, 47
   conversion, 292
   cut-off of a transistor, 193
   doubler, 246, 250
   measurement, 367
   meter, 367
   meter, heterodyne, 370
Frequency Modulation (see FM)
   deviation meter, 331
   discriminator, 325
   IF amplifier, 324
   limiter, 324
   narrow-band, 313
   receiver, 322
   receiver alignment, 330
   sidebands, 311
   transmitter, 316
   wide-band, 313
Frequency monitor, 367
Frequency multipliers, 245
Frequency, resonant, 77
Frequency response, 155, 164
Frequency, ripple, 116
Frequency shift, 275
Frequency-shift keying, 333
Frequency stability of oscillators, 224
Frequency standard, primary, 372
Frequency standard, secondary, 371
Frequency tolerance, 374
Frequency tripler, 246
Full-wave rectifier, 114

441

G

Gain of stage, 147
Galvanometer, 39
Gang tuning, 289
Gas tube, 148
Generators, 92
  AC, 92
  DC, 93
  field, 93
  ripple, 94
  self-excited, 95
  shunt-wound 95
Germanium, 109
Gilbert, 37
Grid, blocked, 135
Grid, control, 133
Grid bias, 135
Grid-dip meter, 369
Grid-leak bias, 220, 240
Grid-leak, cathode bias, 242
Grid-leak detector, 286
Grid modulation, 273
Grid neutralization, 243
Ground radials, 344
Ground wave, 337, 338
Grounded-grid amplifier, 244
Guy wires, 351

H

"H" pad, 210
Half-wave antenna, 341
Half-wave rectifier, 113
Harmonic output, measuring, 240
  minimizing, 239
Hartley oscillator, 222
Hazeltine neutralization, 243
Headphone, 177
Heater-cathode, 104
Helix, 380
Henry, 54
Hertz, 47
Hertz antenna, 342
Heterodyne frequency meter,
  370, 372
High-level modulation, 266
High-pass filters, 255
Hole, 109
Horizontal centering, 150
Horizontal pulse, 393

Horseshoe magnet, 35
Hot-wire meter, 368
Hum, 176
Hum pickup, 301
Hydrogen, 6
Hydrometer, 14
Hysteresis losses, 84

I

Iconoscope, 391
IF amplifier (see Intermediate
  Frequency)
Impedance, 57, 69
  of parallel resonant circuit,
  76
  of series resonant circuit, 74
  of transmission line, 358
Images, 299
Impurity, 109
In phase, 49
Incandescence, 103
Indirectly heated cathode, 104
Induced grid noise, 301
Induced voltage, 38
Inductance, 53
Inductance, mutual, 55
Induction motor, 98
Inductive coupling, 248
Inductive reactance, 56
Inductors in parallel, 54
Inductors in series, 54
Insertion loss, 209
Insulator, 109
Interelectrode capacitance, 143
Interference to TV, 254
Interlaced scanning, 392
Intermediate frequency ampli-
  fier, 294
Intermodulation products, 279
Internal circulating current, 76
Interpolation, 373
Inverse feedback, 174
Ionization, 122, 125
Ionosphere, 337
IR drop, 11
Iron core, 37
Iron core losses, 84
Iron filings, 32
Isolating capacitors, 275

442

Modulation index, 311
Modulation, low-level, 266, 269
    pattern, 277
    percentage, 261, 275, 310
    phase, 312
    plate, 266
Modulator, push-pull, 268
    balanced, 319
    reactance tube, 315
Monitor, frequency, 367
Motor, 96
    induction, 98
    series wound, 98
    shunt wound, 97
Motor-generator, 100
Multi-anode magnetron, 386
Multiplier, frequency, 245
Multiplier, meter, 40
Multipurpose tubes, 148
Multivibrator, 231
Mutual conductance, 141
Mutual inductance, 55

N

N-type material, 109
Narrow-band FM, 313
National Bureau of Standards, 372
Negative carrier shift, 278
Negative feedback, 173
Neutral position, 95
Neutralization, 242
    Balantine, 244
    criss-cross, 243
    grid, 243
    Hazeltine, 243
    plate, 242
    Rice, 243
Neutron, 6
Noise in a receiver, 300
Non-linear meter scale, 368
Non-synchronous vibrator, 128
North pole, 32
Null position of loop antenna, 353

O

Oersted, 37
Ohm, 8
Ohmmeter, 8, 42
Ohm's law, 19

Open circuit, 19
Operating point, 157
Oscillations, damped, 218
    parasitic, 253
    in RF amplifier, 242, 254
    undamped, 218
Oscillator, 217
    Armstrong, 219
    beat frequency, 298
    Colpitts, 223
    crystal-controlled, 226
    electron-coupled, 225
    feed-back, 220
    frequency stability of, 224
    Hartley, 222
    klystron, 384
    parallel-fed, 221
    Pierce, 227
    series-fed, 221
    tuned-plate, tuned-grid, 224
Oscillators, ultra high frequency, 384
Out-of-phase, 50
Overmodulation, 262
Oxygen, 6

P

P-type material, 109
Parallel-fed oscillator, 221
Parallel resistors, 22
Parallel RCL circuit, 72
Parallel resonance, 75
Parallel tubes, 168
Parallelogram law, 50
Parasitic antenna, 347
Parasitic oscillations, 253
Partition noise, 301
Peak, 47
Peak amplitude, 47
Peak-to-peak, 47
Pentode, 145
Percentage of modulation, 261, 275
Permanent magnet, 35
Permeability, 37
Permeability tuning, 294
Pentagrid converter, 293
Percentage of modulation, 310
Persistance, 151

Receiver, T.R.F., 288
Recorder, tape, 208
Rectifier, bridge, 126
  copper-oxide, 108, 115
  full-wave, 114
  half-wave, 113
  mercury vapor, 121
  selenium, 104, 115
Reflector, antenna, 349
Regulation, voltage, 119, 148
Rel, 37
Relays, 37
Reluctance, 37
Residual magnetism, 35, 96
Resistance, 8
Resistance coupling, 163
Resistors, 8, 9
  carbon, 9
  color code, 9
  in parallel, 22
  in series, 21
  variable, 9
  wire-wound, 9
Resonance, parallel, 75
Resonance, series, 74
Resonant frequency, 77
Re-trace, 394
Reverse biasing, 110
RF (see Radio Frequency)
Rheostat, 10
Rice neutralization, 243
Ripple frequency, 116
RMS, 52
Root-Mean-Square, 52
Rules and Regulations, 398

S

Saturation point, 135
Saw-tooth voltage, 150
Saw-tooth wave, 232, 394
Scanning, 392
Schematics, 18
Screen grid, 143
  dissipation, 144
Second detector, 295
Second harmonic distortion, 166
Secondary cell, 12
Secondary of a transformer, 81
Secondary emission, 145

Secondary frequency standard, 371
Selectivity of a receiver, 301
Selenium rectifier, 109, 115
Self-excited generator, 95
Self-induction, 54
Self-oscillation, 176
Semi-conductor, 108
Sensitivity, meter, 41
  receiver, 300, 303
Separately excited generator, 93
Series-fed oscillator, 221
Series-parallel circuits, 24
Series resonance, 74
Series-wound motor, 98
Shielding, magnetic, 35
Shielding in a transformer, 83
Short circuit, 19
Shot effect, 301
Shunt, meter, 41
Shunt-wound generator, 95
Shunt-wound motor, 97
Sideband power, 265
Sidebands, 264
Sidebands, FM, 311
Silicon diodes, 109, 115
Sine wave, 46
Single-button carbon micro-
  phone, 204
Single-sideband reception, 299
Single-sideband transmitter, 279
Skin effect, 57
Skip zone, 337
Sky wave, 337
Slip rings, 92
Soldering, 28
Solenoid, 36
Solid-state detector, 287
Solid state diode, 108
Sound, 155
South pole, 32
Space charge, 103, 107
Sparking, brush, 95
Speaker, 179
Squelch, 331
Squelch, differential, 332
Stability of crystals, 230
Stacked antenna, 350

447